A MANUAL OF
DETERMINATIVE MINERALOGY
WITH TABLES

A MANUAL OF
DETERMINATIVE MINERALOGY
WITH TABLES

FOR THE DETERMINATION OF MINERALS

By means of:

I. Their Physical Characters

II. Blowpipe and Chemical Properties

III. Optical Properties

BY

J. VOLNEY LEWIS

FOURTH EDITION

REVISED AND WITH SUPPLEMENT BY

A. C. HAWKINS

NEW YORK

JOHN WILEY & SONS, Inc.

London: CHAPMAN & HALL, Limited

PREFACE TO THE FOURTH EDITION

Dr. Alfred C. Hawkins, who has become familiar with this manual in the laboratory, has kindly consented to undertake the revision for this edition. In this work we are agreed that the following are the principal changes required: (1) to reduce to the minimum the repetitions in the tables for the determination of minerals by means of their physical properties; (2) to eliminate from the blowpipe tables a number of minerals that are so rare as to have no practical importance; (3) to add a chapter on optical methods, so that the student will know their value and importance both in the study of minerals and in the identification of laboratory and industrial products. The text that accompanies the tables has also been subjected to close scrutiny in order to eliminate errors, insert new information, and in general to bring it abreast of the progress of the science so far as the scope of the book seems to warrant.

I take this occasion to thank Dr. Hawkins for the arduous labor he has given to his task and to bespeak for his work the same kindly consideration and friendly criticism that have always been accorded to my efforts in the preceding editions of this manual.

J. VOLNEY LEWIS.

Chicago, July 28, 1931.

FROM PREFACE TO THE THIRD EDITION

By J. Volney Lewis

The higher degree of accuracy attained in the determination of minerals by means of blowpipe and chemical tests is generally recognized, but in practice the necessary appliances are not always available. Furthermore, the experienced engineer and geologist may often save time by reference to the physical classification. Such tables have peculiar value for the student also, since they require close and accurate observation of streak, hardness, color, luster, form, and cleavage, and because of the emphasis they place on occurrence and mineral associates. By their use the student acquires a practical acquaintance with minerals that is of great value in sight-recognition.

The classification according to physical characters departs radically from the common practice in the construction of physical tables in that luster, so often a matter of uncertainty, has been entirely eliminated as a basis of classification. This keeps down the bulk of the tables somewhat, and to that extent facilitates their use, by avoiding excessive repetition.

Determinations based on physical characters often require confirmatory blowpipe tests, however, and, in the author's opinion, nothing can take the place of thorough drill for the student in blowpipe and chemical methods and in the use of tables based upon them. Chemical composition is the most fundamental property of minerals, and many species, particularly among the ores, can be determined with certainty only by means of chemical tests.

It is intended that the use of the tables shall not only furnish a name by which a mineral may be called, but shall also lead the student to acquire a first-hand knowledge of what the mineral really is, both chemically and physically. The constant use of a good treatise on descriptive mineralogy to supplement the tables is strongly recommended. The instructions and precautions accompanying both the physical classification and the blowpipe tables will, it is hoped, prove adaptable and serviceable. They are intended to aid the student in the development of habits of neatness, orderliness, and accuracy, and at the same time to inculcate a certain respect for mineral specimens, which are so easily damaged or destroyed, but which cannot be reproduced.

CONTENTS

	PAGE
PROPERTIES OF MINERALS	1
Crystallization	1
Optical Properties	6
Physical Properties	10
Chemical Properties	16
PHYSICAL TABLES	18
General Classification	20
DETERMINATION BY BLOWPIPE TESTS	93
Apparatus	93
Reagents	97
Blowpipe Operations and Chemical Tests	98
Reactions of the Elements	117
BLOWPIPE TABLES	135
Laboratory Records	136
General Table	138
MINERALS CLASSIFIED ACCORDING TO CRYSTALLIZATION AND OPTICAL CONSTANTS	8, 198
GLOSSARY	207
ABBREVIATIONS	217
CHEMICAL ELEMENTS	218
BIBLIOGRAPHY	219
SUPPLEMENT	221
INDEX TO SUPPLEMENT	243
INDEX	245

DETERMINATIVE MINERALOGY

PROPERTIES OF MINERALS

Definition.—A *mineral* is a natural substance of definite chemical composition produced by inorganic processes and, with few exceptions, crystalline in structure. When crystallizing under favorable conditions minerals take the form of *crystals* bounded by plane surfaces, and all crystals of the same substance possess the same degree of symmetry and the same fixed angles between corresponding faces, and often different internal properties in different crystallographic directions.

Many minerals are definite compounds only in the sense of varying between fixed limits, according to well-defined chemical principles (see Isomorphism, p. 16). A few like opal and chrysocolla, are amorphous, or noncrystalline, and widely variable in composition. Although included among minerals, such substances are, strictly speaking, not definite mineral species.

In contrast with the definiteness of minerals, *rocks* generally are aggregates of two or more minerals; some, however, like limestone and sandstone, are composed chiefly of one.

CRYSTALLIZATION

Importance.—Crystallography is often useful in the recognition of species. Only a few of the simpler and more common crystal forms are here given. For further details, more elaborate treatises should be consulted. (See bibliography, p. 219.)

The Six Systems.—Crystals give outward expression to the symmetry of the internal molecular structure. All crystals may be grouped under six *systems of crystallization*. These are distinguished from one another by differences in symmetry, expressed in terms of directions and relative lengths of certain lines assumed through the center of the crystal and called crystallographic axes. Thus:

1. *Isometric*, having three equal axes at right angles to one another. (See Figs. 1 to 16.)

2. *Tetragonal*, having three axes at right angles, two of which are equal and the third shorter or longer. (Figs. 17 to 25.)

3. *Hexagonal,* having three equal axes in one plane and inclined at angles of 60 degrees to one another, with a fourth at right angles to these and shorter or longer. (Figs. 26 to 37.)

4. *Orthorhombic,* with three axes at right angles, all unequal. (Figs. 38 to 45.)

5. *Monoclinic,* with three unequal axes, two inclined to each other and the third at right angles to these. (Figs. 46 to 52.)

6. *Triclinic,* three unequal axes, all inclined. (Figs. 53, 54.)

Twin crystals are symmetrical groups of two individuals (or more in case of repeated twinning), which may be simply in contact (*contact twins,* see Figs. 25, 49) or may penetrate each other (*penetration twins,* see Figs. 12, 44, 45, 52).

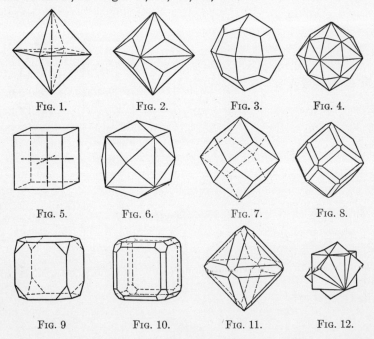

FIG. 1.　　　　FIG. 2.　　　　FIG. 3.　　　　FIG. 4.

FIG. 5.　　　　FIG. 6.　　　　FIG. 7.　　　　FIG. 8.

FIG. 9　　　　FIG. 10.　　　　FIG. 11.　　　　FIG. 12.

ISOMETRIC CRYSTALS: Fig. 1, Octahedron (111) $(a : a : a)$; 2, Trigonal Trisoctahedron (221) $(a : a : 2a)$; 3, Tetragonal Trisoctahedron (Trapezohedron) (211) $(a : 2a : 2a)$; 4, Hexoctahedron (321) $(2a : 3a : 6a)$; 5, Cube, or hexahedron (100) $(a : \infty\, a : \infty\, a)$; 6, Tetrahexahedron (210) $(a : 2a : \infty\, a)$; 7, Dodecahedron (110) $(a : a : \infty\, a)$; 8, Combination of dodecahedron and trapezohedron; 9, Combination of cube and octahedron; 10, Combination of cube, octahedron, and dodecahedron; 11, Combination of octahedron and dodecahedron; 12, Twinned cubes (a *penetration twin*).

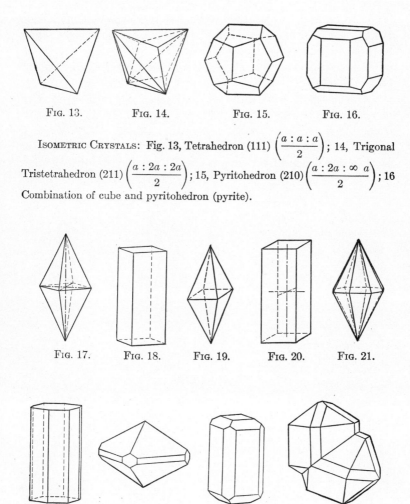

Fig. 13.　　Fig. 14.　　Fig. 15.　　Fig. 16.

Isometric Crystals: Fig. 13, Tetrahedron (111) $\left(\dfrac{a : a : a}{2}\right)$; 14, Trigonal Tristetrahedron (211) $\left(\dfrac{a : 2a : 2a}{2}\right)$; 15, Pyritohedron (210) $\left(\dfrac{a : 2a : \infty\ a}{2}\right)$; 16 Combination of cube and pyritohedron (pyrite).

Fig. 17.　　Fig. 18.　　Fig. 19.　　Fig. 20.　　Fig. 21.

Fig. 22.　　Fig. 23.　　Fig. 24.　　Fig. 25.

Tetragonal Crystals: Fig. 17, Pyramid of the first order (111) $(a : a : c)$; 18, Prism of the first order (110) $(a : a : \infty\ c)$; 19, Pyramid of the second order (101) $(a : \infty\ a : c)$; 20, Prism of the second order (100) $(a : \infty\ a : \infty\ c)$; 21, Ditetragonal pyramid (212) $(a : 2a : c)$; 22, Ditetragonal prism (210) $(a : 2a : \infty\ c)$; 23, Combination of first order prism and pyramid with second order prism (vesuvianite); 24, Combination of basal pinacoid with the same forms as Fig. 23 (vesuvianite); 25, Twin crystal of cassiterite (a *contact twin*).

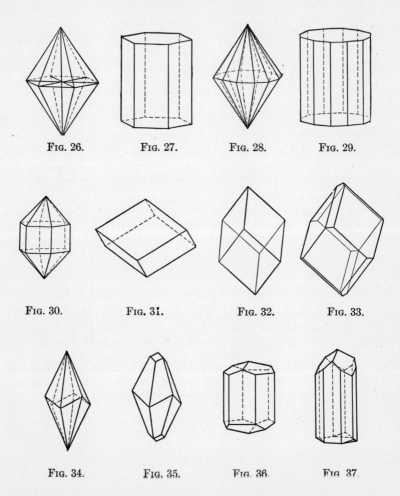

FIG. 26.   FIG. 27.   FIG. 28.   FIG. 29.

FIG. 30.   FIG. 31.   FIG. 32.   FIG. 33.

FIG. 34.   FIG. 35.   FIG. 36.   FIG 37.

HEXAGONAL CRYSTALS: Fig. 26, Pyramid (10$\bar{1}$1) ($a : \infty\, a : a : c$); 27, Prism (10$\bar{1}$0) ($a : \infty\, a : a : \infty\, c$); 28, Dihexagonal pyramid (21$\bar{3}$1) ($3a : 6a : 2a : 6c$); 29, Dihexagonal prism (21$\bar{3}$0) ($3a : 6a : 2a : \infty\, c$); 30, Combination of prism and pyramid; 31, Rhombohedron (10$\bar{1}$1) $\left(\dfrac{a : \infty\; a : a : c}{2}\right)$ (calcite); 32 Rhombohedron (02$\bar{2}$1) $\left(\dfrac{\infty\, a : a : a : 2c}{2}\right)$ (calcite); 33, Combination of the two preceding rhombohedrons (calcite); 34, Scalenohedron (21$\bar{3}$1) (calcite); 35, Combination of scalenohedron and rhombohedron (calcite); 36, Combination of rhombohedron (01$\bar{1}$2) and prism (calcite); 37, Hemimorphic crystal (tourmaline).

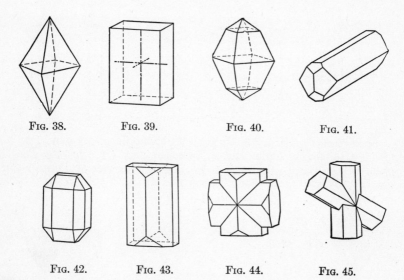

FIG. 38.   FIG. 39.   FIG. 40.   FIG. 41.

FIG. 42.   FIG. 43.   FIG. 44.   FIG. 45.

ORTHORHOMBIC CRYSTALS: Fig. 38, Pyramid (111) ($a : b : c$) (sulphur); 39, Combination of pinacoids (100),($a : \infty\ b : \infty\ c$); (010), ($\infty\ a : b : \infty\ c$); and (001) ($\infty\ a : \infty\ b : c$); 40, Combination of pyramids (111) ($a : b : c$) and (113) ($3a : 3b : c$), (sulphur); 41, Combination of prism, domes, and basal pinacoid (celestite); 42, Combination of prism, pyramid, domes, and pinacoids (olivine); 43, Combination of basal and brachy pinacoids with prism (110) and macro dome (101) (staurolite); 44, 45, Penetration twins (staurolite).

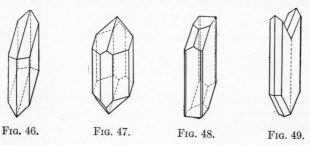

FIG. 46.   FIG. 47.   FIG. 48.   FIG. 49.

MONOCLINIC CRYSTALS: Fig. 46, Hemipyramid (111) ($a : b : c$), prism (110) ($a : b : \infty\ c$), and clino pinacoid (010) ($\infty\ a : b : \infty\ c$), in combination (gypsum); 47, Combination of hemipyramids (111) with ($\bar{2}21$) ($a : b : 2c$), prism (110) and pinacoids (100) ($a : \infty\ b : \infty\ c$), (010) ($\infty\ a : b : \infty\ c$) (pyroxene); 48, Combination of same forms with basal pinacoid (001) ($\infty\ a : \infty\ b : c$) (pyroxene); 49, Contact twin (gypsum).

FIG. 50.   FIG. 51.   FIG. 52.

MONOCLINIC CRYSTALS: Fig. 50, Prism (110), pinacoids (010), (001), and hemi-ortho dome ($\overline{2}01$) (orthoclase), 51, Combination of prism (110), pinacoids (010), (001), and hemi-ortho domes ($\overline{1}01$) and ($\overline{2}01$) (orthoclase); 52, Penetration twin (Carlsbad) (orthoclase).

FIG. 53.   FIG. 54.

TRICLINIC CRYSTALS: Fig. 53, Combination of tetra-pyramids (111), ($1\overline{1}1$), ($a : b : c$); hemi-prisms, (110), ($1\overline{1}0$), ($a : b : \infty$ c) macro pinacoid (100), ($a : \infty$ $b : \infty$ c) and macro dome (201) ($a : \infty$ $b : 2c$) (axinite); 54, Combination of brachy pinacoid (010) (∞ $a : b : \infty$ c) (axinite); 54, Combination of brachy pinacoid (010) (∞ $a : b : \infty$ c), basal pinacoid (001) (∞ $a : \infty$ $b : c$), hemi-prisms (110), ($1\overline{1}0$), and tetra-pyramids ($11\overline{1}$), ($1\overline{1}\overline{1}$) (albite).

NOTE.—Expressions in numerals denoting crystal forms are known as Miller Indices. Those in letters are Weiss Parameters.

In the absence of crystals, evidence of crystalline structure and symmetry may often be observed in the development of cleavage or parting in the broken material.

OPTICAL DETERMINATION AND PROPERTIES OF MINERALS

Determination of minerals in ordinary rock sections may readily be accomplished by following the methods outlined in standard text-books, such as those mentioned in the appended bibliography. The present procedure is suitable for the study of mineral powders and mineral crystals which are often produced in chemical processes, as in commercial manufacturing work.

Microscope.—Any instrument, of standard make, will answer the purpose. For ordinary work, the simpler the instrument is, the better. It must be provided with good nicol prisms. Real efficiency depends upon good lenses also, more than upon the finish or style, or unnecessary complication of the apparatus.

Illumination.—A standard Mazda 100 watt lamp, inside frosted, may be used, blue if preferred, to more nearly simulate daylight. This lamp works well in an ordinary bus light with flat base. The source of light should be so arranged as not to shine over top of microscope stage, as this causes a reflection from the surface of the mineral grains and gives them a frosted translucent appearance, so that observation by transmitted light is not clear and well defined.

Arrangement or tilting of the mirror gives the desired amount and direction of light needed to bring out the shape and relief of the grains, and especially the Becke line by which the refractive index is determined. Experiment with the mirror in different positions.

The position of the substage condenser, which may be moved upward and downward, is varied to suit the circumstances. Its proper position will be different in different individual cases.

Preparation of sample.—Samples to be examined by this method should be either naturally fine grained material, or else should be ground in an agate mortar to a size of 250 mesh or so. Hard particles, like quartz grains, which are larger, will scratch and break the cover-glass if not properly reduced in size.

Mounting of sample.—Object slides are made of clear colorless glass and are, for ordinary use, 25 x 50 mm. (1 x 2 in.) in size. Their short length prevents the fingers from striking them when on the microscope stage. Cover glasses used are usually No. 2's, about 0.2 mm. thick, although No. 1's, somewhat thinner, may be used with high power objectives when necessary. Cover glasses which are very thin are difficult to clean and handle without breaking. Cover glasses are preferably round in shape, but square ones serve very well, and even fragments of cover glasses may be used, being often most desirable where the material to be examined is very small in amount.

It is often convenient to use a wooden toothpick, having a thin flat end, as a spatula to remove to the slide a suitable amount of the powdered sample. After placing the powder on the slide (which has previously been carefully polished with cotton to remove dirt, grease and finger marks), remove a drop of liquid of the desired refractive index from the bottle with a clean dropping rod, place the drop on a clean cover glass, and carefully invert the cover glass over the powder on the slide. This procedure prevents any of the mineral powder from adhering to the dropping rod and possibly contaminating the supply of refractive index liquid. Work the cover glass down smoothly with a rubber pencil eraser (never with the finger); the rubber grips the cover glass without leaving any marks.

Observation of sample.—Now proceed with the tests for refractive index and other optical properties, according to the procedure recommended in Chamot & Mason and Kraus & Hunt (see Bibliography).

A table of the optical properties of a very few of the mineral compounds most often encountered is here appended for convenient reference. The figures quoted are from Larsen's Tables (see Bibliography).

OPTICAL DATA FOR DETERMINATION OF NON-OPAQUE MINERALS

ISOTROPIC GROUP

Refractive Index = n	Mineral	Crystal Habit	Cleavage	Color
n				
1.333	Water			
1.406±	Opal			Varies
1.434	Fluorite	Oct., Cubic	(111) perf.	Colorless, etc.
1.456	Alum (K)	Oct., Cubic		Colorless, etc.
1.487	Analcite	Tet. Tris.		Colorless, etc.
1.490	Sylvite	Cubic	(100) perf.	Colorless, etc.
1.509	Leucite	Tet. Tris.		Colorless, etc.
1.544	Halite	Cubic	(100) perf.	Colorless, etc.
1.723±	Spinel	Oct.	(111) imperf.	Red, etc.
1.778+	Almandite	Tet. Tris., etc.	(110) poor	Red, etc.
2.05±	Limonite	Amor.		Yellow
2.419	Diamond	Oct., etc.	(111) perf.	Colorless
2.47	Sphalerite	Tet., etc.	(110) perf.	Brown
2.849	Cuprite	Dodec., etc.	(111) imperf.	Red

UNIAXIAL POSITIVE GROUP

Refractive Indices

ε	ω				
1.537	1.535	Apophyllite	Tet.	(001) perf.	Colorless
1.553	1.544	Quartz	Hex.		Colorless
1.723	1.694	Willemite	Hex.		Colorless
1.968	1.923	Zircon	Tet.		Colorless
2.903	2.616	Rutile	Tet.		Yellow, etc.

UNIAXIAL NEGATIVE GROUP

Refractive Indices		Mineral	Crystal Habit	Cleavage	Color
ϵ	ω				
1.564	1.568	Beryl	Hex.	(0001) imperf.	Colorless
1.545	1.567	Wernerite	Tet.	(100) perf.	Colorless
1.631	1.634	Apatite	Hex.	(0001) imperf.	Colorless
1.486	1.658	Calcite	Hex.	(10$\bar{1}$1) perf.	Colorless
1.500	1.681	Dolomite	Hex.	(10$\bar{1}$1) perf.	Colorless
1.641	1.687	Tourmaline	Hex.	Parting	Red
1.509	1.700	Magnesite	Hex.	(10$\bar{1}$1) perf.	Colorless
1.760	1.768	Corundum	Hex.	Parting	Red, blue, etc.
1.618	1.818	Smithsonite	Hex.	(10$\bar{1}$1) perf.	Colorless
1.597	1.817	Rhodochrosite	Hex.	(10$\bar{1}$1) perf.	Colorless
1.596	1.830	Siderite	Hex.	(10$\bar{1}$1) perf.	Colorless
2.304	2.402	Wulfenite	Tet.	(111) perf.	Colorless
2.94	3.22	Hematite	Hex.	Parting	Red

BIAXIAL POSITIVE GROUP

α	γ	β				
		1.364	Cryolite	Mon.		Colorless
1.480	1.493	1.482	Natrolite	Orth.		Colorless
1.485	1.488	1.485	Chabazite	Hex.	(10$\bar{1}$1) dist.	Colorless
1.525	1.536	1.529	Albite	Tri.	(010) (001)	Colorless
		1.54±	Chrysotile	Orth.		Green, etc.
1.571	1.614	1.576	Anhydrite	Orth.	(001) (010) (100)	Colorless
1.614	1.636	1.617	Calamine	Orth.	(110) perf.	Colorless
1.619	1.627	1.620	Topaz	Orth.	(001) perf.	Colorless
1.622	1.631	1.624	Celestite	Orth.	(001) (110) (010)	Colorless
1.636	1.648	1.637	Barite	Orth.	(001) (110) (010)	Colorless
1.650	1.658	1.653	Enstatite	Orth.	(110) perf. 87°	Green, etc.
1.662	1.699	1.680	Olivine	Orth.	(010) (100)	Colorless
1.664	1.694	1.671	Diopside	Mon.	(110) perf. 87°	Green, etc.
1.698	1.723	1.704	Augite	Mon.	(110) perf. 90°	Green, etc.
1.726	1.737	1.730	Rhodonite	Tri.	(110) (1$\bar{1}$0) (001)	Colorless
1.736	1.746	1.741	Staurolite	Orth.		Brown
1.877	1.894	1.882	Anglesite	Orth.	(001) (110)	Colorless
1.900	2.034	1.907	Titanite	Mon.	(110) dist.	Brown, etc.
1.950	2.240	2.043	Sulphur	Orth.		Yellow

BIAXIAL NEGATIVE GROUP

1.447	1.472	1.470	Borax	Mon.		Colorless
1.494	1.500	1.498	Stilbite	Mon.		Colorless
1.518	1.526	1.524	Orthoclase	Mon.	(010) (001) perf.	Colorless
1.522	1.530	1.526	Microcline	Tri.	(010) (001) perf.	Colorless
1.541	1.574	1.574	Biotite	Mon.	(001) perf.	Brown
1.539	1.589	1.589	Talc	Mon.	(001)	Colorless
1.562	1.606	1.606	Phlogopite	Mon.	(001)	Brown
1.561	1.594	1.590	Muscovite	Mon.	(001)	Colorless
1.661	1.683	1.673	Hornblende	Mon.	(110) 124°	Green
1.531	1.686	1.682	Aragonite	Orth.	(010) dist.	Colorless
1.712	1.728	1.720	Cyanite	Mon.	(100) (010)	Colorless
1.729	1.768	1.754	Epidote	Mon.	(001) (100)	Green
1.804	2.078	2.976	Cerussite	Orth.	(110) (021)	Colorless

PHYSICAL PROPERTIES

Crystal aggregates, although lacking the definite symmetry of twin groups, may possess a high degree of regularity, as in radiating, globular, and plumose forms. In some aggregates the individuals are well-formed crystals at free ends or sides, but in many they are so closely crowded upon one another as to fill the whole space. This condition gives rise to coarse or fine *granular* texture and, where the individuals are microscopic in size, to *dense* masses.

Cleavage is the capacity possessed by many minerals for breaking with smooth planes parallel to certain actual or possible crystal faces, as in the basal cleavage of the micas, the rhombohedral cleavage of calcite, and the cubic cleavage of galena. Minerals that break with ease in such directions, like the examples named, yielding smooth lustrous faces, are said to have *perfect* cleavage. Inferior degrees are termed *distinct, indistinct, imperfect,* etc. Both the direction of cleavage and the ease with which it may be developed are fixed properties of the species, and hence important in determination.

Cleavage planes, in contrast with crystal faces, are commonly more or less splintery; and the simultaneous reflection of light from numerous small areas often reveals the presence of cleavage where no conspicuous flat surface is seen.

Parting resembles cleavage, but shows this important difference: the capacity for breaking with smooth surfaces is limited to certain definite planes along which weakness has been developed by strain or by twinning lamellae. Hence, one crystal may have parting while another of the same mineral may have none; and even where it is developed the portions between the parting planes do not posses the capacity for breaking in this manner.

Fracture is the term applied to breaking that, unlike cleavage and parting, does not produce smooth planes. Common forms are described as *uneven,* yielding a rough or irregular surface; *conchoidal,* breaking with curved surfaces, often with concentric markings like a shell; *hackly,* giving sharp, jagged surfaces, like broken metal; *splintery,* producing elongated splinters, commonly due to fibrous or columnar structure; and *earthy,* breaking like clay or chalk.

Hardness is resistance to abrasion, or scratching, and is commonly designated approximately by numbers, according to the scale of hardness devised by Mohs, as follows:

1. Talc	6. Orthoclase
2. Gypsum	7. Quartz ⎱ Nearly the
3. Calcite	8. Topaz ⎰ same
4. Fluorite ⎱ Essentially	9. Corundum
5. Apatite ⎰ identical	10. Diamond

Intermediate values are expressed as one-half (as $3\frac{1}{2}$ or 3.5, etc.). Closer determinations are seldom attempted. Approximate hardness can often be determined conveniently by noting the ease or difficulty with which a mineral scratches, or is scratched by, one of the following:

Thumb nail, $2\frac{1}{2}$

Copper or silver coin, 3

Knife blade, $5\frac{1}{2}$–6

Window glass, $5\frac{1}{2}$–6

File, $6\frac{1}{2}$–7

Quartz or flint, 7

Emery (wheel or paper), 8–9

Corundum or "Alundum " (wheel, paper, or whetstone), 9

" Carborundum " (wheel, etc.), $9\frac{1}{2}$

Diamond (glazier's point), 10

With practice hardness can be closely estimated with the knife alone. Rubbing on a fine-cut file is sometimes convenient; a soft mineral yields much powder and little noise, and vice versa. Hardness must be tested on a sound surface, and brittleness must not be confused with softness. Fibrous, scaly, granular, and pulverulent masses often crumble easily and seem much softer than they are. A few minerals show notable differences in hardness in different directions. Cyanite, the most striking example, is easily scratched with a knife lengthwise on the broad faces (H 4–5), but crosswise and on the thin edges it is harder than steel (H 6–7).

The ore minerals of the heavy metals—silver, copper, mercury, lead—are soft, mostly below 3. Sulphides, arsenides, and oxides of iron, nickel, and cobalt are relatively hard; other sulphides are mostly soft, as are also most carbonates, sulphates, and hydrous minerals. The very hard minerals are chiefly oxides and silicates and many of them contain aluminum.

Tenacity is the degree or character of cohesion. The distinctions commonly recognized are: *sectile*, may be cut with a knife, but slices are not malleable; *malleable,* flattens under the hammer; *flexible,* may be bent; *elastic,* springs back after bending; *brittle,* fragile, easily broken, the opposite of *tough*; *friable,* easily crumbled; *pulverulent,* powdery, with little or no cohesion, like chalk or clay.

Specific Gravity is the weight of a substance compared with that of an equal volume of water; thus a mineral with specific gravity 3 is three times as heavy as water. The common methods of determining specific gravity are based on the fact that the loss in weight of a body immersed in water is the weight of an equal volume of water. Thus, if the weight of mineral in air is a and its weight in water is w, sp. gr. $= \dfrac{a}{a-w}$. A porous texture, included or attached impurities, or alteration products will vitiate the result and may render it worthless.

The best-known method of determination of the specific gravity of minerals is by the use of the Jolly balance (figured in Kraus and Hunt's Mineralogy, p. 98). This method depends for its accuracy to a large extent upon the proper adjustment of the spring which is a part of the instrument. A still more accurate method of determination is by means of the pycnometer (*op. cit.,* p. 99). In either method, the total removal of all air bubbles from the sample is essential.

Specific gravity finds important practical application in various processes of ore concentration whereby the heavy metal-bearing minerals are separated from the worthless lighter materials (gangue) which constitute the greater part of most ore deposits. Thus in the *jig* the crushed ore is agitated with water in such manner that the heavy particles gradually work their way to the bottom while the gangue minerals rise to the top. Ores composed of finer mineral particles are often concentrated on inclined *tables,* which are vibrated in such manner as to give the heavier particles a lateral movement, thus separating them from the gangue, as they are moved in a thin sheet of water across the riffles on the inclined surface.

For mineral particles less than one or two millimeters in diameter the most successful method of concentration is *flotation,* in which the heavy minerals rise to the surface of the water and the lighter gangue minerals sink to the bottom. This apparent reversal of gravity is caused by bubbles of air (and in some processes by other gases or by globules of oil) which attach themselves selectively to minerals of metallic, adamantine, or resinous luster, which are not readily wetted by water, and lift them to the surface, where, despite their high specific gravity, they float in the froth. The gangue minerals have vitreous, pearly, or earthy luster and are easily wetted by water; hence the rising bubbles do not attach themselves to these minerals and they quickly fall to the bottom.

Minerals of fixed composition have a definite specific gravity. Many species in which one or more constituents are subject to isomorphous replacement, or substitution, show a corresponding range in specific gravity between certain limits. Whether the specific gravity of a mineral is high, low, or of intermediate value may generally be judged by the hand without weighing.

Color is a fairly definite and fixed characteristic of minerals having metallic luster, but is very variable in most others. In some it varies with isomorphous variations in composition, in some it is due to minute colored inclusions, while in others it is possibly caused by a slight amount of some substance in solid solution. In general the cause of color in minerals is little understood. Some species change or lose their color under the influence of light, heat, x-rays, and radium emanations; and, on the other hand, color appears under these influences in some minerals that were formerly colorless.

Mechanical color effects include *play* or *change of color*, irregular changes and flashes as the mineral is viewed in different directions; *opalescence*, a milky appearance, as in translucent opal; *asterism*, a star effect by reflected or transmitted light, due to structure planes or symmetrically arranged inclusions; *iridescence*, bands of prismatic colors due to cracks within or to a surface film produced by alteration or deposition; *tarnish*, an altered surface coating of different color from the fresh mineral.

Streak is the color of the finest powder of a mineral, or of the mark it will make on a harder substance, such as unglazed porcelain, a clean whetstone, or a fine-cut file. The same result is obtained by scratching the mineral in the test for hardness, or by grinding a fragment in a mortar, or by crushing it to fine flour with a hammer on clean iron or steel. The color of the streak varies but little, even in those minerals that show great color variations in the mass. Rubbing the streak with the finger often brings out the color more distinctly.

Transparency, or diaphaneity.—A mineral is called *transparent* only when objects can be seen clearly through it, *translucent* if light is transmitted but objects are not seen, and *opaque* if no light passes, even through the thinnest edges. Semitransparent and semitranslucent express intermediate degrees. Many minerals that are commonly called opaque are translucent on thin edges and transparent in the thin sections that are prepared for microscopic study.

Luster is the surface appearance of an object, or the manner in which it reflects light. It is largely dependent on the character of the surface, but is modified by the degree of transparency and the refractive index of the substance. Several kinds of luster are commonly recognized. *Metallic* is the luster of metals and of some opaque minerals; *submetallic* and *metalloidal* refer to the same thing in subordinate degree. In mineralogy other types of luster are often referred to collectively as *nonmetallic*, but the following varieties should be readily recognized: *vitreous*, the luster of a broken surface of glass; *adamantine*, somewhat like oiled glass— the luster of the uncut diamond, zircon, cerussite, and other minerals of high refractive index; *resinous*, the luster of resin or sphalerite. *Greasy*, *oily*, *pitchy*, *waxy*, *pearly*, and *silky* are self-explaining terms. Degrees of intensity are designated, in the order of decreasing brilliance, as *splendent*, *shining*, *glistening*, *glimmering*. *Dull* signifies the absence of luster, as in chalk.

Besides the value of luster as an aid in the recognition of minerals, it is to be noted that this optical property is associated with other physical characters that are fundamental in the processes of selective flotation, as noted under "Specific Gravity," page 12.

Fluorescence is the capacity possessed by some minerals for producing in sunlight or ultraviolet light a color different from their own and from that of the exciting light. Thus green or colorless fluorite commonly shows a bluish or purplish color in sunlight.

This property of minerals is sometimes useful, as at Franklin, New Jersey, where the concentration of certain zinc ores is controlled by the aid of fluorescence induced by ultraviolet light. Under the influence of these invisible rays small particles of willemite (zinc silicate) that escape with the tailings, and which cannot be distinguished in ordinary light, are made to glow with a brilliant greenish white fluorescence. This makes it possible so to adjust the processes of concentration as to keep such losses down to the minimum.

Phosphorescence is the glow induced in some minerals by the action of moderate heat, friction, mechanical or electrical stress, ordinary light, ultraviolet light, and radium emanations. The glow may continue a few seconds or minutes after the removal of the cause. Nearly all specimens of some minerals (as diamond, willemite, kunzite, sphalerite) are phosphorescent. In others this property exists only in individual specimens or those from certain localities.

Taste.—Some minerals that are soluble in water have a characteristic taste, which may be *salty*, or *saline*, the taste of common salt (sodium chloride); *alkaline*, the taste of soda (sodium bicarbonate); *acid*, or *sour*, the taste of sulphuric acid; *astringent*, the taste of copperas (ferrous sulphate); *sweetish astringent*, the taste of alum (potassium-aluminum sulphate); *cooling*, the taste of niter (potassium nitrate) or potassium chlorate.

Odor.—Some minerals yield a characteristic odor when struck with a hammer, rubbed, breathed upon, or heated. These are described as *arsenical*, or *alliaceous*, like the odor of garlic (due to arsenic); *selenious*, or *horseradish*, the odor of decaying horseradish (selenium); *sulphurous*, the odor of burning sulphur (sulphur); *fetid*, the odor of rotten eggs (hydrogen sulphide); *argillaceous*, the odor of clay when breathed upon.

Feel is the sensation upon touching or handling minerals. Some that are very soft and greasy, soapy, or *unctuous* to the touch are contrasted with others that are notably rough, harsh, or *meager*.

Magnetism is most pronounced in magnetite, the only mineral that is strongly attracted by a common horseshoe magnet or a magnetized knife blade, which will pick up grains the size of a pea or larger. Pyrrhotite, or magnetic pyrites, and native platinum (alloyed with iron) are also commonly magnetic, and many specimens of hematite, ilmenite, chromite, and franklinite are weakly so and are attracted in minute particles. All iron-bearing minerals, even silicates with small percentages of iron, respond to powerful electromagnets; and magnetic properties are important in some methods of ore concentration. Magnetite that possesses attracting power and polarity is called *lodestone*, or *natural magnet*. This property is utilized in various methods of concentration that are applied to ores of iron, or of iron with other metals, as zinc and manganese. It is also useful in the removal of iron-bearing minerals from mixtures in which they are not desired.

Very recently a method involving static electricity has been developed, whereby small particles of slate and similar materials are quite thoroughly and inexpensively separated from grains of different shape and composition, like quartz sand.

For application of either of the above processes, the mineral material to be treated is usually ground to the size of ordinary sand before treatment.

Pyroelectricity is the capacity for developing electric charges at opposite ends or other parts of a crystal or crystalline fragment when gently heated. This property is most notable in hemimorphic minerals, such as tourmaline and calamine (electric calamine). The poles will attract minute bits of paper and other very light objects.

CHEMICAL PROPERTIES

Composition.—Minerals are either uncombined elements, such as native gold (Au), copper (Cu), sulphur (S), or definite compounds of the elements, as quartz (SiO_2), calcite ($CaCO_3$), gypsum ($CaSO_4 \cdot 2H_2O$). Chemical composition is the most fundamental property of minerals, and for purposes of description they are commonly classified on this basis. Thus the native elements are grouped together, and likewise the sulphides, oxides, carbonates, silicates, phosphates, etc. In determinative tables, such as appear in this book, the object is to group them according to such physical or chemical characters as will most facilitate the identification of unknown specimens.

Chemical analyses of minerals often vary from the formulas by which they are represented on account of one or more of the following causes: (1) Isomorphism (see below); (2) solid solution (e.g., pyrrhotite with excess S); (3) alteration or decomposition; (4) inclusion of crystals or particles of another mineral; (5) other minerals attached to the specimen or particles mixed in an aggregate, as gangue minerals in an ore.

Isomorphism is the capacity possessed by some minerals of analogous composition and similar crystal form of uniting in variable proportions to form homogeneous *mixed crystals*. In the group of the rhombohedral carbonate minerals, for example, calcite, which is essentially $CaCO_3$, may also contain more or less magnesite, $MgCO_3$, siderite, $FeCO_3$, and rhodochrosite, $MnCO_3$. This mingling of isomorphous minerals in the same crystal is equivalent to the substitution of magnesium, iron, and manganese for a part of the calcium in calcite, and may be expressed in the chemical formula thus: $(Ca, Mg, Fe, Mn)CO_3$. Salts of different acids may also be isomorphous, as in the apatite group, which includes phosphates, arsenates, and vanadates. Most minerals are isomorphous mixtures and consequently subject, within limits, to variations in composition, specific gravity, color, and other properties, corresponding to the varying proportions of the interchangeable constituents.

Polymorphism, or **pleomorphism,** is the occurrence of two or more minerals of the same composition but differing in crystallization and in physical and optical properties. In some cases there are also pronounced differences in chemical properties. Native carbon is *dimorphous*, occurring as graphite and diamond; titanium dioxide forms the three minerals, rutile, brookite, and octahedrite, and hence is said to be *trimorphous*. *Allotrophy* and *isomerism* are chemical terms with somewhat similar meaning; thus there are four allotropic forms of sulphur; the butyl alcohols and ordinary ether are isomeric.

IDENTIFICATION OF MINERALS BY MEANS OF THEIR PHYSICAL PROPERTIES

Preliminary Instructions and Precautions

If the *crystal system* can be determined, either from crystals or from cleavage, the crystal tables, pages 198 to 205, will often prove the most convenient means of identification.

Physical properties can be accurately determined only from fresh, homogeneous material, preferably crystalline. If the specimen is tarnished or decomposed at the surface a fresh fracture will often disclose unaltered material within.

Hardness of a mineral is estimated by comparison with a substance that is just hard enough to scratch it, remembering that substances of the same hardness will scratch each other slightly. Press a point or edge of known hardness against a smooth surface of the mineral and move it back and forth in the same line about one-eighth of an inch (3 mm.). Select an inconspicuous place and do not scratch the specimen more than necessary.

A " chalk " mark must not be mistaken for a true scratch. Brush away the powder and examine the smooth surface of the mineral. Rough or altered surfaces do not give reliable results. Alteration products are generally softer than the original mineral.

Powdery, earthy, and fibrous minerals generally appear to be both softer and lighter than they really are. On the other hand, a soft mineral may appear harder than it really is on account of attached or intermingled grains of quartz or other hard substance.

A crystal or other mineral specimen should not be separated entirely from the matrix in which it is imbedded or the rock or mineral aggregate to which it is attached. Mode of occurrence and mineral associates are important aids to identification and shed much light on questions of origin.

Avoid breaking any specimen if there are enough fragments for tests. When it is necessary to break it, hold the specimen firmly in the hand, so as to catch the fragments in the palm, and strike a quick, sharp blow with a light hammer on a projecting

18

edge or corner near the under surface.   Do not break nor otherwise injure a good crystal if it is possible to avoid it.

Luster, which describes the appearance of the surface of the mineral when light is reflected from it (as metallic luster from metal surfaces, vitreous luster from glass or quartz, or dull or earthy luster from chalk or clay), will often serve as an aid in mineral determination.   (See p. 14.)

GENERAL CLASSIFICATION

(For abbreviations used in the tables, see page 217.)

Many minerals of the rarer species, here merely mentioned, or not included, may be found in other books on mineralogy. (See Bibliography, p. 219.)

Streak black or nearly so: SECTION   PAGE

   Mineral silver-white to steel-gray.............. 1   21
   Mineral dark gray, black, blue, or green........ 2   22
   Mineral yellow, red, or brown.................. 3   28

Streak silver-white to steel gray................. 4   30

Streak chalk-white, colorless, or pale colored:

   Mineral white, colorless, or pale colored:
      Distinct cleavage in one direction only..... 5   32
      Distinct cleavage in two directions........ 6   36
      Distinct cleavage in three or more directions. 7   39
      No distinct cleavage [1].................... 8   44

   Mineral dark gray to black:
      Distinct cleavage in one direction only..... 9   52
      Distinct cleavage in two directions........ 10   54
      Distinct cleavage in three or more directions. 11   55
      No distinct cleavage [1].................... 12   57

   Mineral yellow, red or brown:
      Distinct cleavage in one direction only..... 13   59
      Distinct cleavage in two directions........ 14   61
      Distinct cleavage in three or more directions. 15   63
      No distinct cleavage [1].................... 16   66

   Mineral green, blue, or violet:
      Distinct cleavage in one direction only..... 17   71
      Distinct cleavage in two directions........ 18   74
      Distinct cleavage in three or more directions. 19   76
      No distinct cleavage [1].................... 20   77

Streak yellow, red, or brown:

   Mineral black or nearly so................. 21   82
   Mineral yellow, red, or brown.............. 22   85

Streak blue or green........................... 23   90

[1] A microscope, or even a pocket lens, will reveal cleavage in many fine-grained minerals. Without such aid, on specimens with fine granular, fibrous, or dense texture, it may be impossible to determine whether or not the mineral has cleavage. Hence, if not found in this section of the tables, specimens of this character should be sought in the three preceding sections, disregarding altogether the question of cleavage.

SECTION 1

Streak black or nearly so; mineral silver-white to steel-gray.

H.

1½ G. 7.9–8.3 SYLVANITE. (See p. 30.)
2

2 G. 5.5–6.0 JAMESONITE (*Feather Ore*), $Pb_2Sb_2S_5$; Pb 50.8%; often some
3 Fe.

Struct.—Acicular orthorhombic crystals; fibrous, felted, compact; feathery appearance common. **Cleavage** distinct, one direction crosswise (001); brittle; fracture uneven.

Color steel-gray to dark lead-gray. **Streak** grayish black. **Luster** metallic. Opaque. (See p. 142.)

In veins with bournonite, galena, sphalerite, stibnite.

2½ G. 8.3–8.4 KRENNERITE. (See p. 30.)

2½ G. 8.3–8.5 HESSITE, Ag_2Te; Ag 63.3%; often some Au.
3 Struct.—Fine grained to compact; isometric crystals rare. **Cleavage** none; somewhat sectile; fracture uneven.

Color steel-gray to lead-gray. **Streak** gray. **Luster** metallic. Opaque. (See p. 148.)

In veins with other tellurides, pyrite, chalcopyrite, fluorite.

4 G. 4.3–4.5 *Stannite* (*Tin Pyrites*), Cu_2FeSnS_4; Sn 27.5%; Cu 29.5%; also Zn replacing iron up to 10%.

Struct.—Compact, granular, disseminated; small tetragonal crystals rare. **Cleavage** indistinct; brittle; fracture uneven.

Color steel-gray to iron-black; tarnish bluish; may be yellow from admixture of chalcopyrite. **Streak** black. **Luster** metallic. Opaque. (See p. 142.)

In veins with quartz, pyrite, scheelite, chalcopyrite, gold, silver, galena, sphalerite.

5½ G. 6.0–6.3 COBALTITE (*Cobalt Glance*), CoAsS; Co 35.5%; As 45.2%; some Fe.

Struct.—Isometric crystals (cubes, pyritohedrons, Figs. 5 15, 16); granular, compact. **Cleavage** indistinct, three directions at 90 (100); brittle; fracture uneven.

Color silver-white to gray, sometimes reddish. **Streak** grayish black. **Luster** metallic. Opaque. (See p. 140.)

With silver, smaltite, niccolite, pyrrhotite, chalcopyrite; often with pink coating of erythrite.

21

H.

5½ G. 4.8–5.0 LINNAEITE (*Cobalt Pyrites*) (Ni,Co)$_3$S$_4$; Ni 12–43%; Co 11–45%. (See p. 144).

5½ G. 5.6–6.2 GERSDORFFITE, NiAsS; Ni 35.4%; often much Fe. (See p. 140.)

5½ G. 5.9–6.2 ARSENOPYRITE (*Arsenical Pyrites*), FeAsS; As 46%.

6 **Struct.**—Granular, compact; orthorhombic crystals, like marcasite. **Cleavage** indistinct, two directions at 68° and 112° (110); brittle; fracture uneven.
Color silver-white to steel-gray. **Streak** grayish black. **Luster** metallic. Opaque. (See p. 140.)
With ores of gold, silver, lead, tin; with pyrite, chalcopyrite, sphalerite, smaltite.

5½ G. 6.4–6.6 SMALTITE, CoAs$_2$; Co 28.2%; some Ni and Fe.

6 **Struct.**—Granular, compact; isometric-pyritohedral crystals rare. **Cleavage** indistinct, four directions at 70½° and 109½° (111); brittle; fracture uneven.
Color tin-white to steel-gray; often grayish tarnish and pink coating of erythrite. **Streak** grayish black. **Luster** metallic. Opaque. (See p. 140.)
With niccolite, cobaltite, native bismuth and silver, proustite, barite, fluorite, calcite.

5½ G. 6.4–6.6 CHLOANTHITE, NiAs$_2$; Ni 28.1%; some Co and Fe.

6 **Struct.**—Granular, compact; isometric-pyritohedral crystals rare. Cleavage indistinct, four directions at 70½ and 109½° (111); brittle; fracture uneven.
Color tin-white to steel-gray; often grayish tarnish and green coating of annabergite. **Streak** grayish black. **Luster** metallic. Opaque. (See p. 140.)
With niccolite, cobaltite, proustite, native silver and bismuth, fluorite, barite, calcite.

6 G. 4.8–4.0 MARCASITE. (See p. 20.)
6½

6 G. 4.7–4.8 *Braunite*. (See p. 28.)

SECTION 2

Streak black or nearly so; mineral dark gray, black, blue, or green.

0 CHALCOCITE, MELACONITE, ARGENTITE, PYROLUSITE. WAD.

1   Black, powdery, earthy. (See pp. 24, 25, 26.)

1 G. 4.7–4.8 MOLYBDENITE, MoS$_2$; Mo 60.0%.

H.

1½   **Struct.**—Scales, foliated masses, grains; tabular hexagonal crystals rare. **Cleavage** perfect, one direction (0001); thin flakes flexible; sectile; feels greasy.

Color bluish lead-gray. **Streak** grayish black, greenish on glazed paper or porcelain. **Luster** metallic. Opaque. (See p. 152.)

In granite, pegmatite, syenite, gneiss, with cassiterite, pyrrhotite, wolframite, tourmaline, topaz; in crystalline limestone with epidote, chalcopyrite; in crystalline schists; in basic igneous rocks.

1   **G. 1.9–2.3 GRAPHITE** (*Black Lead, Plumbago*), C; often Fe, clay, etc.
2   **Struct.**—Foliated, scaly, granular, earthy; tabular hexagonal crystals rare. **Cleavage** perfect, one direction (0001); thin flakes flexible; sectile; feels greasy.

Color steel-gray to iron-black. **Streak** grayish black, shiny. **Luster** metallic. Opaque. (See p. 152.)

In gneiss and mica schist; in crystalline limestone with garnet, spinel, wollastonite, pyroxene, amphibole; in pegmatite.

1   **G. 3.0–4.3 WAD** (*Bog Manganese*), MnO_2, H_2O; often Fe, Si, Al, Ba, Co.
3   Mn up to 60%.

Struct.—Earthy, porous (floating) to compact; sometimes globular; amorphous. **Cleavage** none; brittle; fracture earthy.

Color bluish or brownish black to dull black. **Streak** brownish black to black. **Luster** metallic to dull. Opaque. (See pp. 150, 186.)

In residual soil, clay, and swamp deposits, with psilomelane, pyrolusite, siderite, limonite.

1½ **G. 4.6**   **COVELLITE**, CuS; Cu 66.4%.
2   **Struct.**—Disseminated, compact, in crusts; tabular hexagonal crystals rare. **Cleavage** perfect, one direction (0001); thin laminæ flexible; brittle in mass; fracture uneven.

Color dark indigo-blue. **Streak** lead-gray to black. **Luster** submetallic, resinous, dull. Opaque. (See p. 144.)

In copper ores with bornite, chalcocite, chalcopyrite.

2   **G. 4.5–4.6 STIBNITE** (*Antimonite, Antimony Glance*), Sb_2S_3; Sb 71.8%.

Struct.—Long prismatic orthorhombic crystals, often bent or twisted; columnar, bladed, granular. **Cleavage** perfect, one direction lengthwise (010); crystals striated lengthwise; brittle; slightly sectile; fracture uneven; crystals slightly flexible.

Color lead-gray; tarnish black, sometimes iridescent. **Streak** dark lead-gray. **Luster** metallic. Opaque. (See p. 140.)

In quartz veins in granite and gneiss with pyrite, sphalerite, galena, barite, cinnabar, realgar.

H.

2 G. 4.7–4.8 PYROLUSITE, MnO_2; commonly a little H_2O; Mn 63.2%.

2½ Struct.—Columnar, acicular, fibrous, radial, dendritic, powdery; crystals pseudomorphous after manganite (orthorhombic). Cleavage none; brittle; fracture splintery, uneven.

Color black to steel-gray. Streak black, bluish black. Luster metallic, dull. Opaque. Rubbed streak characteristic. (See p. 150.)

In residual clays of limestone and slate with manganite, psilomelane, hematite, limonite, barite; dendritic in joint cracks.

2 G. 7.2–7.4 ARGENTITE (*Silver Glance*), Ag_2S; Ag 87.1%.

2½ Struct.—Compact; disseminated, incrusting; rough isometric crystals rare, often distorted. Cleavage indistinct; perfectly sectile, cuts like lead; fracture hackly.

Color lead-gray to black. Streak dark lead-gray, shiny. Luster metallic. Opaque. (See p. 142.)

In veins with silver, ruby silvers, stephanite, galena, smaltite, niccolite.

2 G. 6.2–6.3 STEPHANITE (*Brittle Silver*), Ag_5SbS_4; Ag 68.5%.

2½ Struct.—Disseminated, compact; tabular or thick prismatic orthorhombic crystals, often pseudohexagonal. Cleavage imperfect; brittle; fracture uneven.

Color dark lead-gray to iron-black. Streak iron-black. Luster metallic. Opaque. (See p. 142.)

In veins with other silver minerals, galena, barite.

2
3 G. 6.0–6.2 POLYBASITE, $(Ag,Cu)_9SbS_6$; Ag 62–72%; Cu 3–10%; sometimes As.

Struct.—Tabular six-sided monoclinic crystals with triangular markings on base; compact, disseminated. Cleavage imperfect, one direction (001); brittle; fracture uneven.

Color iron-black; in thin splinters cherry-red. Streak black. Luster metallic. Nearly opaque. (See p. 142.)

In veins with other silver minerals, galena, sphalerite; replacements in limestone.

2
3 G. 5.5–6.0 JAMESONITE. (See p. 21.)

2½ G. 7.4–7.6 GALENA (*Galenite, Lead Glance*), PbS; Pb 86.6%; often Ag.

Struct.—Cleavable masses, granular, compact; isometric crystals (commonly cubes, Fig. 5). Cleavage perfect, three directions at 90° (100); brittle.

Color and streak dark lead-gray. Luster metallic. Opaque. (See p. 142.)

In ore deposits with sphalerite, pyrite, chalcopyrite, barite, fluorite, calcite.

H.

$2\frac{1}{2}$ G. 5.5–5.8   CHALCOCITE *(Copper Glance)*, Cu_2S;   Cu 79.8%;   some-
3   times Fe.

Struct.—Granular compact, disseminated; rarely in pseudohexagonal orthorhombic crystals, deeply striated. **Cleavage** indistinct; rather brittle; fracture conchoidal.

Color dark lead-gray; tarnish dull black, blue, or green. May be coated with malachite (green) or azurite (blue). **Streak** dark gray to black, shiny. **Luster** metallic. Opaque. (See p. 144.)

In veins with pyrite, chalcopyrite, bornite, tetrahedrite, hematite, galena.

$2\frac{1}{2}$ G. 5.7–5.9   BOURNONITE   *(Cogwheel Ore)*, $PbCuSbS_3$;   Pb 42.5%;   Cu
3   13%.

Struct.—Fine grained, compact; thick tabular orthorhombic crystals or cross "cogwheel" twins. **Cleavage** indistinct; brittle; fracture uneven.

Color steel-gray to iron-black. **Streak** dark gray to black. **Luster** metallic. Opaque. (See p. 142.)

In veins with galena, sphalerite, tetrahedrite, siderite, stibnite, chalcocite.

$2\frac{1}{2}$ G. 8.3–8.5   HESSITE.   (See p. 31.)
3

$2\frac{1}{2}$ G. 8.7–9.0   PETZITE.   (See p. 148.)
3

3   G. 4.4–4.5   ENARGITE, Cu_3AsS_4;   Cu 48.3%;   As 19.1%;   some Sb.

Struct.—Compact, columnar, granular; small prismatic orthorhombic crystals rare. **Cleavage** distinct, two directions lengthwise (110) at 82° and 98°; brittle; fracture uneven.

Color and **streak** grayish black. **Luster** metallic. Opaque. (See p. 140.)

In veins with pyrite, chalcopyrite, bornite, chalcocite, tennantite.

3   G. 4.4–5.1   TETAHEDRITE *(Gray Copper)*, Cu_3SbS_3; often some Fe
4   Zn, Pb, Ag, As.   Cu 46.8%;   *Freibergite* has Ag 3–15%. With increasing As grades into *Tennantite*, Cu_3AsS_3.

Struct.—Isometric-tetrahedral crystals (Figs. 13, 14); granular, compact. **Cleavage** none; brittle; fracture uneven.

Color steel-gray to iron-black. Sometimes coated with brass-yellow chalcopyrite. **Streak** dark gray, black, reddish brown. **Luster** metallic. Opaque. (See p. 140.)

In veins with silver, lead, and copper ores.

H.

3   G. 5.8–6.2   MELACONITE (*Tenorite, Black Oxide of Copper*), CuO; Cu
4   79.8%.

Struct.—Earthy massive and powder (*melaconite*). Thin scaly pseudo-hexagonal monoclinic crystals (*tenorite*) rare; Cleavage indistinct; crystals brittle; fracture uneven.

Color steel-gray to black. Streak black. Earthy varieties soil the fingers. Luster metallic; dull. Opaque. (See p. 246.)

Black coatings and crusts on native copper and various copper minerals.

3   G. 3.0–4.3   WAD (*Bog Manganese*), MnO_2, H_2O; often Fe, Si, Al, Ba, Co.
4   Black, compact; H 1–6.   (See p. 186.)

$3\frac{1}{2}$ G. 4.2–4.4   MANGANITE.   (See p. 83.)
4

4   G. 4.3–4.5   *Stannite*.   (See p. 21.)

5   G. 7.2–7.5   WOLFRAMITE   (Fe,Mn)WO_4;   grades into *Ferberite*,
$5\frac{1}{2}$ FeWO_4, and *Huebnerite*, MnWO_4; WO_3 about 76%.

Struct.—Thick tabular, short columnar, and bladed monoclinic crystals, resembling orthorhombic; cleavable, granular, compact. Cleavage perfect, one direction (010); brittle; fracture uneven.

Color dark gray, black, brownish black, reddish brown. Streak brownish black, black. Luster metallic, submetallic. Opaque. May be slightly magnetic. (See pp. 148, 162, 178.)

In veins in granite with cassiterite, quartz, mica, fluorite, apatite, scheelite, pyrite, galena, sphalerite; also in sands.

5   G. 4.5–5.0   ILMENITE (*Titanic Iron Ore*), FeTiO$_3$; Fe 36.8%.
6   Ti 31.6%; sometimes Mg.

Struct.—Thin plates, granular, compact, disseminated; pebbles, sand; thick tabular hexagonal-rhombohedral crystals. Cleavage none; sometimes partings; brittle; fracture conchoidal.

Color and streak iron-black, brownish black. Luster metallic, submetallic. Opaque. May be slightly magnetic. (See pp. 150, 152.)

Disseminated and masses in igneous rocks, gneiss, schist; with hematite, magnetite, titanite, apatite, rutile, quartz. Common in black sands.

5   G. 3.7–4.7   PSILOMELANE, MnO_2, MnO, H_2O, BaO, K_2O.
6   Struct.—Compact, botryoidal, reniform, stalactitic; no crystals. Cleavage none; brittle; fracture conchoidal, uneven.

Color iron-black, bluish black, steel-gray. May have sooty coating of pyrolusite or be in layers with it. Streak black, brownish balck. Luster metallic, dull. Opaque. (See p. 150.)

With other manganese minerals, limonite, barite.

H.

5   G. 3.0–4.3   WAD (*Bog Manganese*), MnO_2, H_2O; often Fe, Si, Al, Ba, Co.
6   Black, compact. H 1–6. (See p. 186.)

5½   G. 9.0–9.7   URANINITE (*Pitchblende*), UO_3, UO_2, Pb, Th, La, Y, He, Ra,
         etc.

   Struct.—Botryoidal, granular, lamellar, compact; isometric crystals
rare. **Cleavage** none; brittle; fracture conchoidal.
   Color greenish or brownish black, pitch-black. **Streak** brownish black,
grayish black, olive green. **Luster** pitch-like, submetallic, dull. Opaque.
(See p. 152.)
   With ores of silver, lead, copper, bismuth; also in pegmatites.

5½   G. 4.0–4.1   *Ilvaite*, $CaFe_3(OH)(SiO_4)_2$.
6   **Struct.**—Prismatic orthorhombic crystals, striated lengthwise; columnar, compact. **Cleavage** indistinct, two directions at 90° (010) (001);
brittle; fracture uneven.
   Color black, greenish to brownish black; often softer yellowish altered
coating. **Streak** black with greenish or brownish tinge. **Luster** submetallic,
vitreous. Opaque.
   In limestone and dolomite; with pyroxene, actinolite, iron minerals.

5½   G. 4.9–5.2   MAGNETITE (*Magnetic Iron Ore*), $FeFe_2O_4$; Fe 72.4%;
6½   sometimes Mg, Mn, Ti.

   Struct.—Granular, compact, lamellar, disseminated; sand; isometric
crystals, commonly octahedrons and dodecahedrons (Figs. 1, 7). **Cleavage**
none; may have octahedral **parting** (111) four directions at 70½° and 109½°;
brittle; fracture conchoidal, uneven.
   Color iron-black. **Streak** black. **Luster** metallic. Opaque. Strongly
attracted by magnet; may be natural magnet (*lodestone*). (See pp. 146,
148.)
   Ore bodies and disseminated in igneous and metamorphic rocks; black
sands; with hornblende, pyroxene, feldspars, chlorite, pyrite, apatite,
ilmenite, zircon.

5½   G. 5.1–5.2   FRANKLINITE, $(Fe,Mn,Zn)(Fe,Mn)_2O_4$; Fe 39–47%; Mn
6½   10–20%; Zn 5.5–18.5%.

   Struct.—Compact, granular, rounded disseminated grains; isometric
crystals (octahedrons, Fig. 1). **Cleavage** none; indistinct octahedral parting (111) four directions at 70½° and 109½°; brittle; fracture conchoidal,
uneven.
   Color iron-black. **Streak** black, brownish black, reddish brown. **Luster**
metallic, dull. Opaque. May be slightly magnetic. (See p. 150.)
   In crystalline limestone (New Jersey) with zincite, willemite, rhodonite,
tephroite.

6   G. 5.3–7.3   COLUMBITE. (See pp. 84, 148.)

H.

6   G. 4.7–4.8   *Braunite,* $3Mn_2O_3 . MnSiO_3$; Mn 64.4%.

6½   **Struct.**—Granular; drusy crusts; minute tetragonal crystals, resembling octahedrons. **Cleavage** distinct, four directions at 70° and 110° (111); brittle; fracture uneven.

    Color brownish black to steel-gray. **Streak** black, brownish black. **Luster** submetallic, greasy. Opaque. (See p. 150.)

    With manganese minerals, magnetite, hematite, barite.

SECTION 3

Streak black or nearly so; mineral yellow, red, or brown.

2   G. 6.0–6.2   P OLYBASITE.   (See p. 24.)
3

2½   G. 9.0   C ALAVERITE.   (See p. 30.)

2½   G. 8.3–8.4   K RENNERITE.   (See p. 148.)

3   G. 4.9–5.4   BORNITE (*Peacock Ore, Horseflesh Ore*), Cu_5FeS_4; Cu 63.3%.

    Struct.—Compact, granular; isometric crystals (cubes) rare. **Cleavage** none; brittle; fracture uneven.

    Color copper-red to bronze-brown; tarnish deep blue, purple, and variegated. **Streak** grayish black. **Luster** metallic. Opaque. (See p. 142.)

    In veins and ore deposits with other copper minerals, pyrite, siderite.

3   G. 8.1–8.2   *Altaite,* PbTe; Pb 62.3%. (See p. 148.)

3   G. 5.3–5.7   M ILLERITE (*Nickel Pyrites*), NiS; Ni 64.7%.

3½   **Struct.**—Needle-like to hair-like crystals (hexagonal-rhombohedral); fibrous crusts, compact. **Cleavage** rhombohedral, difficult to observe; brittle; slender crystals elastic; fracture splintery, uneven.

    Color brass-yellow, bronze-yellow. **Streak** greenish black. **Luster** metallic. Opaque. (See p. 144.)

    In cavities in hematite ore and limestone; with pyrrhotite, chalcopyrite, chloanthite, barite, fluorite, siderite.

3½   G. 4.1–4.3   CHALCOPYRITE (*Copper Pyrites*), $CuFeS_2$; Cu 34.5%
4

    Struct.—Compact, granular, disseminated; sometimes tetragonal crystals resembling tetrahedrons. **Cleavage** indistinct; brittle; fracture uneven.

    Color brass-yellow, golden yellow; tarnish often iridescent or deep blue, purple, and black. **Streak** greenish black. **Luster** metallic. Opaque. (See p. 142.)

    In schists, veins, and contact deposits with quartz, calcite, pyrite, bornite, chalcocite, galena, sphalerite.

H.

$2\frac{1}{2}$ G. 4.6–5.1   Pentlandite (Fe,Ni)S; Ni 18–40%.   (See p. 144.)
4

$3\frac{1}{2}$ G. 4.5–4.6   PYRRHOTITE (*Magnetic Pyrites*), FeS;   S 36.4%;   **may**
$4\frac{1}{2}$ have up to 3.5% additional S in solution.

Struct.—Compact, granular; tabular hexagonal crystals rare. **Cleavage** indistinct, one direction (0001); brittle; fracture uneven.

Color yellowish to brownish bronze; tarnish dark brown. **Streak** dark grayish black. **Luster** metallic. Opaque. Particles generally attracted by magnet. (See p. 144.)

In veins, schists, contacts, with pyrite, chalcopyrite, pentlandite, **galena**, apatite; accessory in basic igneous rocks; in magmatic segregations.

4   G. 4.3–4.5   *Stannite*.   (See p. 21.)

5   G. 7.2–7.5   WOLFRAMITE. ,   (See p. 26.)
$5\frac{1}{2}$

5   G. 7.3–7.7   Niccolite, NiAs; Ni 43.9%; some Fe, Co, Sb, S.

$5\frac{1}{2}$ **Struct.**—Compact, disseminated; small hexagonal crystals rare. **Cleavage** none; brittle; fracture uneven.

Color light copper-red; tarnish gray to blackish. May have coating of green (annabergite). **Streak** brownish black. **Luster** metallic. Opaque. (See p. 140.)

With cobalt, nickel, and silver minerals, bismuth, arsenic, calcite.

$5\frac{1}{2}$ G. 6.0–6.3   Cobaltite.   (See p. 21.)

6   G. 4.9–5.2   PYRITE (*Pyrites, Iron Pyrites, Fool's Gold*), FeS$_2$; S 53.3%;
$6\frac{1}{2}$ Fe 46.7%; sometimes Ni, Co, Cu, Au.

Struct.—Isometric crystals, cubes, pyritohedrons, octahedrons (Figs. 1, 5, 15, 16), often striated; compact, granular, botryoidal, stalactitic. Cleavage none; brittle; fracture uneven.

Color pale to full brass-yellow; tarnish brown, variegated, sometimes iridescent. **Streak** greenish black, brownish black. **Luster** metallic. Opaque. (See p. 144.)

Lenticular bodies in schists; concretions, disseminated in clay, **shale**, coal; in veins with other sulphides; accessory in all kinds of rocks.

6   G. 4.8–4.9   MARCASITE, FeS$_2$; Fe 46.6%; S 53.4%.
$6\frac{1}{2}$

Struct.—Tabular orthorhombic crystals and twin groups, often cockscomb or spear-head forms (*cockscomb pyrites, spearhead pyrites*); compact, stalactitic, rounded concretions. **Cleavage** indistinct, two directions at 75° and 105° (110); brittle; fracture uneven.

Color pale brass-yellow to almost white; tarnish deeper yellow to brown. **Streak** dark greenish to brownish black. **Luster** metallic. Opaque. (See p. 144.)

H.

Alters readily on exposure to capillary melanterite and to limonite; much less stable than pyrite. With lead and zinc ores, pyrite, chalcopyrite, cinnabar; concretions in clay, shale, and coal.

6   G. 4.7–4.8 . *Braunite.* (See p. 28.)
6½

SECTION 4

Streak silver-white to steel gray.

0   G. 13.6   *Mercury* (*Native Mercury, Quicksilver*), Hg; sometimes Ag.

Struct.—Small liquid globules; isometric crystals (octahedrons) at −39° C. **Cleavage** cubic; sp. g. of crystals 14.4.
Color tin-white. **Luster** metallic. Opaque. (See p. 146.)
With cinnabar and other mercury minerals and quartz, in shales, schists, some hot springs.

1½   G. 7.9–8.3   SYLVANITE, AuAgTe₄; Au 24.5%; Ag 13.4%.

2   **Struct.**—Branching aggregates, bladed, columnar, granular; monoclinic crystals rare. **Cleavage** distinct, one direction (010); brittle; fracture uneven.
Color silver-white to steel-gray, sometimes brassy tinge. **Streak** whitish steel-gray. **Luster** metallic. Opaque. (See p. 148.)
In veins with gold, calaverite, sphalerite, pyrite, tetrahedrite.

2   G. 9.7–9.8   BISMUTH (*Native Bismuth*), Bi; often also As, S, Te.

2½   **Struct.**—Laminated, granular, branching, disseminated; rarely distinct hexagonal-rhombohedral crystals. **Cleavage** distinct, one direction crosswise (0001); sectile; somewhat malleable.
Color silver-white, reddish; tarnish often brassy. **Streak** silver-white, shiny. **Luster** metallic. Opaque. (See p. 146.)
With ores of silver, cobalt, nickel, lead, zinc, tin, tungsten.

2   G. 6.1–6.3   *Tellurium* (*Native Tellurium*), Te; sometimes Se, Au, Fe. (See
2½   p. 148.)

2½   G. 9.0   CALAVERITE, (Au,Ag)Te₂; Au 38–41%; Ag 2–4%. (See p. 148.)

2½   G. 8.3–8.4   KRENNERITE, AuAgTe₄; Au 24.5%; Ag 13.4%. (See p. 148.)

2½   G. 10–12   SILVER (*Native Silver*), Ag; some Au, Cu.

3   **Struct.**—Grains, scales, plates, wire; isometric crystals commonly distorted. **Cleavage** none; malleable and ductile; fracture hackly.
Color silver-white; tarnish yellow, brown, black. **Streak** silver-white to light lead-gray, shiny. **Luster** metallic. Opaque. (See p. 146.)
In veins with silver, copper, and lead minerals, fluorite, calcite, barite, stibnite.

H.

$2\frac{1}{2}$　G. 8.3–8.5　HESSITE, Ag_2Te; Ag 63.3%; often some Au.

3　　**Struct.**—Fine grained to compact; isometric crystals rare. **Cleavage** none; somewhat sectile; fracture uneven.
　　　Color steel-gray to lead-gray. **Streak** gray. **Luster** metallic. Opaque. (See p. 148.)
　　　In veins with other tellurides, pyrite, chalcopyrite, fluorite.

$2\frac{1}{2}$　G. 8.7–9.0　PETZITE. (See p. 148.)

3

3　　G. 8.1–8.2　*Altaite*, PbTe; Pb 62.3%; some Ag and Au. (See p. 148.)

3　　G. 13.7–14.1　*Amalgam (Silver Amalgam)*, (Ag,Hg); Ag 27.5–95.8%. (See
$3\frac{1}{2}$　　　　　　　p. 146.)

3　　G. 6.6–6.7　*Antimony (Native Antimony)*, Sb; sometimes Ag, Fe, As.

$3\frac{1}{2}$　　**Struct.**—Granular, cleavable, radiated, botryoidal; rarely hexagonal-rhombohedral crystals. **Cleavage** distinct, one direction (0001); brittle; fracture uneven.
　　　Color and **streak** tin-white to light steel-gray. **Luster** metallic. Opaque. (See p. 140.)
　　　In veins with silver, arsenic, and antimony minerals.

3　　G. 5.6–5.7　ARSENIC (*Native Arsenic*), As; often some Sb.

3　　**Struct.**—Mammillary, concentric crusts, scaly, fine grained, compact; hexagonal-rhombohedral crystals rare. **Cleavage** distinct, one direction (0001); brittle; fracture uneven.
　　　Color and **streak** tin-white, tarnishing soon to dark gray. **Luster** metallic. Opaque. (See p. 140.)
　　　In veins with antimony minerals, ruby silver ores, realgar, orpiment, sphalerite.

$3\frac{1}{2}$　G. 9.4–9.9　*Dyscrasite (Antimonial Silver)*, Ag_3Sb to Ag_6Sb; Ag 73–84%.

4　　G. 14–19.　PLATINUM (*Native Platinum*), Pt; Fe up to 15%, also Pd, Rh,
$4\frac{1}{2}$　　　　　　　Ir, Os

　　　Struct.—Grains, scales, lumps; rarely distorted isometric crystals; **Cleavage** none; malleable, ductile; fracture hackly.
　　　Color tin-white, steel-gray; does not tarnish. **Streak** light steel-gray, shiny. **Luster** metallic. Opaque. May be magnetic. (See p. 152.)
　　　In placers with gold, chromite, iridium.

6　　G. 22.6–22.8　*Iridium (Native Iridium, Platiniridium)*, Ir; some Pt, Pd,
7　　　　　　　　Rh.

6　　G. 18.9–21.2　*Iridosmium (Iridosmine, Osmiridium)*, Ir, Os; also Rh,
7　　　　　　　　Pt, Ru.

SECTION 5

Streak chalk-white, colorless, or pale colored; mineral white, colorless, or pale colored; distinct cleavage in one direction only.

H.

0   G. 1.4–1.5   *Sassolite* (*Native Boric Acid*), H_3BO_3; B_2O_3 56.4%. (See p. 59.)
1

1   G. 2.8–2.9   PYROPHYLLITE, $H_2Al_2(SiO_3)_2$.
2   **Struct.**—Foliated, granular, fibrous, radial, compact; indistinct, orthorhombic crystals rare.   **Cleavage** perfect, one direction (001); fracture uneven, splintery; thin flakes flexible, not elastic; feel greasy.
    Color white, apple-green, gray, yellow.   **Streak** white.   **Luster** pearly to dull.   Translucent to opaque.   (See p. 190.)
    In schistose rocks with cyanite, topaz, graphite, lazulite.

1   G. 2.5–2.8   TALC (*Steatite, Soapstone*), $H_2Mg_3(SiO_3)_4$.
2½   **Struct.**—Foliated, granular; fibrous; compact (soft, *French chalk*); waxy; indistinct tabular monoclinic crystals rare.   **Cleavage** perfect, one direction (001); fracture uneven; sectile; thin flakes flexible, not elastic; greasy feel.   H. sometimes 3–4.
    Color apple-green, gray, white.   **Streak** white.   **Luster** pearly, greasy.   Transparent to opaque.   (See pp. 172, 182, 190.)
    In crystalline schists; with serpentine, dolomite, magnesite, chlorite, actinolite.

1½   G. 2.6–2.7   VIVIANITE.   (See p. 72.)
2

1½   G. 2.3–2.4   GYPSUM (*Selenite, Alabaster, Satin Spar*), $CaSO_4 \cdot 2H_2O$.
2   **Struct.**—Granular, foliated, fibrous; earthy; diamond-shaped monoclinic crystals with beveled edges (Figs. 46, 49).   **Cleavage** perfect, one direction (010); two others less conspicuous (111) (100) at 90°, 66°, 114° brittle; thin flakes flexible; fracture conchoidal, splintery.
    Color white, colorless, gray, yellow, red.   **Streak** white.   **Luster** vitreous; pearly on (010); silky.   Transparent to opaque.   (See pp. 162, 164.)
    Beds and masses with limestone, shale, clay, rock salt; near volcanic vents; with anhydrite, celestite, sulphur, calcite, aragonite.

2   G. 2.3–2.4   BRUCITE, $Mg(OH)_2$; sometimes Fe and Mn.
2½   **Struct.**—Foliated, scaly; fibrous (*nemalite*); rarely broad tabular hexagonal-rhombohedral crystals.   **Cleavage** perfect, one direction (0001); sectile; thin flakes and fibers flexible.
    Color white, grayish, bluish, greenish.   **Streak** white.   **Luster** pearly, on cleavage; vitreous, waxy.   Transparent to translucent.   (See pp. 184, 186.)
    With serpentine, dolomite, magnesite, chromite.

H.

2   G. 1.7   Borax, $Na_2B_4O_7 \cdot 10H_2O$; B_2O_3 36.6%.

$2\frac{1}{2}$ **Struct.**—Compact, earthy, incrusting; short columnar monoclinic crystals. **Cleavage** distinct, one direction (100); brittle; fracture conchoidal.

Color white, colorless, grayish, bluish, greenish. **Streak** white. **Luster** vitreous, greasy. Translucent to opaque. Sweetish alkaline taste. (See pp. 164, 166.)

In mud of alkaline lakes and marshes with halite, gypsum, colemanite.

2   G. 2.7–3.0 MUSCOVITE (*Common or White Mica, Potash Mica, Isin-*
3   *glass*), $H_2KAl_3(SiO_4)_3$; often a little Na, Ca, Mg, Fe, and F.

Struct.—Foliated, flaky; fine scaly to fibrous (*sericite*); dense; rarely distinct monoclinic (pseudohexagonal) crystals. **Cleavage** perfect, one direction (001); thin flakes tough, very elastic.

Color white, gray, yellowish, greenish, brownish. **Streak** white. **Luster** vitreous, pearly. Transparent to translucent. (See p. 172.)

In pegmatite, granite, gneiss, schists, contacts; with feldspars, quartz, tourmaline, beryl, garnet.

2   G. 2.8–2.9 PHLOGOPITE. (See p. 72.)

3

2   G. 2.8–2.9 Lepidolite (*Lithia Mica*), $(Li,K)_2Al_2(OH,F)_2(SiO_3)_3$;
**3   ** Li_2O 3.8–5.8%.

Struct.—Foliated, scaly, compact; rarely monoclinic crystals, small tubular or prismatic. **Cleavage** perfect, one direction (001); laminæ tough, elastic.

Color pink, lilac, yellowish, grayish white, white. **Streak** white. **Luster** pearly. Translucent. (See p. 172.)

In pegmatite with pink and green tourmaline, cassiterite, topaz, amblygonite, spodumene.

2   G. 2.8–2.9 *Paragonite* (*Soda Mica*), $H_2NaAl_3(SiO_4)_3$.

3   Fine scaly masses, compact; strong pearly luster. Otherwise like muscovite, above. In schists with cyanite, staurolite, tourmaline, garnet, actinolite.

2   G. 2.7   Thenardite, Na_2SO_4; Na_2O 56.3%.

3   **Struct.**—Orthorhombic crystals, often cross twins; granular. **Cleavage** one direction (001); brittle; fracture uneven.

Color white to brownish. **Streak** white. **Luster** vitreous. Transparent to translucent. Soluble in water. (See p. 162.)

About salt lakes and dry lake beds.

H.

2½ G. 2.7–2.8   *Glauberite*, $Na_2Ca(SO_4)_2$.

Struct.—Thick tabular monoclinic crystals; reniform, lamellar. **Cleavage** distinct, one direction (001); brittle; fracture conchoidal.

Color white, colorless, yellowish, grayish; white powdery coating forms on exposure. **Streak** white. **Luster** vitreous, greasy. Transparent to translucent. Taste slightly salty. (See p. 164.)

With halite, thenardite, mirabilite, hanksite, ulexite.

2½ G. 2.7–2.8   *Polyhalite*.   (See p. 60.)

3

3   G. 2.5–2.8   TALC.   (See p. 32.)

4

3½ G. 2.1–2.2   STILBITE (a zeolite), $H_4(Ca,Na_2)Al_2(SiO_3)_6 \cdot 4H_2O$.

4   **Struct.**—Sheaf-like, radial, globular; tabular monoclinic crystals, commonly in twinned groups, orthorhombic in appearance. **Cleavage** distinct, one direction (010); brittle; fracture uneven.

Color white, grayish, yellowish, red to brown. **Streak** white. **Luster** vitreous; pearly on cleavage. Translucent. (See p. 170.)

Amygdules and veins in igneous rocks, chiefly basic; in metalliferous veins; with other zeolites, prehnite, datolite, pectolite, native copper, calcite, quartz, epidote, pyrite, chalcopyrite, chlorite.

3½ G. 2.2   HEULANDITE (a zeolite), $H_4(Ca,Na_2)Al_2(SiO_3)_6 \cdot 3H_2O$.

4   **Struct.**—Tabular monoclinic crystals, often look orthorhombic; diamond-shaped, striated; foliated, globular, granular. **Cleavage** prominent, one direction (010); brittle; fracture uneven.

Color white, grayish, red, brown. **Streak** white. **Luster** vitreous; pearly on cleavage. Transparent to translucent. (See p. 170.)

Occurrence and associations as for stilbite, above.

3½ G. 3.0–3.1   MARGARITE, $H_2CaAl_4Si_2O_{12}$; some Fe, Na, K.

1½ **Struct.** Micaceous, scaly, granular; six-sided scales, plates (monoclinic). **Cleavage** perfect, one direction (001); flakes rather brittle, not elastic.

Color pink, grayish, white, yellowish. **Streak** white. **Luster** pearly on cleavage; vitreous. Translucent. (See pp. 172, 190.)

Coating or associated with corundum; also chlorite, spinel, emery, diaspore.

4½ APATITE.   (See p. 68.)

4½ G. 2.3–2.4   APOPHYLLITE, $(H,K)_2Ca(SiO_3)_2 \cdot H_2O$; a little F.

5   **Struct.**—Square, tabular, or cube-like tetragonal crystals; lamellar granular, compact. **Cleavage** perfect, one direction (001); brittle; fracture uneven.

H.

Color white, greenish, yellowish, reddish. Streak white. Luster vitreous; pearly on cleavage. Transparent to nearly opaque. (See p. 170.)

Amygdules and veins in igneous rocks, chiefly basic; in metalliferous veins; with zeolites, prehnite, datolite, pectolite, native copper, calcite, quartz, epidote, pyrite, chalcopyrite, chlorite.

$5\frac{1}{2}$ DIOPSIDE. (See p. 176.)

6   G. 3.2–3.4 ZOISITE, $Ca_2Al_3(OH)(SiO_4)_3$; often some Fe.

$6\frac{1}{2}$ Struct.—Columnar, bladed, fibrous, compact; prismatic orthorhombic crystals striated lengthwise, without terminations. Cleavage conspicuous, one direction lengthwise (010); brittle; fracture uneven.

Color gray, yellowish brown, greenish; also red. Streak white. Luster vitreous; pearly on cleavage. Transparent to opaque. (See 180.)

In crystalline schists with hornblende, vesuvianite, cyanite, epidote, garnet, feldspars, quartz.

6   G. 3.2–3.3 SILLIMANITE (*Fibrolite*), Al_2SiO_5, or $Al(AlO)SiO_4$.

7   Struct.—Fibrous, columnar, radiating; slender orthorhombic crystals without terminations. Cleavage, one direction lengthwise (010); brittle; fracture splintery, uneven.

Color grayish white, hair-brown, greenish. Streak white. Luster vitreous, silky. Transparent to translucent. (See p. 194.)

In gneiss; in contacts of aluminous rocks; with andalusite, cordierite, garnets, corundum.

6   G. 3.3–3.5 DIASPORE, $AlO \cdot OH$; Al 45%; sometimes Fe.

7   Struct.—Scaly, bladed, fibrous; columnar and tabular orthorhombic crystals rare. Cleavage distinct, one direction (010); brittle; fracture conchoidal.

Color white, grayish, greenish, hair-brown, yellow, colorless. Streak white. Luster vitreous; pearly on cleavage. Transparent to opaque. (See p. 194.)

With corundum, emery, dolomite, margarite, chlorite, magnetite.

6   G. 3.3–3.4 AXINITE, $HCa_3Al_2B(SiO_4)_4$; sometimes Mn, Fe, Mg.

7   Struct.—Tabular wedge-shaped triclinic crystals (Fig. 53); lamellar, granular. Cleavage distinct, one direction (010); brittle; fracture conchoidal.

Color clove-brown, yellow, greenish, grayish blue, gray. Streak white. Luster vitreous. Transparent to translucent. (See p. 178.)

In veins with quartz, feldspars, hornblende, chlorite.

8   G. 3.4–3.6 TOPAZ. (See p. 61.)

SECTION 6

Streak chalk-white, colorless, or pale colored; mineral white, colorless, or pale colored; distinct cleavage two directions.

H.

$3\frac{1}{2}$ G. 3.7.   STRONTIANITE, $SrCO_3$; SrO 70.1%; sometimes Ca.
4

Struct.—Chisel- or spear-shaped orthorhombic crystals, pseudohexagonal prisms; columnar, acicular, fibrous, divergent; granular, compact. **Cleavage** distinct, two directions at 63° and 117° (110); brittle; fracture uneven.

Color white, colorless, grayish, greenish, yellowish. **Streak** white. **Luster** vitreous, greasy. Transparent to translucent. (See p. 182.)

In ore deposits with galena, barite, calcite, celestite, fluorite, pyrite; veins in limestone, chalk, marl.

4   G. 2.3–2.5   COLEMANITE, $HCa(BO_2)_3 \cdot 2H_2O$.

$4\frac{1}{2}$ **Struct.**—Short prismatic monoclinic crystals; cleavable, granular, compact, incrusting. **Cleavage** distinct, two directions at 90° (010) (001); fracture uneven, conchoidal.

Color white, colorless, grayish, yellowish. **Streak** white. **Luster** vitreous, dull. Transparent to opaque. (See p. 166.)

Pandermite is compact, porcelain-like; *priceite* is loosely compacted, chalky. Beds in sediments with gypsum, celestite, quartz.

4   G. 2.2   *Phillipsite* (a zeolite), $(Ca,K_2)Al_2(SiO_3)_4 \cdot 5H_2O$; often **Na**.
$4\frac{1}{2}$

$4\frac{1}{2}$ G. 2.4–2.5   HARMOTOME (a zeolite), $H_2BaAl_2(SiO_3)_5 \cdot 4H_2O$; some **Na** and **K**.

4   G. 3.5–3.7   CYANITE.   (See p. 174.)
5

$4\frac{1}{2}$ G. 3.4–3.5   CALAMINE (*Electric Calamine*), $(ZnOH)_2SiO_3$; **Zn 54.2%**.
5

Struct.—Tabular orthorhombic-hemimorphic crystals, commonly divergent cockscomb groups; mammillary, stalactitic, granular. **Cleavage**, two directions lengthwise at 76° and 104° (110); brittle; fracture uneven, conchoidal.

Color white, colorless, yellowish, brownish, greenish, bluish. **Streak** white. **Luster** vitreous, adamantine, dull. Transparent to translucent. (See p. 186.)

In oxidized zinc ores, usually in limestone or clay, with smithsonite, cerussite, anglesite, galena, sphalerite, calcite, limonite.

H.
4½   G. 2.8–2.9   WOLLASTONITE (a pyroxene), $CaSiO_3$.
5   **Struct.**—Granular, fibrous, compact, cleavable; tabular monoclinic crystals. **Cleavage** distinct, two directions at 84½° and 95½° (100) (001); brittle; fracture uneven.
        Color white, grayish, yellowish, reddish, brownish. **Streak** white. **Luster** vitreous, silky; pearly on cleavage. Translucent to opaque. (See p. 172.)
        In limestone contacts with pyroxene, tremolite, garnet, vesuvianite, epidote, graphite.

5   G. 2.2–2.3   NATROLITE, $Na_2Al(AlO)(SiO_3)_3 \cdot 2H_2O$.
5½   **Struct.**—Slender orthorhombic (pseudotetragonal) crystals; fibrous, radial, granular, compact. **Cleavage**, two directions lengthwise at 89° and 91° (110); brittle; fracture uneven.
        Color white, colorless, grayish, yellowish, reddish. **Streak** white. **Luster** vitreous, silky. Transparent to translucent. (See p. 166.)
        Amygdules and veins in igneous rocks, chiefly basic; in metalliferous veins; with other zeolites, prehnite, datolite, pectolite, native copper, calcite, quartz, epidote, pyrite, chalcopyrite, chlorite.

5   G. 2.2–2.4   *Scolecite* (a zeolite), $CaAl(AlO)(SiO_3)_3 \cdot 3H_2O$.
5½

5   G. 2.9–3.1   TREMOLITE (an amphibole), $CaMg_3(SiO_3)_4$.
6   **Struct.**—Bladed, columnar, fibrous, compact; bladed monoclinic crystals without terminations; prism angle and **cleavage** (distinct, two directions lengthwise) at 56° and 124° (110); brittle; fracture uneven; small fibers flexible (*asbestos*). *Nephrite* or *jade*, in part tremolite, is dense, compact, tough.
        Color white to dark gray, yellowish, colorless. **Streak** white. **Luster** vitreous, silky, pearly. Transparent to opaque. (See p. 174.)
        In limestone, dolomite, schist; common at contacts; with pyroxene, garnet, vesuvianite, epidote, wollastonite.

5   G. 3.2–3.6   DIOPSIDE (*Malacolite*, a pyroxene), $CaMg(SiO_3)_2$; some Fe.
6   **Struct.**—Prismatic monoclinic (pseudotetragonal) crystals, stout, terminated (Figs. 47, 48); lamellar, granular compact. **Cleavage** two directions lengthwise at 87° and 93° (110) sometimes distinct; often conspicuous transverse parting (001); brittle; fracture uneven.
        Color white, colorless, grayish, green to black. **Streak** white, grayish, greenish. **Luster** vitreous, dull. Transparent to opaque. (See p. 176.)
        In basic igneous rocks; in crystalline limestones with wernerite, vesuvianite, garnet.

5   G. 3.1–3.3   ENSTATITE (a pyroxene), $MgSiO_3$; FeO up to 12%.
6   **Struct.**—Lamellar, columnar, fibrous, compact; prismatic orthorhombic crystals rare. **Cleavage** distinct, two directions at 88° and 92° (110); parting one direction (010), bisecting cleavage angle; brittle; fracture uneven

H.

Color grayish white, yellowish, greenish, to olive-green and brown. Streak white. Luster vitreous, pearly; submetallic, bronzy (*bronzite*). Translucent to opaque. (See pp. 176, 192.)

In basic igneous rocks (gabbro, peridotite) and serpentine.

5 G. 3.0–3.2 *Anthophyllite.* (See p. 54.)
6

6 G. 3.0–3.1 AMBLYGONITE, $Li(AlF)PO_4$; Li_2O 10.1%; often Na and sometimes OH. Resembles feldspars, but heavier. (See p. 178.)

6 G. 2.5–2.6 ORTHOCLASE (*Potash Feldspar*), $KAlSi_3O_8$; K_2O 16.9%;
6½ often Na.

Struct.—Cleavable, granular, disseminated grains; prismatic and tabular monoclinic crystals and twins (Figs. 50 to 52). Cleavage distinct, two directions at 90° (010) (001); brittle; fracture conchoidal, uneven.

Color white, red, gray, green, colorless. Streak white. Luster vitreous; often pearly on cleavage. Transparent to opaque. (See p. 174.)

In many igneous and metamorphic rocks; in veins and contacts; with quartz, other feldspars, mica, hornblende, pyroxene; in pegmatites with beryl, topaz, tourmaline. *Adularia* is transparent or opalescent (*moonstone*). *Sanidine* is glassy, often transparent, in lavas. *Sunstone*, or *aventurine feldspar*, contains brilliant scales of hematite. *Perthite* and *microperthite* are interlaminated orthoclase and albite. *Microcline* and *anorthoclase* are triclinic and have cleavage angles not quite 90°, the former sometimes bright green (*amazonstone, amazonite*), the latter with Na_2O up to 8%. *Hyalophane*, with BaO 7–15%, likewise triclinic.

6 G. 2.6–2.8 PLAGIOCLASE (*Soda-lime* and *Lime-soda Feldspars*), rang-
6½ ing from $NaAlSi_3O_8$ (ab)to $CaAl_2Si_2O_8$ (an), often some K.

	Comp.	Sp. G.
Albite	ab–ab$_6$an$_1$	2.62–2.64
Oligoclase	ab$_6$an$_1$–ab$_3$an$_1$	2.65–2.67
Andesine	ab$_3$an$_1$–ab$_1$an$_1$	2.68–2.69
Labradorite	ab$_1$an$_1$–ab$_1$an$_3$	2.70–2.72
Bytownite	ab$_1$an$_3$–ab$_1$an$_6$	2.73–2.75
Anorthite	ab$_1$an$_6$–an	2.75–2.76

Struct.—Lamellar, granular, disseminated; small triclinic crystals (Fig. 54). Cleavage distinct, two directions at 86°–86½° and 94°–93½° (001) (010); often striations on one cleavage; cleavage often curved; brittle; fracture uneven.

Color white, colorless, gray, green, bluish, reddish; sometimes play of colors—blue, green, yellow, red. Streak white. Luster vitreous; often pearly on cleavage. Transparent to opaque, sometimes opalescent (*moonstone*), or with bright reddish or yellowish reflections from included scales (*aventurine feldspar*, or *sunstone*). (See p. 174.)

H.

In igneous rocks, gneisses, schists, with other feldspars, quartz, mica, chlorite, zeolites; sometimes in veins.

6 G. 3.5–3.7 CYANITE. (See p. 74.)
7

6 G. 3.1–3.2 SPODUMENE (a pyroxene), $LiAl(SiO_3)_2$; Li_2O 8.4%; some Na.

7 Struct.—Cleavable, columnar, compact; rough prismatic or flattened monoclinic crystals, striated lengthwise. **Cleavage** conspicuous, two direc-tions lengthwise at 87° and 93° (110); parting sometimes prominent, one direction (100), bisecting larger cleavage angle; brittle; fracture uneven, splintery.

Color white, gray, yellowish; emerald-green (*hiddenite*); pink to purple (*kunzite*). **Streak** white. **Luster** vitreous, pearly. Transparent to opaque. (See p. 176, 178.)

In pegmatites with tourmaline, lepidolite, beryl, amblygonite, cas-siterite.

6½ G. 3.1–3.2 ANDALUSITE (*Chiastolite*), Al_2SiO_5, or $Al(AlO)SiO_4$.

7½ Struct.—Columnar, granular, disseminated; rough orthorhombic prisms, nearly square. **Cleavage** distinct, two directions at 89° and 91° (110); brittle; fracture uneven.

Color white, pink, reddish brown, olive-green; sometimes black and white cross or checkered pattern on cross-fracture (*chiastolite*, or *macle*). **Streak** white. **Luster** vitreous, dull. Translucent to opaque. (See p. 194.)

In slate, schists, and gneiss; with sillimanite, garnet, biotite, tour-maline, cordierite.

8½ G. 3.5–3.8 CHRYSOBERYL, $BeAl_2O_4$. (See p. 76.)

SECTION 7

Streak chalk-white, colorless, or pale colored; mineral white, colorless, or pale colored; distinct cleavage three or more direc-tions.

1½ G. 2.3–2.4 GYPSUM. (See p. 32.)
2

2 G. 2.1–2.6 HALITE (*Common Salt, Rock Salt*), NaCl; Na 60.6%; often
2½   Ca and Mg.

Struct.—Granular, cleavable, compact; isometric crystals (cubes, Fig. 5). **Cleavage** distinct, three directions at 90° (100); brittle; fracture conchoidal.

Color white, colorless, grayish, reddish, bluish. **Streak** white. **Luster** vitreous. Transparent to translucent. Taste salty. (See p. 162.)

Beds in sedimentary strata with gypsum, anhydrite, sylvite, calcite, clay, sand; in dry lakes; in brines. (Compare cryolite, p. 48.)

H.

2   G. 1.9–2.0 SYLVITE, KCl; K 52.4%; sometimes Na.

2½   **Struct.**—Granular, compact; isometric crystals (cubes, Fig. 5). **Cleavage** distinct, three directions at 90° (100); brittle; fracture conchoidal.
Color white, colorless, grayish, bluish, reddish. **Streak** white. **Luster** vitreous. Transparent to translucent. Taste salty, bitter; becomes damp in moist air. (See p. 162.)
In salt deposits; with halite, kainite, carnallite.

2½   G. 2.0–2.2 KAINITE, $KMgClSO_4 \cdot 3H_2O$; K 18.9%. (See p. 162.)
3

2½   G. 4.3–4.6 BARITE (*Barytes, Heavy Spar*), $BaSO_4$; sometimes Ca and Sr.

3½   **Struct.**—Tabular and prismatic orthorhombic crystals, divergent groups; compact, lamellar, fibrous. **Cleavage** distinct, three directions at 78½°, 90°, and 101½° (001) (110); brittle; fracture uneven.
Color white, colorless, light shades of yellow, brown, red, blue. **Streak** white. **Luster** vitreous, pearly. Transparent to opaque. (See p. 164.)
In veins with galena, sphalerite, fluorite, chalcopyrite; in limestones and residual clays with oxides of manganese and iron.

3   G. 2.7 CALCITE (*Calc Spar*), $CaCO_3$; often Mg, Fe, Mn, sometimes Pb.

Struct.—Hexagonal-rhombohedral crystals, prismatic, scalenohedral, rhombohedral, tabular, or acicular inhabit (Figs. 31 to 35); twins; cleavable, granular, stalactitic, oolitic, earthy. **Cleavage** perfect, three directions, at 75° and 105° (10$\bar{1}$1); brittle; fracture conchodial, seldom observed.
Color white, colorless, pale shades of gray, yellow, red, green, blue, violet; brown to black when impure. **Streak** white. **Luster** vitreous, dull. Transparent to opaque. (See p. 182.)
Chief constituent of limestone, marble, chalk, calcareous marl; in veins with metallic ores, quartz, pyrite, zeolites. *Dog tooth spar* and *nail head spar* are suggestive crystal habits; *Fontainbleau limestone*, crystals containing much sand; *satin spar*, fibrous, silky; *Iceland spar*, transparent, suitable for optical uses; *chalk*, soft, white, yellowish, earthy; *calcareous marl*, soft, earthy, with clay; *stalactites* and *stalagmites*, cave deposits; *calc sinter*, *calc tufa*, *travertine*, deposits of springs or streams, porous, cavernous; *thinolite*, layers of yellow to brown cellular and skeleton crystals forming extensive tufa in dry lakes (N. W. Nevada), apparently tetragonal pseudomorphs.

3   G. 6.1–6.4 ANGLESITE, $PbSO_4$; Pb 68.3%.

Struct.—Orthorhombic crystals; granular, compact. **Cleavage** not conspicuous, three directions at 76°, 90° and 104° (001) (110); brittle; fracture conchoidal.

H.

   Color white, colorless, gray, brown, green. **Streak** white. **Luster** adamantine, vitreous. Transparent to translucent. (See p. 154.)
   In oxidized parts of ore deposits with lead, zinc, and iron minerals.

3   G. 2.9–3.0   ANHYDRITE (*Anhydrous Gypsum*), $CaSO_4$.

3½   **Struct.**—Granular, compact, fibrous, cleavable; rarely orthorhombic crystals. **Cleavage** distinct, three directions at 90° (001) (100) (010); brittle; fracture conchoidal.
   Color white, grayish, bluish, reddish to brick-red. **Streak** white to grayish. **Luster** vitreous; pearly on (001). Translucent to opaque. (See p. 164.)
   In limestones, shales, salt deposits; with halite, gypsum, calcite.

3   G. 3.9–4.0   CELESTITE, $SrSO_4$; sometimes Ca and Ba.

3½   **Struct.**—Tabular or prismatic orthorhombic crystals (Fig. 41); fibrous, cleavable, rarely granular. **Cleavage** distinct, three directions at 76°, 90°, and 104° (001) (110); brittle; fracture uneven.
   Color white, colorless, bluish, reddish. **Streak** white. **Luster** vitreous, pearly. Transparent to translucent. (See p. 164.)
   In limestones and shales with gypsum, halite, sulphur, galena, aragonite.

3½   G. 2.8–2.9   DOLOMITE, $CaMg(CO_3)_2$; often Fe, Mn; much iron,
4   *Ankerite.*

   Struct.—Granular, cleavable, compact; hexagonal-rhombohedral crystals, faces often curved (*pearl spar*). **Cleavage** perfect, three directions at 74° and 106° (10$\overline{1}$1); brittle; fracture conchoidal, uneven.
   Color white, colorless, gray, red, green, brown, black. **Streak** white. **Luster** vitreous, pearly. Transparent to opaque. (See p. 182.)
   Extensive strata as dolomitic limestone and marble; gangue with ores of lead, zinc, etc.; with serpentine, talc, gypsum, and ordinary limestone.

3½   G. 3.8–3.9   SIDERITE (*Spathic Iron, Chalybite, Clay Ironstone, Black*
4   *Band Ore*), $FeCO_3$; Fe 48.3%.

   Struct.—Granular, cleavable, compact; hexagonal-rhombohedral crystals, curved and saddle-shaped common. **Cleavage** perfect, three directions at 73° and 107° (10$\overline{1}$1); brittle; fracture uneven.
   Color gray, yellow, brown, black, sometimes white. **Streak** white, pale yellow. **Luster** vitreous, pearly, dull. Translucent to opaque. (See pp. 158, 184.)
   In veins with silver minerals, pyrite and other sulphides, cryolite; beds and concretions in limestone, shale, and coal.

3½   G. 2.9–3.0   ARAGONITE (*Flos Ferri*), $CaCO_3$; sometimes Sr and Pb.

4   **Struct.**—Chisel- or spear-shaped orthorhombic crystals, pseudohexagonal prisms; acicular, columnar, stalactitic, coral-like. **Cleavage** three directions at 64°, 90°, and 116° (110) (010); brittle; fracture conchoidal.

H.

Color white, gray, yellow, pale green, violet. Streak white. Luster vitreous, resinous. Transparent to translucent. (See p. 182.)

In gypsum beds, basalt, serpentine, beds of limonite and siderite; with celestite, sulphur, metallic sulphides, zeolites; constitutes some shells (pearly layers of many) and some coral.

$3\frac{1}{2}$ G. 3.9–4.1 SPHALERITE. (See p. 164.)
4

$3\frac{1}{2}$ G. 2.2–2.3 LAUMONTITE (a zeolite), $H_4Ca(AlO)_2(SiO_3)_4 \cdot 2H_2O$. (See p.
4   168.)

$3\frac{1}{2}$ G. 3.4–3.6 RHODOCHROSITE. (See p. 64.)
$4\frac{1}{2}$

$3\frac{1}{2}$ G. 3.0–3.5 MAGNESITE, $MgCO_3$; sometimes much Fe, also Mn.
$4\frac{1}{2}$

Struct.—Compact like unglazed porcelain, granular, cleavable; rarely hexagonal-rhombohedral crystals. Cleavage conspicuous, three directions at $72\frac{1}{2}°$ and $107\frac{1}{2}°$ ($10\bar{1}1$); tough to brittle; fracture conchoidal.

Color white, yellowish, grayish, brown. Streak white. Luster vitreous, dull. Transparent to opaque. (See p. 184.)

Forming extensive beds; disseminated in talc and chlorite schists; veins in serpentine, dolomite, limestone; with gypsum.

4 G. 3.0–3.2 FLUORITE. (See p. 77.)

4 G. 2.0–2.2 CHABAZITE (a zeolite), $CaAl_2(SiO_3)_4 \cdot 6H_2O$; often K, Na
5   Ba, Sr.

Struct.—Hexagonal-rhombohedral crystals (cube-like rhombohedrons), also modified forms, twins; compact. Cleavage distinct, three directions at 85° and 95° ($10\bar{1}1$); brittle; fracture uneven.

Color white, yellow, flesh-red. Streak white. Luster vitreous. Transparent to translucent. (See p. 170.)

Amygdules and veins in igneous rocks, chiefly basic; in metalliferous veins; with other zeolites, prehnite, datolite, pectolite, native copper, calcite, quartz, epidote, pyrite, chalcopyrite, chlorite.

4 G. 3.5–3.7 CYANITE. (See p. 74.)
5

$4\frac{1}{2}$ G. 5.9–6.1 SCHEELITE. (See p. 65.)
5

H.

5 G. 4.3–4.5 SMITHSONITE (*Calamine*, in England), $ZnCO_3$; Zn 52.1%.

Struct.—Mammillary, stalactitic, incrusting, cellular (*dry bone*); rarely small hexagonal-rhombohedral crystals. **Cleavage** distinct, three directions at 72° and 108° ($10\bar{1}1$); brittle; fracture uneven, splintery.

Color white, grayish, colorless, greenish, blue, pink, brown. **Streak** white. **Luster** vitreous, adamantine, pearly, dull. Transparent to opaque. (See p. 184.)

In oxidized zinc ores, usually in limestone or clay, with cerusite anglesite, galena, sphalerite, calcite, limonite.

5 G. 3.2–3.6 DIOPSIDE. (See p. 37.)
6

5 G. 3.1–3.3 Enstatite. (See p. 37.)
6

5 G. 2.5–2.6 NEPHELITE (a feldspathoid), $NaAlSiO_4$; also K (up to
6   7% K_2O).

Struct. Compact, disseminated grains; small hexagonal crystals rare. **Cleavage** distinct, three directions at 60° and 120° ($10\bar{1}0$); brittle; fracture conchoidal, uneven.

Color reddish, brownish, greenish, gray, white, colorless. **Streak** white. **Luster** greasy, vitreous. Transparent to opaque. (See p. 168.)

In lavas and granular igneous rocks with feldspars, sodalite, cancrinite, biotite, zircon, corundum; not with quartz.

5 G. 3.9–4.2 Willemite. (See p. 65.)
6

5 G. 2.6–2.8 Wernerite (*Scapolite*), $n(Ca_4Al_6Si_6O_{25}) \cdot m(Na_4Al_3Si_9O_{24}Cl)$.

6 **Struct.**—Stout prismatic tetragonal crystals; compact, fibrous, granular. **Cleavage** three directions lengthwise at 45° and 90° (100) (110), not conspicuous; brittle; fracture conchoidal, uneven.

Color white, gray, greenish, bluish, reddish. **Streak** white. **Luster** vitreous, greasy. Translucent to opaque. (See pp. 172, 180.)

In crystalline limestones and schists with pyroxenes, amphiboles, apatite, garnet, biotite.

5 G. 2.4–2.5 Cancrinite. (See p. 65.)
6

6 G. 3.5–3.7 CYANITE. (See p. 74.)
7

6½ G. 3.5–3.7 Grossularite. (See p. 70.)
7½

H.

$7\frac{1}{2}$ G. 2.9–3.0 PHENACITE.   (See p. 66.)
8

9   G. 3.9–4.1 CORUNDUM, Al_2O_3.

Struct.—Rough hexagonal-rhombohedral crystals, prismatic, pyramidal, tabular, tapering (barrel-shaped), often striated; lamellar, granular, compact. Cleavage none; often conspicuous parting, three directions at 86° and 94° $(10\bar{1}1)$; sometimes transverse parting (0001); brittle, tough when compact; fracture uneven, conchoidal.

Color white, gray, brown to black; deep red (*ruby*); blue (*sapphire*); black from admixture of magnetite, hematite, or spinel (*emery*). Streak white. Luster vitreous, adamantine. Transparent to opaque. (See p. 194.)

In peridotite, gneiss, schist, syenite, crystalline limestone; with olivine, chlorite, serpentine, magnetite, spinel, vermiculite; cyanite, diaspore, muscovite.

10 G. 3.5   DIAMOND, C.

Struct.—Isometric crystals (octahedron, hexoctahedron, Figs. 1, 4), usually with curved surfaces; rounded and irregular grains, pebbles, often with radial structure. Cleavage distinct, four directions at $70\frac{1}{2}$° and $109\frac{1}{2}$° (111); brittle; fracture conchoidal.

Color white, colorless; pale shades of yellow, red, orange, green, blue, brown; occasionally black. Streak white. Luster adamantine, greasy, Transparent to opaque. *Bort*, rough rounded masses with radial or confused crystalline structure, without distinct cleavage; grayish to black; sp. g. 3.5 *Carbonado*, or *black diamond*, granular to compact, without cleavage; sp. g. 3.1–3.3. (See p. 196.)

In peridotite or serpentine; in sands, gravels, quartzite; with pyrope, magnetite, chromite, zircon, gold.

SECTION 8

Streak chalk-white, colorless, or pale colored; mineral white, colorless, or pale colored; no distinct cleavage.

0   G. 2.6   KAOLINITE (*Kaolin, China Clay*), $H_4Al_2Si_2O_9$.

1   Earthy, powdery; white, gray, yellowish, reddish; commonly soapy feel and plastic when wet. (See p. 46.)

0   G. 2.4–2.6 BAUXITE (*Beauxite*), mixture of $AlO \cdot OH$ and $Al(OH)_3$;
1   Al 30–40%.

Clay-like, powdery, pisolitic; white, gray, yellowish, reddish. A mark made with heavy pressure on glass not easily rubbed off. (See p. 46.)

H.

0   G. 2.7   CHALK (*Marl*, earthy, impure), $CaCO_3$; a variety of calcite.

1   Powdery, clay-like, earthy; white, gray, yellowish; harsh feel. (See p. 40.)

0   G. 2.3–2.4 GYPSITE (earthy gypsum), $CaSO_4 \cdot 2H_2O$.

1   Powdery, clay-like, earthy; white, gray yellowish. (See Gypsum, p. 32.)

0   G. 2.1–2.2 TRIPOLITE (*Tripoli, Diatomaceous Earth, Infusorial Earth*),
1 $SiO_2 \cdot nH_2O$; the composition of *opal*.

Powdery, earthy; a chalk-like opal; apparently soft, but particles scratch glass; harsh feel. White, gray, yellowish. (See p. 50.)

0   G. 1.7–1.8 EPSOMITE (*Epsom Salt*), $MgSO_4 \cdot 7H_2O$.

1   Fibrous efflorescence, earthy powder; colorless, white, gray. Bitter saline taste. (See p. 47.)

0   G. 1.6–1.7 ULEXITE, $NaCaB_5O_9 \cdot 8H_2O$.

1   **Struct.**—Fine fibrous masses (" cotton balls "), easily pulverized (monoclinic).
Color white. **Streak** white. **Luster** silky. Translucent. (See p. 166.)
In dry lakes or about salt lakes with halite, gypsum, borax, glauberite.

1   G. 5.5–5.6 CERARGYRITE (*Horn Silver*), AgCl; Ag 75.3%; sometimes
1½   Hg. (See p. 156.)

1   G. 2.5–3.2 ASBESTOS: Two varieties: (1) *Chrysotile* (fibrous serpen-
2   tine), $H_4Mg_3Si_2O_9$; (2) *Fibrous amphiboles*: anthophyllite, $(Mg,Fe)SiO_3$; tremolite, $CaMg_3(SiO_3)_4$; actinolite,
$Ca(Mg,Fe)_3(SiO_3)_4$; crocidolite, $NaFe''Fe'''(SiO_3)_3$.

Struct.—Parallel flexible fibers; felted aggregates (*mountain paper, mountain cork, mountain leather, mountain wood*).
Color white, gray, yellowish; also lavender-blue (*crocidolite*). **Luster** silky, dull. Translucent to opaque. (See pp. 54, 90, 160, 174, 192.)
Chrysotile is chiefly short cross-fiber, perpendicular to walls of veins in serpentine, fibers fine silky, very flexible, tough; some slip-fiber parallel to walls. *Amphibole asbestos*, chiefly long fiber parallel to walls of veins in peridotite or pyroxenite, or chief constituent of latter, is dull, coarser fiber, little strength or toughness. The crocidolite variety is exceptional in most of these respects, being fine silky and tough.

1   G. 1.6   CARNALLITE, $KMgCl_3 \cdot 6H_2O$; KCl 26.8%.   (See p. 162.)
2

1   G. 6.4–6.5 *Calomel*, Hg_2Cl_2; Hg 84.9%.   (See p. 154.)
2

H.

1   G. 2.4–2.6   KAOLINITE (*Kaolin, China Clay, Porcelain Clay*),
$H_4Al_2Si_2O_9$.

$2\frac{1}{2}$ **Struct.**—Friable, clay-like, compact; minute scaly monoclinic crystals
(pseudohexagonal or pseudorthorhombic) rare; brittle; fracture earthy.
Color white, gray, yellowish, reddish. **Streak** white. **Luster** dull,
pearly. Opaque to translucent. Generally plastic when moist. (See p.
192.)

With quartz, feldspar; largely from decomposition of latter, chief constituent of most clay. *Halloysite*, amorphous variety, little or no plasticity;
translucent to transparent in water; infusible. *Bentonite*, amorphous
variety, brittle; soapy feel; very plastic when wet; absorbs three times its
weight and seven times its volume of water; finally a glue-like paste.
Fuller's earth, absorbent variety, decolorizes oils and other liquids.

1   G. 2.4–2.6   BAUXITE, mixture of colloidal $AlO \cdot OH$ (*Diaspore*) and
$Al(OH)_3$ (*Gibbsite*); often Fe, Si, Ca, Mg; Al 30–40%.

Struct.—Amorphous, earthy, pisolitic, oolitic; brittle.
Color white, gray, yellow, red. **Streak** white. **Luster** dull. Opaque.
A mark made with heavy pressure on glass not easily rubbed off. (See p.
192.)

Nodules and beds in clay or limestone, with iron oxides.

1   G. 2.1–2.2   TRIPOLITE (*Tripoli, Infusorial Earth, Diatomite, Diatoma-*
3   *ceous Earth*), $SiO_2 \cdot nH_2O$; the composition of *opal*.

Struct.—Amorphous, porous, earthy, chalk-like; particles scratch glass;
harsh feel; not plastic when wet.
Color white, gray, yellowish. **Streak** white. **Luster** dull. Opaque.
(See p. 50.)

Associted and in part mingled with clay, sand, peat.

$1\frac{1}{2}$ GYPSUM.   (See p. 32.)

$1\frac{1}{2}$ G. 2.2–2.3   SODA NITER (*Chile Saltpeter*), $NaNO_3$; N_2O_5 63.5%.

Struct.—Granular, crusts, efflorescences; rarely hexagonal-rhombohedral crystals, like calcite. **Cleavage** distinct, three directions at $73\frac{1}{2}°$ and
$106\frac{1}{2}°$ ($10\bar{1}1$); brittle, somewhat sectile; fracture conchoidal.
Color white, colorless, grayish, yellowish, brownish. **Streak** white.
Luster vitreous. Transparent to translucent. Taste cool, salty; becomes
damp in moist air. (See p. 164.)

Extensive deposits in some arid districts (Chile); with gypsum, sand,
clay, guano.

$1\frac{1}{2}$ G. 1.4–1.5   Mirabilite (*Glauber Salt*), $Na_2SO_4 \cdot 10H_2O$.

2   **Struct.**—Mealy efflorescences, fibrous crusts, powder; monoclinic crystals rare. **Cleavage** perfect, one direction (100); brittle; fracture conchoidal.

H.

Color white, colorless, yellowish.   Streak white.   Luster vitreous. Transparent to opaque.   Taste cool, saline.   (See p. 164.) In dry lakes with halite, gypsum, clay, marl.

$1\frac{1}{2}$ G. 2.0–2.1   SULPHUR.   (See p. 67.)
$2\frac{1}{2}$

$1\frac{1}{2}$ G. 2.3–2.4   GYPSUM.   (See p. 32.)
$2\frac{1}{2}$

2   G. 1.9   MELANTERITE.   (See p. 78.)

2   G. 2.1–2.2   NITER (Saltpeter), KNO_3; K_2O 46.5%.

Struct.—Crusts, efflorescences, needle-like aggregates; rarely slender orthorhombic (pseudohexagonal) crystals.   Cleavage distinct, two directions at 70° and 110° (011); brittle; fracture uneven.
Color white, colorless, grayish.   Streak white.   Luster vitreous.   Translucent.   Taste cool, saline; remains dy in moist air.   (See p. 164.)
On rocks, walls, earth; in earth of some caves; in soil.

2   G. 1.0–2.0   SEPIOLITE (Meerschaum), $H_4Mg_2Si_3O_{10}$; sometimes Cu and Ni.

$2\frac{1}{2}$ Struct.—Compact, nodular, earthy, clay-like; rarely fibrous; floats when dry.   Cleavage none; brittle; fracture conchoidal, uneven; smooth feel; adheres to tongue.
Color white, grayish, yellowish.   Streak white.   Luster dull.   Opaque. (See p. 170, 188.)
In peridotites and serpentine with magnesite, chlorite; masses in stratified earthy deposits.

2   G. 1.7–1.8   EPSOMITE (Epsom Salt), $MgSO_4 \cdot 7H_2O$.

$2\frac{1}{2}$ Struct.—Granular, fibrous, capillary, incrusting, earthy; rarely prismatic orthorhombic crystals.   Cleavage distinct, one direction (010); brittle; fracture conchoidal.
Color white, colorless, gray.   Streak white.   Luster vitreous, dull. Transparent to translucent.   Taste bitter, salty.   (See p. 164.)
On walls and floors of caves and mines with limestone, gypsum, serpentine, talc, magnesite.

2   G. 3.6–3.8   Hydrozincite, $Zn_3(OH)_4CO_3$; Zn 60.8%.   (See p. 184.)
$2\frac{1}{2}$

2   G. 5.2–5.3   Senarmontite, Sb_2O_3; Sb 83.3%.

$2\frac{1}{2}$ Struct.—Isometric crystals (octahedrons, Fig. 1).

H.

$2\frac{1}{2}$ G. 2.9–3.0 CRYOLITE, Na₃AlF₆; Na 32.8; Al 12.8%.

Struct.—Cleavable, granular, compact; rarely small monoclinic crystals, like cubes and octahedrons. Cleavage none; parting, often three directions at 88°, 90°, 92° (001) (110); brittle; fracture uneven.

Color white, colorless, grayish. Streak white. Luster vitreous. Translucent. Taste cool, saline; remains dry in moist air. (See p. 166.)

On rocks, walls, earth; in earth of some caves; in soil.

$2\frac{1}{2}$ G. 2.3–2.4 GIBBSITE, Al(OH)₃. (See p. 192.)
$3\frac{1}{2}$

3 CALCITE. (See p. 40.)

3 G. 6.7–7.0 WULFENITE. (See p. 68.)

3 G. 1.8–1.9 ALLOPHANE, approx. Al₂SiO₅·5H₂O; variable. (See p. 188.)

3 G. 6.4–6.6 CERUSSITE (*White Lead Ore*), PbCO₃; Pb 77.5%.

$3\frac{1}{2}$ Struct.—Pseudohexagonal orthorhombic crystals, clusters, star-shaped groups; granular, fibrous, compact. Cleavage indistinct; brittle; fracture conchoidal.

Color white, gray, colorless, or yellow, brown, etc., from impurities. Streak white. Luster adamantine, greasy, silky. Transparent to translucent. (See p. 154.)

In oxidized parts of lead ores with lead, zinc, iron, and copper minerals.

$3\frac{1}{2}$ ANHYDRITE, DOLOMITE. (See p. 41.)

3 G. 2.5–2.6 SERPENTINE. (See p. 79.)
4

3 G. 4.3–4.4 WITHERITE, BaCO₃; BaO 77.7%.

4 Struct.—Compact, granular, radial, fibrous, lamellar; pseudohexagonal orthorhombic crystals resembling quartz. Cleavage indistinct; brittle; fracture uneven.

Color white, grayish, yellowish. Streak white. Luster vitreous, greasy. Transparent to translucent. (See p. 164.)

In veins with galena, barite, fluorite, calcite.

$3\frac{1}{2}$ G. 6.5–7.1 PYROMORPHITE. (See p. 79.)
4

$3\frac{1}{2}$ G. 7.0–7.3 MIMETITE. (See p. 68.)
4

$3\frac{1}{2}$ G. 2.3–2.4 WAVELLITE. (See p. 80.)
4

H.

$3\frac{1}{2}$ G. 2.6–2.8 ALUNITE (*Alum Stone*), $KAl_3(OH)_6(SO_4)_2$; K_2O 11.4%;
4   Al_2O_3 37%.   (See pp. 184, 190.)

4 DOLOMITE (p. 41), MAGNESITE (p. 42).

$4\frac{1}{2}$ G. 3.1–3.2 APATITE. (See p. 68.)
5

$4\frac{1}{2}$ G. 2.7–2.8 PECTOLITE, $HNaCa_2(SiO_3)_3$; sometimes Mn.

5   Struct.—Fibrous, radiating, compact; rarely distinct monoclinic crystals. Cleavage two directions at 85° and 95° (100) (001); brittle; fracture splintery, uneven.

Color white, grayish, reddish. Streak white. Luster vitreous, silky. Translucent to opaque. (See p. 170.)

Amygdules and veins in igneous rocks, chiefly basic; in metalliferous veins; with zeolites, prehnite, datolite, native copper, calcite, quartz, epidote, pyrite, chalcopyrite, chlorite.

5   G. 4.3–4.5 SMITHSONITE. (See p. 43.)

5   G. 2.9–3.0 DATOLITE, $Ca(BOH)SiO_4$.

$5\frac{1}{2}$ Struct.—Complex monoclinic crystals; granular, compact; botryoidal. Cleavage none; brittle; fracture conchoidal, uneven.

Color greenish, colorless, yellowish, reddish, grayish. Streak white. Luster vitreous, greasy, dull. Transparent to opaque. (See p. 168.)

Amygdules and veins in igneous rocks, chiefly basic; metalliferous veins; with zeolites, prehnite, pectolite, native copper, calcite, quartz, epidote, pyrite, chalcopyrite, chalorite.

5   G. 2.2–2.3 ANALCITE (a zeolite), $NaAl(SiO_3)_2 \cdot H_2O$.

$5\frac{1}{2}$ Struct.—Isometric crystals (trapezohedrons, Fig. 3); granular, compact. Cleavage none; brittle; fracture uneven, conchoidal.

Color white, colorless, grayish, greenish, yellowish, reddish. Streak white. Luster vitreous. Transparent to opaque. (See p. 170.)

Amygdules and veins in igneous rocks, chiefly basic; in metalliferous veins; with other zeolites, prehnite, pectolite, datolite, native copper, calcite, quartz, epidote, pyrite, chalcopyrite, chlorite. Sometimes primary constituent of igneous rocks.

5   G. 2.3–2.4 THOMSONITE (a zeolite), $(Ca,Na_2)_2 Al_4(SiO_4)_4 \cdot 5H_2O$. (See p.
$5\frac{1}{2}$ 168.)

5   G. 2.1–2.3 SODALITE. (See p. 80.)
6

H.

5½ G. 2.4–2.5 LEUCITE (a feldspathoid), $KAl(SiO_3)_2$; K_2O 21.5%.

6   Struct.—Isometric crystals (trapezohedrons, Fig. 3), rounded disseminated grains. Cleavage indistinct, brittle; fracture conchoidal.
Color white, gray, yellowish, reddish, colorless. Streak white. **Luster** vitreous, greasy. Translucent to opaque. (See p. 188.)
In lavas with sanidine, augite, nephelite, olivine; not with quartz.

5½ G. 3.0–3.3 JADE, $NaAl(SiO_3)_2$ (*Jadeite*); or $Ca(Mg,Fe)_3(SiO_3)_4$ (*Nephrite*).

6½   Struct.—Very tough compact varieties of the amphiboles, tremolite and actinolite (*nephrite*), or of the pyroxene, *jadeite*; fracture splintery.
Color greenish, grayish, white. Streak white. **Luster** vitreous, waxy, dull. Translucent to opaque. (See p. 176.)
Rolled pebbles in clay; ancient or oriental utensils and art objects.

5½ G. 2.1–2.2 OPAL, $SiO_2 \cdot nH_2O$; H_2O 2–16%, chiefly 3–9%.

6½   Struct.—Amorphous, botryoidal, reniform, stalactitic, earthy. **Cleavage** none; brittle; fracture conchoidal, conspicuous when compact.
Color white, yellow, red, brown, green, gray, blue, colorless; sometimes a rich play of colors (*precious opal*). Streak white. **Luster** vitreous, pearly, dull. Transparent to opaque. (See pp. 190, 194, 196.)
In cavities and veins in igneous and sedimentary rocks. *Precious opal*, play of colors; *fire opal*, red, transparent or translucent; *hyalite*, colorless, transparent, like melted glass; *common opal*, translucent to opaque, greasy luster, many colors, but no play of colors—including *opal-agate*; *geyserite*, *siliceous sinter*, porous, hot water deposit; *tripolite*, earthy, from leached limestone; *diatomaceous earth*, *infusorial earth*, chalk-like, clay-like, composed of diatom remains; *wood opal*, replacing fossil wood.

6   G. 2.8–3.0 PREHNITE. (See p. 81.)
6½

6   G. 3.1–3.2 CHONDRODITE. (See p. 69.)
6½

6   G. 6.8–7.1 CASSITERITE. (See p. 70.)
7

6½   G. 3.5–3.7 GROSSULARITE. (See p. 70.)
7½

7   G. 2.65 QUARTZ (*Rock Crystal*), SiO_2.

Struct.—Prismatic hexagonal crystals striated crosswise, commonly terminated by double rhombohedron (like hexagonal pyramid); granular, disseminated, compact. **Cleavage** indistinct; brittle; fracture conchoidal.

H.

Color white, colorless, various shades (see varieties, below). **Streak** white. **Luster** vitreous, greasy. Transparent to opaque. (See p. 196.)

In igneous rocks, gneiss, schists, sand, sandstone, quartzite; common vein mineral with many metallic ores.

Varieties: *Rock crystal*, colorless, transparent; *amethyst*, purple, blue violet (color destroyed by heat); *rose quartz*, pink to rose-red (may fade on exposure); *false topaz, citrine*, clear yellow; *smoky quartz, cairngorm*, smoky yellow to black; *milky quartz*, milk-white, nearly opaque; *cat's eye*, opalescent from inclosed parallel fibers of asbestos; *tiger eye*, with lustrous yellow to brown parallel fibers; *aventurine*, glistening with inclosed scales (mica, hematite, etc.); *ferruginous quartz*, yellow, red, or brown from ferric oxides.

7   G. 2.6–2.64 CHALCEDONY (*Agate, Flint, Hornstone*), SiO_2.

Struct.—Compact, botryoidal, mammillary, banded. **Cleavage** none; brittle to tough; fracture conchoidal.

Color white, grayish, brownish to black (see varieties, below). **Streak** white. **Luster** waxy, vitreous to nearly dull. Translucent to opaque. (See p. 196.)

Lining or filling cavities (*agate*, etc.); concretions in chalk (*flint*) or limestone (*chert, hornstone*).

Varieties: *Carnelian, sard*, clear red to brownish red; *chrysoprase*, apple-green; *heliotrope, bloodstone*, bright green with small spots of red; *agate*, variegated, generally banded; *moss agate*, with moss-like or tree-like inclusions; *onyx*, banded colors in flat planes; *sardonyx*, an onyx including layers of sard, or carnelian; *siliceous sinter*, cellular deposition from siliceous water (see also opal); *flint*, whitish, dull gray, smoky brown to black (nodules in chalk); *chert, hornstone*, like flint, but more brittle, with splintery fracture (in limestone); *basanite, touchstone*, compact, velvet-black; *jasper*, impure opaque, red, brown, or yellow from ferric oxides.

7   G. 2.3   *Tridymite*, SiO_2.

Struct.—Minute thin tabular hexagonal crystals; twins common, groups resembling octahedron, fan-shaped, spherical rosettes. **Cleavage** indistinct; brittle; fracture conchoidal.

Color white or colorless. **Luster** vitreous, pearly. Transparent.

In cavities in acid and intermediate volcanic rocks; with **sanidine**, hornblende, augite, hematite, opal.

7   G. 2.3   *Cristobalite*, SiO_2.

Struct.—Minute white octahedrons, pseudoisometric, with complicated twinning, in cavities of igneous rocks.

H.

7   G. 2.9–3.0   BORACITE, $Mg_7Cl_2B_{16}O_{30}$.

Struct.—Isometric-tetrahedral crystals (tetrahedron, cube), small, isolated; groups rare; granular. **Cleavage** indistinct; brittle; fracture conchoidal, uneven.

Color white, colorless, grayish, yellow, green. **Streak** white. **Luster** vitreous. Transparent to opaque. (See pp. 166, 178.)

Commonly disseminated glassy crystals with gypsum, anhydrite, halite, carnallite.

7   G. 3.0–3.2   TOURMALINE.   (See p. 59.)
7½

7   G. 3.0   DANBURITE.   (See p. 178.)
7½

7½   G. 4.5–4.8   ZIRCON, $ZrSiO_4$; ZrO 67.2%; commonly a little Fe.

Struct.—Square tetragonal crystals with prism and pyramid; irregular lumps, disseminated grains. **Cleavage** indistinct; brittle; fracture uneven.

Color gray, brown, yellow, green; red transparent (*hyacinth*); colorless or smoky (*jargon*). **Streak** white. **Luster** adamantine, vitreous. Opaque to transparent. (See p. 196.)

Minute grains in feldspathic igneous rocks; rare in crystalline limestone, gneiss, schist; with magnetite, apatite, biotite, wollastonite, titanite; in placers with gold, corundum, spinel, garnet, monazite.

7½   G. 2.6–2.8   BERYL.   (See p. 81.)

9   G. 3.9–4.1   CORUNDUM.   (See p. 44.)

SECTION 9

Streak chalk-white, colorless, or pale colored; mineral dark gray to black; distinct cleavage one direction only.

1   G. 2.8–2.9   PYROPHYLLITE.   (See p. 32.)
2

1   G. 2.5–2.8   TALC.   (See p. 32.)
2½

1½   G. 2.6–2.7   VIVIANITE.   (See p. 32.)
2

1½   G. 2.3–2.4   GYPSUM.   (See p. 32.)
2

2   G. 1.7   BORAX.   (See p. 33.)
2½

H.

$\dfrac{2}{3}$ G. 2.7–3.0   MUSCOVITE.   (See p. 33.)

$\dfrac{2}{3}$ G. 2.8–3.1   BIOTITE (*Black Mica*), $(H,K)_2(Mg,Fe)_2Al_2(SiO_4)_3$; a little F; often Ti.

Struct.—Plates, scales; pseudohexagonal monoclinic crystals rare. **Cleavage** conspicuous, one direction (001); thin flakes tough, very elastic, becoming more brittle with alteration. Often shows triangular parting.

Color black, brownish black, greenish black, dark green. **Streak** white. **Luster** pearly, submetallic. Transparent to opaque. (See pp. 148, 160, 172.)

Common in granite, syenite, gneiss, mica schist; less common in basic igneous rocks and contacts.

$\dfrac{2}{3}$ G. 2.8–2.9   PHLOGOPITE.   (See p. 72.)

$\dfrac{2}{3}$ G. 2.8–2.9   *Paragonite.*   (See p. 33.)

$\dfrac{3}{4}$ G. 2.5–2.8   TALC.   (See p. 32.)

$\dfrac{3\frac{1}{2}}{4\frac{1}{2}}$ G. 3.0–3.1   MARGARITE.   (See p. 34.)

$\dfrac{5}{6}$ G. 3.3–3.5.   HYPERSTHENE (a pyroxene), $(Fe,Mg)SiO_3$; sometimes Al.

Struct.—Foliated, cleavable, granular; orthorhombic crystals rare. **Cleavage** perfect, one direction (010), less distinct in two directions (110), at 46°, 88°, 92°, 134°; brittle; fracture uneven.

Color grayish, greenish, and brownish black to bronze. **Streak** brownish gray, grayish white. **Luster** metalloidal, bronzy, pearly. Opaque to translucent. (See pp. 160, 192.)

In basic igneous rocks with plagioclase feldspars, olivine, amphibole, pyroxene, magnetite, titanite; seldom with quartz.

$5\frac{1}{2}$ PYROXENE, DIOPSIDE.   (See p. 176.)

$\dfrac{6}{6\frac{1}{2}}$ G. 3.2–3.4   ZOISITE.   (See p. 35.)

$\dfrac{6}{7}$ G. 3.2–3.5   EPIDOTE.   (See p. 61.)

$\dfrac{6}{7}$ G. 3.3–3.5   DIASPORE.   (See p. 35.)

H.

$\begin{smallmatrix}6\\7\end{smallmatrix}$ G. 3.3–3.4   Axinite.   (See p. 35.)

$\begin{smallmatrix}6\\7\end{smallmatrix}$ G. 3.5–3.6   *Chloritoid (Ottrelite)*, $H_2FeAl_2SiO_7$; some Mg, sometimes Mn.

$\begin{smallmatrix}7\\7\frac{1}{2}\end{smallmatrix}$ G. 2.6–2.7   Cordierite.   (See p. 73.)

SECTION 10

Streak chalk-white, colorless, or pale colored; mineral dark gray to black; distinct cleavage two directions.

$\begin{smallmatrix}3\frac{1}{2}\\4\end{smallmatrix}$ G. 3.7   STRONTIANITE.   (See p. 36.)

$\begin{smallmatrix}4\\5\end{smallmatrix}$ G. 3.5–3.7   CYANITE.   (See p. 74.)

$\begin{smallmatrix}5\\5\frac{1}{2}\end{smallmatrix}$ G. 3.4–3.6   TITANITE.   (See p. 62.)

5   G. 2.9–3.4   HORNBLENDE (an amphibole), Silicate of Ca, Mg, Fe, Al, etc.

6   **Struct.**—Granular, columnar, fibrous, radiated; long prismatic monoclinic crystals, often rhombohedron-like terminations; prism angle 124°; some prisms short, six-sided. **Cleavage** perfect, two directions lengthwise at 56° and 124° (110); brittle; fracture uneven, splintery.

Color green, black, brown, gray. **Streak** brown, green, yellow, gray, white. Luster, submetallic, vitreous, pearly, silky. Translucent to opaque. (See pp. 160, 174.)

Common in igneous and metamorphic rocks with feldspars, pyroxenes, chlorite, quartz, calcite.

$\begin{smallmatrix}5\\6\end{smallmatrix}$ G. 2.9–3.1   TREMOLITE.   (See p. 37.)

$\begin{smallmatrix}5\\6\end{smallmatrix}$ G. 3.0–3.2   *Anthophyllite* (an amphibole), $(Mg,Fe)SiO_3$; sometimes Al.

Struct.—Lamellar, columnar, fibrous; prismatic orthorhombic crystals rare. **Cleavage** two directions lengthwise at $54\frac{1}{2}°$ and $125\frac{1}{2}°$ (110); brittle; fracture splintery; fine fibers flexible (*asbestos*).

Color gray, clove-brown, greenish to emerald. **Streak** white. **Luster** vitreous, pearly, silky, sometimes metalloidal. Translucent to opaque. (See pp. 160, 174, 192.)

In schists with talc, hornblende, chlorite, mica.

H.

5 G. 3.2–3.6 PYROXENE. (See p. 74.)
6

5 G. 3.2–3.6 DIOPSIDE. (See p. 37.)
6

5½ G. 4.0–4.1 *Tephroite,* Mn_2SiO_4; commonly also Mg and a little Fe.

6 Struct.—Cleavable, granular, compact; orthorhombic crystals rare. Cleavage distinct, two directions at 90°; brittle; fracture conchoidal, uneven.

Color ash-gray, flesh-red, brown. Streak pale gray. Luster vitreous, greasy. Translucent to opaque. (See p. 168.)

In crystalline limestone with zincite, willemite, franklinite, rhodonite (Franklin, N. J.); with other manganese minerals.

6 G. 2.5–2.6 ORTHOCLASE. (See p. 38.)
6½

6 G. 2.6–2.8 PLAGIOCLASE. (See p. 38.)
6½

6 G. 3.5–3.6 *Aegirite.* (Acmite, a pyroxene.)
6½

6 G. 3.5–3.7 CYANITE. (See p. 74.)
7

6 G. 3.1–3.2 Spodumene. (See p. 39.)
7

6½ RUTILE. (See p. 58.)

6½ G. 3.1–3.2 ANDALUSITE. (See p. 39.)
7½

SECTION 11

Streak chalk-white, colorless, or pale colored; mineral dark gray to black; distinct cleavage three or more directions.

1½ G. 2.3–2.4 GYPSUM. (See p. 32.)
2

2 G. 2.1–2.6 HALITE. (See p. 39.)
2½

2 G. 1.9–2.0 Sylvite. (See p. 40.)
2½

H.

3   G. 2.7   CALCITE. (See p. 40.)

3   G. 6.1–6.4   ANGLESITE. (See p. 40.)

3   G. 2.9–3.0   ANHYDRITE. (See p. 41.)
$3\frac{1}{2}$

$3\frac{1}{2}$ G. 2.8–2.9   DOLOMITE. (See p. 41.)
4

$3\frac{1}{2}$ G. 3.8–3.9   SIDERITE. (See v. 41.)
4

$3\frac{1}{2}$ G. 2.9–3.0   ARAGONITE. (See p. 41.)
4

$3\frac{1}{2}$ G. 3.9–4.1   SPHALERITE. (See p. 64.)
4

4   G. 3.5–3.7   CYANITE. (See p. 74.)
5

5   G. 3.2–3.6   PYROXENE. (See p. 74.)
6

5   G. 3.2–3.6   DIOPSIDE. (See p. 37.)
6

5   G. 2.5–2.6   NEPHELITE. (See p. 43.)
6

5   G. 3.3–3.5   HYPERSTHENE. (See p. 53.)
6

5   G. 2.4–2.5   CANCRINITE. (See p. 65.)
6

$5\frac{1}{2}$ G. 3.8–3.9   *Octahedrite (Anatase)*, TiO_2; Ti 60%.
6   Struct.—Tetragonal crystals, pyramidal, tabular, rarely prismatic.

$5\frac{1}{2}$ G. 4.0   *Perovskite.* (See p. 66.)
6

6   G. 3.5–3.7   CYANITE. (See p. 74.)
7

$6\frac{1}{2}$ G. 3.4–4.3   GARNET, $R_3''R_2'''(SiO_4)_3$; $R''=$Ca, Mg, Fe, Mn; $R'''=$Al,
$7\frac{1}{2}$ Fe, Cr, cometimes Ti

Struct.—Isometric crystals (dodecahedrons, trapezohedrons, Figs. 3, 7 8); granular, lamellar, compact, disseminated, sand. **Cleavage** none;

H.

parting sometimes distinct, six directions at 60°, 90°, and 120° (110); brittle; fracture conchoidal, uneven.

Color red, brown, black, green, purple, etc. (See varieties, p. 70.)

Streak white. **Luster** vitreous. Transparent to opaque. (See p. 180.)

For varieties and occurrence, see p. 70.

9　G. 3.9–4.1　CORUNDUM. (See p. 44.)

10　G. 3.5　　DIAMOND. (See p. 44.)

SECTION 12

Streak chalk-white, colorless, or pale colored; mineral dark gray to black; no distinct cleavage.

1　G. 5.5–5.6　CERARGYRITE. (See p. 45.)
1½

1　G 2.2–2.4　GLAUCONITE. (See p. 78.)
2

1　G. 6.4–6.5　*Calomel.* (See p. 45.)
2

2　G. 5.2–5.3　*Senarmontite.* (See p. 47.)
2½

3　G. 6.4–6.6　CERUSSITE. (See p. 48.)
3½

3　G. 2.5–2.6　SERPENTINE. (See p. 79.)
4

3　G. 4.3–4.4　WITHERITE. (See p. 48.)
4

3½　G. 6.5–7.1　PYROMORPHITE. (See p. 79.)
4

3½　G. 3.1–3.3　SCORODITE. (See p. 80.)
4

5　G. 2.1–2.3　SODALITE. (See p. 80.)
6

5½　G. 2.4–2.5　LEUCITE. (See p. 50.)
6

H.

5½ G. 3.0–4.2 ALLANITE (*Orthite*), (Ca,Fe)₂(Al,Fe,Ce)₃OH(SiO₄)₃; also La,
6   Nd, Pr, Y. (See pp. 148, 160, 168.)

5¼ G. 3.9–4.1 *Brookite*, TiO₂; Ti 60%.

6 **Struct.**—Orthorhombic crystals, often tabular (pseudohexagonal), also prismatic, faces often striated. **Cleavage** indistinct; brittle; fracture uneven.
    Color hair-brown, yellowish and reddish brown to iron-black. **Streak** white, grayish, yellowish, brownish. **Luster** adamantine, metallic. Opaque.
(See pp. 152, 196.)
    In igneous rocks, gneiss, crystalline limestone; in veins with quartz, feldspars, metallic sulphides; with rutile, octahedrite, titanite, adularia, nephelite; in gold placers.

5¼ G. 4.3–5.8 *Fergusonite*, (Y,Er,Ce,U)(Cb,Ta)O₄; some Ca, Fe, H₂O.
6

5¼ G. 2.1–2.2 OPAL. (See p. 50.)
6½

6   G. 2.8–3.0 PREHNITE. (See p. 81.)
6½

6   G. 4.1–4.3 RUTILE, TiO₂; Ti 61%; often Fe.

7   **Struct.**—Prismatic tetragonal crystals striated lengthwise; knee-shaped and rosette twins; acicular, compact, disseminated. **Cleavage** indistinct, sometimes distinct 2 directions at 45° (100) (110); brittle; fracture uneven.
    Color red, reddish brown, black (deep red when transparent). **Streak** white, gray, pale brown. **Luster** metallic, adamantine. Transparent to opaque. (See pp. 152, 196.)
    In veins with quartz, feldspars, hematite, ilmenite; hair-like inclusions in quartz; in igneous contacts and metamorphic rocks.

6   G. 6.8–7.1 CASSITERITE. (See p. 70.)
7

6   G. 4.0–4.5 *Gadolinite*, FeBe₂(YO)₂(SiO₄)₂; some Ce, La, Nd, Pr, Er,
7   Sc, etc.

6½ G. 3.4–4.3 GARNET. (See p. 70.)

7   G. 2.65   QUARTZ. (See p. 50.)

7   G. 2.6–2.64 CHALCEDONY. (See p. 51.)

H.

7 G. 3.0–3.2   TOURMALINE, $R_9Al_3(BOH)_2(SiO_5)_4$; R = Mg, Fe, Ca, Na,
7½   K, Li.

Struct.—Prismatic hexagonal-rhombohedral crystals, hemimorphic, curved triangular in cross-section, striated lengthwise (Fig. 37); radiating, columnar, compact. Cleavage indistinct; brittle; fracture uneven, conchoidal.

Color black, blue (*indicolite*), pink to red (*rubellite*), brown, green; rarely white or colorless. Streak white. Luster vitreous, resinous. Transparent to opaque. (See pp. 162, 178, 192.)

In pegmatite, gneiss, mica schist, slate, gravels; common at contacts; with quartz, feldspars, beryl, topaz, cassiterite, fluorite.

7 G. 3.6–3.8   STAUROLITE.   (See p. 71.)
7½

7½ G. 4.5–4.8   ZIRCON.   (See p. 52.)

7½ G. 3.6–4.6   SPINEL.   (See p. 82.)
8½

9 G. 3.9–4.1   CORUNDUM.   (See p. 44.)

SECTION 13

Streak chalk-white, colorless, or pale colored; mineral yellow, red, or brown; distinct cleavage one direction only.

0 G. 1.4–1.5 *Sassolite.* (*Native Boric Acid*), H_3BO_3; B_2O_3 56.4%. (See p. 32.)
1

Struct.—Small pearly scales; rarely thin tabular triclinic crystals. Cleavage perfect, one direction (001); greasy feel; brittle.

Color white, grayish, yellowish. Streak white. Luster pearly. Translucent. Acid taste.

In hot lagoons, fumaroles, volcanic craters, lakes, springs.

1 G. 2.3–2.8   VERMICULITE (*Jefferisite*), Hydrated micas and chlorites;
1½   silicates of Mg, Fe, Al.

Struct.—Scaly, flaky; monoclinic pseudomorphous crystals. Cleavage perfect, one direction (001); thin flakes flexible—some very slightly so; not elastic.

Color golden yellow, yellowish brown, brownish red, yelowish green, dark green. Streak white. Luster pearly to nearly dull, metallic. Translucent to opaque. (See p. 170.)

With peridotite, serpentine, talc, chlorite, corundum, micas.

1 2.8–2.9   PYROPHYLLITE.   (See p. 32.)
2

H.

$1\frac{1}{2}$ G. 2.3–2.4   GYPSUM.   (See p. 32.)
2

$1\frac{1}{2}$ G. 2.1   Copiapite, $Fe_4(OH)_2(SO_4)_5 \cdot 17H_2O$; often Al and Mg. (See
$2\frac{1}{2}$ p. 158.)

2   G. 2.7–3.0   MUSCOVITE.   (See p. 72.)
3

2   G. 2.8–2.9   *Paragonite*.   (See p. 33.)
3

2   G. 2.8–3.1   BIOTITE.   (See p. 53.)
3

2   G. 2.8–2.9   PHLOGOPITE.   (See p. 72.)
3

2   G. 2.8–2.9   Lepidolite.   (See p. 33.)
3

2   G. 2.7   Thenardite.   (See p. 33.)
3

$2\frac{1}{2}$ G. 2.7–2.8   *Polyhalite*, $K_2MgCa_2(SO_4)_4 \cdot 2H_2O$; K_2O 15.6%.

Struct.—Fibrous, lamellar, compact; triclinic. **Cleavage** distinct, one direction; brittle; fracture splintery. Fourling twins.

Color flesh- to brick-red; yellowish red to white. **Streak** white, reddish to yellowish white. **Luster** greasy, pearly. Translucent to opaque. Taste weakly bitter and astringent. (See p. 164.)

In beds of salt, gypsum, and clay.

$2\frac{1}{2}$ G. 2.3–2.4   Gibbsite.   (See p. 48.)
$3\frac{1}{2}$

$3\frac{1}{2}$ G. 2.1–2.2   STILBITE.   (See p. 34.)
4

$3\frac{1}{2}$ G. 2.2   Heulandite.   (See p. 34.)
4

$3\frac{1}{2}$ G. 3.0–3.1   Margarite.   (See p. 34.)
$4\frac{1}{2}$

$4\frac{1}{2}$ APATITE.   (See p. 68.)

$4\frac{1}{2}$ G. 2.3–2.4   APOPHYLLITE.   (See p. 34.)
5

H.

5   G. 3.3–3.5   Hypersthene.   (See p. 53.)
6

6   G. 3.2–3.4   Zoisite.   (See p. 35.)
6½

6   G. 3.2–3.5   EPIDOTE (*Pistacite*), $Ca_2(Al,Fe)_3(OH)(SiO_4)_3$.

7   Struct.—Long monoclinic crystals striated lengthwise, commonly terminated by two sloping faces; columnar, divergent acicular, granular. Cleavage distinct, one direction lengthwise (001); brittle; fracture uneven.
Color yellowish green to brown and black, gray, yellow, red. Streak white to grayish. Luster vitreous. Transparent to opaque. (See pp. 162, 180.)
In gneiss, schists, crystalline limestone, greenstone; with garnet, magnetite, chlorite, native copper, zeolites.

6   G. 3.2–3.3   Sillimanite.   (See p. 35.)
7

6   G. 3.3–3.5   Diaspore.   (See p. 35.)
7

6   G. 3.3–3.4   Axinite.   (See p. 35.)
7

7   G. 2.6–2.7   Cordierite.   (See p. 73.)
7½

8   G. 3.4–3.6   TOPAZ, $Al_2(F,OH)_2SiO_4$.

Struct.—Prismatic orthorhombic crystals striated lengthwise; granular, pebbles, compact. Cleavage perfect, one direction crosswise (001); brittle; fracture conchoidal, uneven.
Color white, colorless, yellow, pink, bluish, greenish. Streak white. Luster vitreous. Transparent to opaque. (See p. 194.)
Veins in pegmatite, rhyolite, granite; contacts; placers; with tourmaline, cassiterite, apatite, fluorite, beryl, garnet.

SECTION 14

Streak chalk-white, colorless, or pale colored; mineral yellow, red, or brown; distinct cleavage two directions.

3½   G. 3.7   STRONTIANITE.   (See p. 36.)
4

4   G. 2.2   *Phillipsite*.   (See p. 36.)
4½

H.

4½ G. 3.4–3.5 CALAMINE. (See p. 36.)
5

4½ G. 2.8–2.9 Wollastonite. (See p. 37.)
5

5 G. 2.2–2.3 NATROLITE. (See p. 37.)

5 G. 3.4–3.6 TITANITE (*Sphene*), CaSiTiO$_5$; commonly a little Fe.

5½ **Struct.**—Tabular or wedge-shaped monoclinic crystals; lamellar, compact. **Cleavage** distinct, two directions at 66½° and 113½° (110); parting often distinct four directions at 54° and 126° (221); brittle; fracture conchoidal.

   Color brown to black, yellow, gray, green; rarely rose-red. **Streak** white. **Luster** vitreous, resinous, adamantine. Transparent to opaque. (See pp. 172, 182.)

   Accessory in many igneous rocks; in gneiss, chlorite schist, crystalline limestone; with chlorite, iron oxides, pyroxene, amphibole, zircon, apatite, feldspars, quartz, rutile.

5 G. 2.9–3.4 HORNBLENDE. (See p. 54.)
6

5 G. 2.9–3.1 TREMOLITE. (See p. 37.)
6

5 G. 3.0–3.2 *Anthophyllite*. (See p. 54.)
6

5 G. 3.2–3.6 PYROXENE. (See p. 74.)
6

5 G. 3.1–3.3 Enstatite. (See p. 37.)
6

5½ G. 4.0–4 1 *Tephroite*. (See p. 55.)
6

5½ G. 3.4–3.7 RHODONITE, MnSiO$_3$; often Ca, Fe; sometimes Zn (*Fow-*
6½   *lerite*).

   Struct.—Granular, cleavable, compact; triclinic crystals, tabular, commonly rough, with rounded edges. **Cleavage** distinct, two directions at 92½° and 87½° (110); brittle, tough when compact; fracture conchoidal, uneven.

   Color brownish red, flesh-red, pink; sometimes yellowish or greenish; may tarnish brown or black on exposure. **Streak** white. **Luster** vitreous. Transparent to opaque. (See p. 176.)

   In veins; in crystalline limestone with willemite, franklinite, zincite.

H.

6   G. 3.0–3.1 Amblygonite. (See p. 38.)

6   G. 2.5–2.6 ORTHOCLASE. (See p. 38.)
6½

6   G. 2.6–2.8 PLAGIOCLASE. (See p. 38.)
6½

6   G. 3.5–3.6 *Aegirite*. (See p. 55.)
6½

6   G. 3.1–3.2 Spodumene. (See p. 39.)
7

6½ RUTILE. (See p. 58.)

6½ G. 3.2–3.6 OLIVINE (*Chrysolite, Peridot*), $(Mg,Fe)_2SiO_4$, ranging from
7   *Forsterite*, Mg_2SiO_4, to *Fayalite*, Fe_2SiO_4; sometimes a
                little Ni, Sn, Ti.

     Struct.—Granular, disseminated; prismatic or tabular orthorhombic crystals (Fig. 42) rare. **Cleavage** indistinct, two directions at 90° (100) (010); brittle; fracture conchoidal, uneven.

     Color yellowish green, yellowish brown, reddish. **Streak** white, yellowish white. **Luster** vitreous. Transparent to translucent. (See p. 188.)

     In basic igneous rocks (gabbro, basalt, peridotite) with augite, chromite, corundum, spinel, pyrope; rarely in crystalline dolomite.

6½ G. 3.1–3.2 ANDALUSITE. (See p. 39.)
7½

8½ G. 3.5–3.8 Chrysoberyl. (See p. 76.)

SECTION 15

    Streak chalk-white, colorless, or pale colored; mineral yellow, red, or brown; distinct cleavage three or more directions.

1½ G. 2.3–2.4 GYPSUM. (See p. 32.)
2

2   G. 2.1–2.6 HALITE. (See p. 39.)
2½

2   G. 1.9–2.0 Sylvite. (See p. 40.)
2½

2½ G. 2.0–2.2 Kainite. (See p. 40.)
3

H.

2½   G. 4.3–4.6   BARITE.   (See p. 40.)
3½

3   G. 2.7   CALCITE.   (See p. 40.)

3   G. 6.1–6.4   ANGLESITE.   (See p. 40.)

3   G. 2.9–3.0   ANHYDRITE.   (See p. 41.)
3½

3   G. 3.9–4.0   CELESTITE.   (See p. 41.)
3½

3½   G. 2.8–2.9   DOLOMITE.   (See p. 41.)
4

3½   G. 3.8–3.9   SIDERITE.   (See p. 41.)
4

3½   G. 2.9–3.0   ARAGONITE.   (See p. 41.)
4

3½   G. 3.9–4.1   SPHALERITE (*Blende, Zinc Blende, Black Jack, Rosin*
4   *Jack*), ZnS; Zn 67%; may be replaced by Fe up to 18%.

Struct.—Cleavable masses, granular, compact, botryoidal; rounded isometric-tetrahedral crystals. **Cleavage** pronounced, six directions at 60°, 90°, and 120° (110); brittle; fracture conchoidal.

Color yellow, brown, red, green, black; rarely white or pale gray (*cleiophane*). **Streak** white, light to dark brown. **Luster** resinous, adamantine, submetallic. Transparent to opaque. (See pp. 144, 166, 184, 190.)

Ore deposits and veins with galena, pyrite, chalcopyrite, fluorite, **barite**; also in limestones.

3½   G. 2.2–2.3   LAUMONTITE.   (See p. 42.)
4

2½   G. 3.4–3.6   RHODOCHROSITE, MnCO₃; Mn 47.8%; sometimes **Fe**,
4½   Ca, Mg.

Struct.—Cleavable, granular, compact, botryoidal, incrusting; hexagonal-rhombohedral crystals rare, commonly with curved faces. **Cleavage** conspicuous, three directions at 73° and 107° (10$\bar{1}$1); brittle; fracture uneven.

Color reddish white, rose-red, dark red, brown; brown to black on exposure. **Streak** white. **Luster** vitreous, pearly. Transparent to translucent. (See p. 184.)

In veins with other manganese minerals, ores of silver, lead, and copper pyrite.

$3\frac{1}{2}$ G. 3.0–3.1   MAGNESITE.   (See p. 42.)
$4\frac{1}{2}$

4   G. 3.0–3.2   FLUORITE.   (See p. 77.)

4   G. 2.0–2.2   CHABAZITE.   (See p. 42.)
5

$4\frac{1}{2}$ G. 5.9–6.2   Scheelite, $CaWO_4$; WO_3 80.6%; some Mo; sometimes Cu.
5

   Struct.—Small pyramidal tetragonal crystals resembling octahedrons, sometimes tabular; incrusting, granular, compact.   Cleavage distinct, four directions at $80\frac{1}{2}°$, $110\frac{1}{2}°$, and $130\frac{1}{2}°$ (111); brittle; fracture conchoidal, uneven.
   Color white, yellow, brownish, greenish, reddish.   Streak white to yellowish.   Luster greasy, adamantine.   Transparent to translucent.   (See pp. 172, 188, 192.)
   In veins and contacts with quartz, cassiterite, topaz, fluorite, apatite, molybdenite.

5   G. 4.3–4.5   SMITHSONITE.   (See p. 43.)

5   G. 3.2–3.6   PYROXENE.   (See p. 74.)
6

5   G. 3.1–3.3   Enstatite.   (See p. 37.)
6

5   G. 2.5–2.6   NEPHELITE.   (See p. 43.)
6

5   G. 2.6–2.8   Wernerite.   (See p. 43.)
6

5   G. 3.9–4.2   Willemite, Zn_2SiO_4; Zn 58%; may contain Mn (*Troostite*);
6   some Fe.

   Struct.—Compact granular, disseminated; prismatic hexagonal-rhombohedral crystals rare.   Cleavage distinct, three directions at 60° and 120° ($11\bar{2}0$); brittle; fracture conchoidal, uneven.
   Color yellow, green, red, brown, white.   Streak white.   Luster vitreous. Transparent to opaque.   (See pp. 168, 186.)
   In crystalline limestone with franklinite, zincite, rhodonite.

5   G. 3.3–3.5   Hypersthene.   (See p. 53.)
6

5   G. 2.4–2.5   Cancrinite (a feldspathoid), $H_6Na_6Ca(NaCO_3)_2Al_8(SiO_4)_9$.
6   (See p. 168.)

H.

$5\frac{1}{2}$ G. 3.8–3.9   *Octahedrite*.   (See p. 56.)
6

$5\frac{1}{2}$ G. 4.0   *Perovskite (Perofskite)*, $CaTiO_3$; some Fe.
6

$6\frac{1}{2}$ G. 3.4–4.3   GARNET.   (See p. 70.)
$7\frac{1}{2}$

$7\frac{1}{2}$ G. 2.9–3.0   Phenacite, Be_2SiO_4.

8   **Struct.**—Hexagonal-rhombohedral crystals, prismatic, lenticular. **Cleavage** indistinct, three directions at 60° and 120° ($11\overline{2}0$); brittle; fracture conchoidal.

Color colorless, wine-yellow, rose-red, brown. **Streak** white. **Luster** vitreous. Transparent to translucent. (See p. 196.)

In pegmatite and metamorphic rocks with quartz, topaz, beryl, microcline, chrysoberyl.

9   G. 3.9–4.1   CORUNDUM.   (See p. 44.)

10   G. 3.5   DIAMOND.   (See p. 44.)

SECTION 16

Streak chalk-white, colorless, or pale colored; mineral yellow, red, or brown; no distinct cleavage.

0   Kaolinite, Bauxite, Chalk, Tripolite, Gypsite.

1   Powdery, earthy, or clay-like minerals, which may be colored yellow, red, or brown by ferric oxides, although white when pure. (See pp. 44, 46, 45, 32.)

0   G. 4.5   *Molybdite*, $Fe_2(MoO_4)_3 \cdot 7\frac{1}{2}H_2O$; MoO_3 59.4%.

$1\frac{1}{2}$ **Struct.**—Earthy powder, crusts; rarely fibrous, radiating, or hair-like orthorhombic crystals. **Cleavage** distinct, one direction crosswise (001); brittle.

Color and **streak** straw-yellow, yellowish white. **Luster** dull, silky. Translucent to opaque. (See p. 85.)

With molybdenite, of which it is an alteration product.

1   G. 5.5–5.6   Cerargyrite.   (See p. 45.)
$1\frac{1}{2}$

1   G. 5.3–5.8   Embolite, $Ag(Cl,Br)$; Ag 60–70%.   (See p. 156.)
$1\frac{1}{4}$

H.

1 G. 1.6   CARNALLITE.   (See p. 45.)
2

1 G. 6.4–6.5 *Calomel.*   (See p. 45.)
2

1 G. 2.4–2.6 KAOLINITE.   (See p. 44.)
2½

1 G. 2.1–2.2 TRIPOLITE (*Infusorial Earth, Diatomaceous Earth*),
3 $SiO_2 \cdot nH_2O$; the composition of *opal*.

Struct.—Amorphous, porous, earthy, chalk-like; particles scratch glass; harsh feel; not plastic when wet.

Color white, gray, yellowish. **Streak** white. **Luster** dull. Opaque. (See p. 50.)

Associated with and in part mingled with clay, sand, peat.

1½ G. 2.2–2.3 SODA NITER.   (See p. 46.)
2

1½ G. 2.0–2.1 SULPHUR, S; traces of Te, Se, As.
2½   **Struct.**—Granular, fibrous, compact, earthy; reniform, stalactitic, incrusting; orthorhombic crystals, pyramidal (Figs. 38, 40), or tabular. **Cleavage** indistinct; very brittle; fracture conchoidal.

Color yellow, greenish or reddish yellow, brown, gray. **Streak** white, pale yellow. **Luster** resinous, greasy, adamantine. Transparent to translucent. (See p. 152.)

In beds with gypsum; about vents of volcanoes and fumaroles; in oxidized parts of sulphide ores; with celestite, gypsum, calcite, aragonite.

2 G. 1.9   MELANTERITE.   (See p. 78.)

2 G. 1.0–2.0 SEPIOLITE.   (See p. 47.)
2½

2 G. 3.6–3.8 *Hydrozincite.*   (See p. 47.)
2½

2½ G. 2.9–3.0 CRYOLITE.   (See p. 48.)

3 G. 6.6–7.2 VANADINITE, $Pb_5Cl(VO_4)_3$; Pb 73%; V_2O_5 19.4%; sometimes P, As.

Struct.—Small hexagonal crystals (prisms, Fig. 27), sometimes hollow; fibrous, incrusting, compact, globular. **Cleavage** none; brittle; fracture uneven, conchoidal.

Color ruby-red, brown, yellow. **Streak** white, pale yellow. **Luster** greasy, resinous. Translucent to opaque. (See p. 154.)

In oxidized parts of lead ores; in gold and silver veins; with pyromorphite, wulfenite, galena.

H.

3 G. 6.7–7.0 WULFENITE, $PbMoO_4$; Pb 56.4%; sometimes Ca.

Struct.—Thin square tabular tetragonal crystals; sometimes acute pyramidal; granular. **Cleavage** indistinct; brittle; fracture conchoidal, uneven.

Color yellow, orange, olive-green, brown, yellowish gray, whitish. **Streak** white. **Luster** adamantine, resinous. Transparent to translucent. (See p. 154.)

In oxidized parts of lead veins with galena, pyromorphite, vanadinite.

3 G. 1.8–1.9 ALLOPHANE. (See p. 188.)

3 G. 6.4–6.6 CERUSSITE. (See p. 48.)
$3\frac{1}{2}$

3 G. 2.5–2.6 SERPENTINE. (See p. 79.)
4

3 G. 4.3–4.4 WITHERITE. (See p. 48.)
4

$3\frac{1}{2}$ G. 6.5–7.1 PYROMORPHITE. (See p. 79.)
4

$3\frac{1}{2}$ G. 2.6–2.8 ALUNITE. (See p. 49.)
4

$3\frac{1}{2}$ G. 2.3–2.4 WAVELLITE. (See p. 80.)
4

$3\frac{1}{2}$ G. 7.0–7.3 MIMETITE, $Pb_5Cl(AsO_4)_3$; Pb 69.5%; sometimes Ca and P.

4 **Struct.**—Prismatic, tabular, and barrel-shaped hexagonal crystals; globular, reniform, incrusting. (See p. 154.)

$3\frac{1}{2}$ G. 3.1–3.3 SCORODITE. (See p. 80.)
4

$4\frac{1}{2}$ G. 3.1–3.2 APATITE, $Ca_5F(PO_4)_3$; P_2O_5 42.3%; often some Cl.
5

Struct.—Prismatic hexagonal crystals, sometimes tabular; granular, compact. **Cleavage** distinct to poor, one direction crosswise (0001); brittle; fracture conchoidal, uneven.

Color green, blue, violet, red, brown, white, colorless. **Streak** white. **Luster** vitreous, greasy. Transparent to opaque. (See pp. 166, 186.)

In crystalline limestones with graphite, fluorite, pyrrhotite; in igneous rocks (minute crystals); in magnetite ores; with fluorite in tin and tungsten ores; amorphous in stratified deposits with limestone and marl (*phosphate rock, phosphatic nodules*).

H.

$4\frac{1}{2}$ G. 2.7–2.8 PECTOLITE. (See p. 49.)
5

5   G. 4.3–4.5 SMITHSONITE. (See p. 43.)

5   G. 2.2–2.3 ANALCITE. (See p. 49.)
$5\frac{1}{2}$

5   G. 2.9–3.0 DATOLITE. (See p. 49.)
$5\frac{1}{2}$

5   G. 2.3–2.4 THOMSONITE. (See p. 49.)
$5\frac{1}{2}$

5   G. 4.9–5.3 MONAZITE, $(Ce,La,Nd,Pr)PO_4$; also Th, Y; ThO_2 up to 10%+.
$5\frac{1}{2}$

Struct.—Sands, disseminated grains; small monoclinic crystals rare. Cleavage indistinct; sometimes parting one direction (001); brittle; fracture conchoidal, uneven.

Color yellow, yellowish green, yellowish brown, reddish brown. Streak white. Luster resinous, vitreous. Translucent to opaque. (See p. 190.)

In pegmatite, gneiss; in sands of streams or seashore; with magnetite, ilmenite, garnet, corundum, gold, platinum.

5   G. 2.1–2.3 SODALITE. (See p. 80.)
6

$5\frac{1}{2}$ G. 2.4–2.5 LEUCITE. (See p. 50.)
6

$5\frac{1}{2}$ 3.9–4.1 *Brookite.* (See p. 58.)
6

$5\frac{1}{2}$ G. 2.1–2.2 OPAL. (See p. 50.)
$6\frac{1}{2}$

6   G. 3.1–3.2 CHONDRODITE, $Mg_5(F,OH)_2(SiO_4)_2$; some Fe replaces Mg.

$6\frac{1}{2}$ Struct.—Rounded disseminated grains, compact; small complex monoclinic crystals rare. Cleavage sometimes distinct, one direction (001); brittle; fracture conchoidal, uneven.

Color brownish red, yellow, white. Streak white. Luster vitreous, greasy. Translucent to opaque. (See p. 188.)

In crystalline limestone with spinel, magnetite, pyroxene, vesuvianite, phlogopite, corundum.

6   G. 4.1–4.3 RUTILE. (See p. 58.)
7

H.

6   G. 6.8–7.1   CASSITERITE (*Tinstone*), SnO_2; Sn 78.6%.

7   **Struct.**—Granular, disseminated; reniform with radiating fibrous structure (*wood tin*); sand and pebbles (*stream tin*); thick prismatic tetragonal crystals, knee-shaped twins common (Fig. 25). **Cleavage** indistinct, brittle; fracture uneven.

Color brown to black; rarely yellow, red, gray, white. **Streak** white, grayish, brownish. **Luster** adamantine, greasy, dull. Transparent to opaque. (See p. 196.)

In granite, gneiss; with wolframite, scheelite, molybdenite, tourmaline, fluorite, topaz, apatite, lepidolite; in pegmatites; in sands and gravels.

6½   G. 3.3–3.5   VESUVIANITE, $Ca_6Al_3(OH,F)(SiO_4)_5$; often Mg, Fe, Mn.

Struct.—Short prismatic tetragonal crystals (Figs. 23, 24); columnar, granular; compact, like jade. **Cleavage** indistinct; brittle; fracture uneven.

Color brown or green, rarely yellow or blue. **Streak** white. **Luster** vitreous, greasy, resinous. Translucent to opaque. (See p. 180.)

In limestone contacts with garnet, pyroxene, tourmaline, chondrodite, wollastonite, epidote.

6½   G. 3.2–3.6   OLIVINE.   (See p. 63.)
7

6½   G. 3.4–4.3   GARNET, $R''_3R'''_2(SiO_4)_3$; $R'' = Ca$, Mg, Fe, Mn; $R''' = Al$,
7½   Fe, Cr, sometimes Ti.

Struct.—Isometric crystals (dodecahedrons, trapezohedrons, Figs. 3, 7, 8); granular, lamellar, compact, disseminated, sand. **Cleavage** none; parting sometimes distinct, six directions at 60°, 90°, 120° (110); brittle; fracture conchoidal, uneven.

Color red, brown, black, etc. (See varieties below.) **Streak** white. **Luster** vitreous. Transparent to opaque.

Pyrope, $Mg_3Al_2(SiO_4)_3$; deep red to reddish black, rarely purple; sp. g. 3.7. Rounded grains in peridotite and serpentine.

Almandite, $Fe_3Al_2(SiO_4)_3$; deep red to brownish black; sp. g. 3.9–4.2. In schists and gneiss with mica, staurolite, andalusite, cyanite.

Spessartite, $Mn_3Al_2(SiO_4)_3$; brownish red to hyacinth-red; sp. g. 4.0–4.3. In granite and pegmatite with topaz, tourmaline, quartz, orthoclase.

Grossularite (*essonite*), $Ca_3Al_2(SiO_4)_3$; white, yellow, green, pink; sp. g. 3.5–3.6. In limestone contacts with wollastonite, vesuvianite, diopside, scapolite.

Andradite, $Ca_3Fe_2(SiO_4)_3$; wine-red, greenish, yellow, brown, black (*melanite*); sp. g. 3.8–3.9. In phonolite, nephelinite, leucitophyre, and contacts, with magnetite, epidote, feldspar, nephelite, leucite.

Much *common garnet* is a mixture of grossularite, almandite, and andradite.

H.

7   G. 2.65   QUARTZ.   (See p. 50.)

7   G. 2.6–2.64 CHALCEDONY.   (See p. 51.)

7   G. 2.9–3.0 Boracite.   (See p. 52.)

7   G. 3.0–3.2 TOURMALINE.   (See p. 59.)
7½

7   G. 3.6–3.8 STAUROLITE, Fe(AlO)₄(AlOH)(SiO₄)₂; sometimes Mg,
7½   Mn.

    Struct.—Prismatic orthorhombic crystals; cross twins at 60° and 90°
common (Figs. 43 to 45); often rough. **Cleavage** not conspicuous, one direction lengthwise (010); brittle; fracture conchoidal, uneven.
    Color yellowish brown, reddish to brownish black, weathering gray.
Streak white to grayish. **Luster** vitreous, dull. Translucent to opaque.
(See p. 194.)
    In slate, schists, gneiss, with garnet, cyanite, sillimanite, tourmaline.

7   G. 3.0   Danburite, CaB₂(SiO₄)₂.   (See p. 178.)
7½

7½ G. 4.5–4.8 ZIRCON.   (See p. 52.)

7½ G. 2.6–2.8 BERYL.   Rare pink varieties (*rose beryl, morganite*).   (See
        p. 81.)

7½ G. 3.6–4.6 SPINEL.   (See p. 82.)
8½

9   G. 3.9–4.1 CORUNDUM.   Brown, pink and ruby varieties. (See p. 44.)

SECTION 17

    Streak chalk-white, colorless, or pale colored; mineral green,
blue, or violet; distinct cleavage one direction only.

1   G. 2.3–2.8 Vermiculite.   (See p. 59.)
1½

1   G. 2.8–2.9 Pyrophyllite.   (See p. 32.)
2

H.

1   G. 2.5–2.8   TALC.   (See p. 32.)
2½

1 G. 2.6–3.0 CHLORITE (*Clinochlore, Prochlorite*), H, Fe, Mg, Al silicates.
2½   **Struct.**—Foliated, scaly, granular, compact, earthy; tabular six-sided monoclinic crystals rare. **Cleavage** perfect, one direction (001); fracture scaly, earthy; thin flakes flexible, tough, not elastic; slight soapy feel.
   Color light to dark green. **Streak** white, greenish white, grayish. **Luster** pearly, vitreous, dull. Translucent to opaque. (See pp. 172, 190.)
   In schists, greenstones, green slates, serpentines, peridotites; with magnetite, chromite, garnet, talc, pyroxene, serpentine, corundum.

1½ G. 2.6–2.7 VIVIANITE (*Blue Iron Earth*), $Fe_3(PO_4)_2 \cdot 8H_2O$; P_2O_5 28.3%.
2   **Struct.**—Radial fibrous, earthy; prismatic and tabular monoclinic crystals. **Cleavage** distinct, one direction (010); sectile; thin flakes flexible, fracture splintery, earthy.
   Color blue, green, greenish black; colorless when fresh, turns blue on exposure to light or grinding in a mortar. **Streak** white, blue, greenish blue. **Luster** pearly on cleavage; vitreous, dull. Transparent to opaque. (See p. 158.)
   In clay, marl, peat; in cavities of fossils; with limonite; in veins with pyrrhotite, pyrite, gold.

1½ G. 2.1   COPIAPITE.   (See p. 60.)
2½

2   G. 2.3–2.4   BRUCITE.   (See p. 32.)
2½

2   G. 1.7   BORAX.   (See p. 33.)
2½

2   G. 2.7–3.0   MUSCOVITE.   (See p. 33.)
3

2   G. 2.8–3.1   BIOTITE.   (See p. 53.)
3

2   G. 2.8–2.9   PHLOGOPITE (*Amber Mica, Bronze Mica, Magnesia Mica*),
3 $H_2KMg_3Al(SiO_4)_3$; some F and Fe.
   Struct.—Plates, scales; prismatic or tabular monoclinic crystals with hexagonal or orthorhombic outlines, commonly rough. **Cleavage** conspicuous, one direction (001); thin flakes tough, very elastic.
   Color yellowish brown, brownish red, gray to green; rarely colorless. **Streak** white. **Luster** pearly, submetallic. Translucent to transparent. (See pp. 148, 172.)
   Contacts in crystalline limestone; in serpentine; with pyroxene, amphibole, serpentine, graphite, apatite, corundum.

H.

2   G. 2.8–2.9   Lepidolite.   (See p. 33.)
3

2   G. 2.8–2.9   *Paragonite.*   (See p. 33.)
3

2½   G. 2.3–2.4   Gibbsite.   (See p. 48.)
3½

3   G. 2.5–2.8   TALC.   (See p. 32.)
4

4½   G. 2.3–2.4   APOPHYLLITE.   (See p. 34.)
5

5   APATITE (p. 68), PYROXENE, DIOPSIDE (p. 176).

5   G. 3.3–3.5   Hypersthene.   (See p. 53.)
6

6   G. 3.2–3.4   Zoisite.   (See p. 35.)
6½

6   G. 3.2–3.5   EPIDOTE.   (See p. 61.)
7

6   G. 3.2–3.3   Sillimanite.   (See p. 35.)
7

6   G. 3.3–3.5   Diaspore.   (See p. 35.)
7

6   G. 3.3–3.4   Axinite.   (See p. 35.)
7

6   G. 3.5–3.6   *Chloritoid.*   (See p. 54.)
7

7   G. 2.6–2.7   Cordierite   (*Iolite*), $(Mg,Fe)_4Al_8(OH)_2(Si_2O_7)_5$.   (See pp.
7½   180, 194.)

8   G. 3.4–3.6   TOPAZ.   (See p. 61.)

SECTION 18

Streak chalk-white, colorless, or pale colored; mineral green, blue, or violet; distinct cleavage two directions.

H.

$3\frac{1}{2}$ G. 3.7   STRONTIANITE. (See p. 36.)
4

4   G. 3.5–3.7 CYANITE, Al_2SiO_5, or $(AlO)_2SiO_3$.

5   **Struct.**—Long tabular or bladed triclinic crystals rarely terminated; may be curved or radiating. **Cleavage** pronounced, two directions lengthwise at 74° and 106° (100) (010); transverse parting (001) common; brittle; fracture splintery.

Color blue, white, gray, green nearly black; often streaked. **Streak** white. **Luster** vitreous. Transparent to translucent. (See pp. 190, 194.)

Hardness lengthwise 4–5, crosswise 6–7. In gneiss and mica schist with staurolite, garnet, corundum.

$4\frac{1}{2}$ G. 3.4–3.5 CALAMINE. (See p. 62.)
5

5   G. 3.4–3.6 TITANITE. (See p. 62.)
$5\frac{1}{2}$

5   G. 2.9–3.4 HORNBLENDE. (See p. 54.)
6

5   G. 3.0–3.2 ACTINOLITE (an amphibole), $Ca(Mg,Fe)_3(SiO_3)_4$.

6   **Struct.**—Bladed or acicular monoclinic crystals; columnar, fibrous, divergent, granular, compact. **Cleavage** conspicuous, two directions lengthwise at 56° and 124° (110); brittle; fracture splintery, uneven.

Color bright to dark green, grayish green. **Streak** white. **Luster** vitreous, silky, pearly. Transparent to opaque. (See p. 174.)

In talc, chlorite, and hornblende schists and greenstones, with epidote, talc, serpentine.

5   G. 3.0–3.2 *Anthophyllite.*   (See page 54.)
6

5   G. 3.2–3.6 PYROXENE, $Ca(Mg,Fe)(SiO_3)_2$, ranging from *Diopside*,
6                 $CaMg(SiO_3)_2$, to *Hedenbergite*, $CaFe(SiO_3)_2$; often some Al, Mn, and Na.

AUGITE (a pyroxene), like common pyroxene above, with Al_2O_3 up to 15% or 20%; sometimes alkali metals, Na and K.

Struct.—Granular, columnar, rarely fibrous; lamellar (*diallage*); thick monoclinic prisms four- to eight-sided (Figs. 47, 48). **Cleavage** two directions

H.

    lengthwise at 87° and 93° (110) sometimes distinct; parting often prominent crosswise (001); *diallage* has fine lamellar parting one direction lengthwise (100); brittle; fracture uneven.

    Color bright to dark green, grayish green, black, brown. **Streak** greenish, brownish, grayish to white. **Luster** vitreous, submetallic, dull. **Transparent** to opaque. (See pp. 160, 176.)

    Common in basic igneous rocks; in crystalline limestones with garnet, chlorite, amphibole, wollastonite, magnetite, pyrite.

5   G. 3.2–3.6 DIOPSIDE. (See p. 37).
6

5   G. 3.1–3.3 Enstatite. (See p. 37.)
6

5   G. 3.3–3.5 Hypersthene. (See p. 53.)
6

$5\frac{1}{2}$ G. 3.4–3.7 RHODONITE. (See p. 62.)
$6\frac{1}{2}$

6   G. 3.0–3.1 Amblygonite. (See p. 38.)

6   G. 2.5–2.6 ORTHOCLASE. (See p. 38.)
$6\frac{1}{2}$

6   G. 2.6–2.8 PLAGIOCLASE (*Soda-lime* and *Lime-soda Feldspars*),
$6\frac{1}{2}$ ranging from $NaAlSi_3O_8$ (ab) to $CaAl_2Si_2O_8$ (an), generally also some K.

    Struct.—Lamellar, granular, disseminated; small triclinic crystals (Fig. 54). **Cleavage** distinct, two directions at $86°–86\frac{1}{2}°$ and $94°–93\frac{1}{2}°$ (001) (010); often striations on one cleavage; cleavage often curved; brittle; fracture uneven.

    Color white, colorless, gray, green, bluish, reddish; sometimes play of colors—blue, green, yellow, red. **Streak** white. **Luster** vitreous, pearly. Transparent to opaque, sometimes opalescent. (See p. 174.) (For description of varieties, see p. 38.)

    In igneous rocks, gneisses, schists, with other feldspars, quartz, mica, chlorite, zeolites; sometimes in veins.

6   G. 3.5–3.6 *Aegirite* (*Aegirine, Acmite*; a pyroxene), $NaFe'''(SiO_3)_2$.
$6\frac{1}{2}$ (See p. 55.)

6   G. 3.5–3.7 CYANITE. (See p. 74.)
7

6   G. 3.1–3.2 Spodumene. (See p. 39.)
7

H.

6½   G. 3.2–3.6   OLIVINE.   (See p. 63.)
7

6½   G. 3.1–3.2   ANDALUSITE.   (See p. 39.)
7½

8½   G. 3.5–3.8   CHRYSOBERYL, $BeAl_2O_4$.

Struct.—Tabular orthorhombic crystals, heart-shaped or pseudohexagonal twins, disseminated plates. **Cleavage** two directions at 60° and 120° (011); brittle; fracture uneven, conchoidal.

Color yellowish green, deep green, greenish white, greenish brown, yellow. **Streak** white. **Luster** vitreous, greasy. **Transparent** to translucent. (See p. 194.)

Alexandrite, the deep green variety, is red by gas or lamp light; *cat's eye* is yellowish green, opalescent.

In granite, gneiss, mica schist, placers; with beryl, garnet, tourmaline, sillimanite.

SECTION 19

Streak chalk-white, colorless, or pale colored; mineral green, blue, or violet; distinct cleavage three or more directions.

2   G. 2.1–2.6   HALITE.   (See p. 39.)
2½

2   G. 1.9–2.0   SYLVITE.   (See p. 40.)
2½

2½   G. 4.3–4.6   BARITE.   (See p. 40.)
3½

3   G. 2.7   CALCITE.   (See p. 40.)

3   G. 6.1–6.4   ANGLESITE.   (See p. 40.)

3   G. 3.9–4.0   CELESTITE.   (See p. 41.)
3½

3½   G. 2.8–2.9   DOLOMITE   (See p. 41.)

3½   G. 2.9–3.0   ARAGONITE.   (See p. 41.)
4

3½   G. 3.9–4.1   SPHALERITE.   (See p. 64.)
4

H.

4   G. 3.0–3.2   FLUORITE (*Fluor Spar*), CaF₂; F 48.9%; sometimes Cl.

Struct.—Isometric crystals (cubes, Figs. 5, 9), penetration twins; cleavable masses, granular, columnar. **Cleavage** perfect, four directions at 70½° and 109½° (111); brittle; fracture uneven.

Color violet, blue, green, yellow, colorless, brown. **Streak** white. **Luster** vitreous. Transparent to translucent. (See p. 166.)

Common in veins and contacts with galena, sphalerite, calcite, barite, cassiterite, apatite, topaz, lepidolite; in limestones; rare in igneous rocks.

4   G. 3.5–3.7   CYANITE.   (See p. 74.)
5

4½ G. 5.9–6.2   Scheelite.   (See p. 65.)
5

5   G. 4.3–4.5   SMITHSONITE.   (See p. 43.)

5   G. 2.5–2.6   NEPHELITE.   (See p. 43.)
6

5   G. 2.4–2.5   Cancrinite.   (See p. 65.)
6

5   G. 2.6–2.8   Wernérite.   (See p. 43.)
6

5   G. 3.9–4.2   Willemite.   (See p. 65.)
6

5½ G. 3.8–3.9   *Octahedrite*.   (See p. 56.)
6

6   G. 3.5–3.7   CYANITE.   (See p. 74.)
7

6¼ G. 3.4–4.3   GARNET,   (See p. 70.)
7½

9   G. 3.9–4.1   CORUNDUM.   (See p. 44.)

10 G. 3.5   DIAMOND.   (See p. 44.)

SECTION 20

Streak chalk-white, colorless, or pale colored; mineral green, blue, or violet; no distinct cleavage.

1   G. 5.5–5.6   Cerargyrite.   (See p. 45.)
1⅓

H.

1 G. 5.3–5.8 EMBOLITE. (See p. 66.)
1½

1 G. 2.2–2.4 GLAUCONITE (*Greensand, Green Earth*), approx. $KFe(SiO_3)_2 \cdot$
2 H_2O; K_2O 6–9%; some Al and Mg.

Struct.—Granular, earthy, disseminated; amorphous. Cleavage none; brittle; fracture earthy, uneven. Monoclinic (?)
Color yellowish green, grayish green, blackish green. Streak light green, greenish white. Luster vitreous, dull. Opaque. (See p. 160.)
Abundant in greensand beds (so-called marls); disseminated in sands, clays, sandstones, limestones.

1   G. 3.0–3.1 ANNABERGITE, $Ni_3(AsO_4)_2 \cdot 8H_2O$; Ni 29.4%; sometimes Co
2½   and Ca.

Struct.—Earthy, incrusting, compact, stains; capillary monoclinic crystals rare. Cleavage none; brittle; fracture uneven.
Color apple-green, light green. Streak pale green, greenish white. Luster dull, vitreous. Opaque to translucent. (See p. 158.)
Oxidation product of nickel arsenides; with smaltite, niccolite, chloanthite, calcite.

1   G. 2.3–2.8 GARNIERITE, approx. $H_2(Ni,Mg)SiO_4 \cdot nH_2O$; Ni 8–35%.
2½

Struct.—Compact, botryoidal, incrusting, earthy. Cleavage none; fracture conchoidal, earthy; brittle. Sometimes greasy feel. Hardness sometimes 3–4.
Color pale yellowish green to emerald-green. Streak white, greenish white. Luster greasy, resinous, dull. Opaque. (See pp. 188, 192.)
Veins in peridotites, serpentine; with chromite, talc, chlorite.

1½ G. 2.0–2.1 SULPHUR. (See p. 67.)
2½

2   G. 1.9   MELANTERITE (*Copperas, Green Vitriol*), $FeSO_4 \cdot 7H_2O$.

Struct.—Capillary, fibrous, compact, stalactitic, concretionary, powdery; monoclinic crystals rare. Cleavage inconspicuous, one direction crosswise (001); brittle; fracture conchoidal, earthy.
Color green, yellowish green, white; dull yellowish white on exposure. Streak white. Luster vitreous, dull. Transparent to translucent. Sweet astringent taste. (See p. 158.)
Oxidation product of iron sulphide minerals—marcasite, pyrite, chalcopyrite, pyrrhotite, etc.

2   G. 2.0–2.2 CHRYSOCOLLA, approx. $CuSiO_3 \cdot 2H_2O$; variable; Cu 20–50%.
3   Struct.—Amorphous, compact, reniform, incrusting, stains, earthy.
Cleavage none; brittle; fracture conchoidal.

H.

Color green, greenish blue, blue; brown to black from impurities. **Streak** white to pale blue or green. **Luster** vitreous, greasy, dull. Translucent to opaque. (See p. 188.)

In oxidized parts of copper deposits, with malachite, azurite, cuprite, native copper.

$2\frac{1}{2}$　G. 2.1–2.3　CHALCANTHITE (*Blue Vitriol*), $CuSO_4 \cdot 5H_2O$; Cu 25.4%.

Struct.—Crystalline crusts, reniform, stalactitic, fibrous, powdery; small tabular triclinic crystals rare. **Cleavage** indistinct; brittle; fracture conchoidal, earthy.

Color deep blue, sky-blue, greenish blue. **Streak** white. **Luster** vitreous, dull. Translucent. Plates wet iron with copper by contact. Nauseous metallic taste. (See p. 156.)

In oxidized parts of copper veins; often deposited by mine waters.

3　G. 6.7–7.0　WULFENITE. (See p. 68.)

3　G. 1.8–1.9　ALLOPHANE, approx. $Al_2SiO_5 \cdot 5H_2O$; variable. (See p. 188.)

3　G. 2.5–2.6　SERPENTINE, $H_4Mg_3Si_2O_9$; commonly Fe, sometimes Ni.
4　**Struct.**—Massive compact; fibrous (*chrysotile, asbestos*); lamellar; columnar; brittle; fibers flexible and tough. **Cleavage** none; fracture conchoidal, splintery.

Color olive-green, blackish green, yellowish green, yellow; rarely white. **Streak** white. **Luster** greasy, waxy, silky. Translucent to opaque. (See pp. 170, 188.)

Common alteration product of olivine rocks (peridotites); in dolomitic limestone; with magnesite, talc, chromite, magnetite, corundum, platinum, diamond. Mixed with dolomite, calcite, or magnesite in a mottled or clouded green marble (*verdantique*, or *ophicalcite*).

$\frac{3}{4}$　G. 2.3–2.8　GARNIERITE. (See p. 78.)

$3\frac{1}{2}$　G. 6.5–7.1　PYROMORPHITE, $Pb_5Cl(PO_4)_3$; Pb 76.3%; P_2O_5 15.7%.
4

Struct.—Small prismatic hexagonal crystals, often rounded, barrel-shaped, sometimes hollow; incrusting, reniform, disseminated. **Cleavage** none; brittle; fracture conchoidal, uneven.

Color green, yellow, brown, white, gray. **Streak** pale yellow, greenish yellow, white. **Luster** resinous, greasy, adamantine. Translucent to opaque (See p. 154.)

In oxidized parts of lead veins with galena, cerussite, mimetite, barite, limonite.

H.

$3\frac{1}{2}$ G. 2.3–2.4 Wavellite, $(AlOH)_3(PO_4)_2 \cdot 5H_2O$; P_2O_5 34.5%; sometimes F.

4   **Struct.**—Radial fibrous, globular with crystalline surface, stalactitic distinct orthorhombic crystals rare. **Cleavage** three directions at 73°, 90°, and 107° (101) (010); brittle; fracture uneven, conchoidal.

Color green, yellow, white, brown. **Streak** white. **Luster** vitreous, pearly. Translucent. (See pp. 186, 190.)

In clays and in veins and joint cracks of rocks; with oxides of iron and manganese, pyrite, actinolite, amblygonite.

$3\frac{1}{2}$ G. 3.1–3.3 Scorodite, $FeAsO_4 \cdot 2H_2O$.   (See p. 158.)
4

$4\frac{1}{2}$ G. 3.1–3.2 APATITE. (See p. 68.)
5

5   G. 4.3–4.5 SMITHSONITE. (See p. 43.)

5   G. 2.9–3.0 DATOLITE. (See p. 49.)
$5\frac{1}{2}$

5   G. 2.2–2.3 ANALCITE. (See p. 49.)
$5\frac{1}{2}$

5   G. 2.3–2.4 Thomsonite. (See p. 49.)
$5\frac{1}{2}$

5   G. 4.9–5.3 Monazite. (See p. 69.)
$5\frac{1}{2}$

5   G. 2.1–2.3 Sodalite (a feldspathoid), $Na_4Al_3Cl(SiO_4)_3$.

6   **Struct.**—Compact, disseminated grains, nodular; isometric crystals (dodecahedrons) rare. Cleavage indistinct, six directions at 60°, 90°, and 120° (110); brittle; fracture conchoidal, uneven.

Color blue, gray, white, red, green. **Streak** white. **Luster** vitreous, greasy. Transparent to translucent. (See p. 168.)

In igneous rocks with nephelite, leucite, cancrinite; not with quartz.

5   G. 3.0–3.1 *Lazulite*, $(Fe,Mg)(AlOH)_2(PO_4)_2$; P_2O_5 45.4%.

6   **Struct.**—Acute pyramidal or tabular monoclinic crystals; granular, compact. **Cleavage** indistinct; brittle; fracture uneven.

Color sky-blue, pale greenish blue. **Streak** white. **Luster** vitreous. Translucent to opaque.

In veins and metamorphic rocks with siderite, corundum, cyanite, rutile.

H.

5½ G. 2.6–2.8 Turquois, $Al_2(OH)_3PO_4 \cdot H_2O$, with 1.5–6.5% Cu.
6

Struct.—Compact, reniform, stalactitic, incrusting, thin seams, disseminated; triclinic crystals rare. Cleavage none; brittle; fracture conchoidal.

Color sky-blue, bluish green, apple-green. Streak white, pale green. Luster waxy, dull. Opaque to translucent. (See pp. 186, 190, 194.)

Veins and seams in partly decomposed igneous rocks.

5½ G. 2.1–2.2 OPAL. (See p. 50.)
6½

5½ G. 3.0–3.3 JADE. (See p. 50.)
6½

6   G. 2.8–3.0 PREHNITE, $H_2Ca_2Al_2(SiO_4)_3$; often some Fe.

6½ Struct.—Botryoidal, stalactitic, radial fibrous; rounded groups of tabular orthorhombic crystals; distinct crystals rare. Cleavage indistinct, one direction (001); brittle; fracture uneven.

Color light green, oil-green, gray, white; often fading on exposure. Streak white. Luster vitreous, waxy. Transparent to translucent. (See pp. 170, 180.)

With zeolites, datolite, apophyllite, pectolite, native copper, calcite, quartz, epidote, chlorite—in igneous rocks, chiefly basic.

6½ G. 3.3–3.5 VESUVIANITE. (See p. 70.)

6½ G. 3.2–3.6 OLIVINE. (See p. 63.)
7

6½ G. 3.4–4.3 GARNET. (See p. 70.)
7½

7   G. 2.65 QUARTZ. (See p. 50.)

7   G. 2.6–2.64 CHALCEDONY. (See p. 51.)

7   G. 2.9–3.0 Boracite. (See p. 52.)

7   G. 3.0–3.2 TOURMALINE. (See p. 59.)
7½

7½ G. 4.5–4.8 ZIRCON. (See p. 52.)

7½ G. 2.6–2.8 BERYL, $Be_3Al_2(SiO_3)_6$; a little H, sometimes Na, Li, Cs.

8   Struct.—Prismatic hexagonal crystals, often large, rough, and striated lengthwise (Fig. 27); columnar, granular, compact. Cleavage indistinct; brittle; fracture uneven, conchoidal.

H.

Color bright green (*emerald*), blue, greenish blue (*aquamarine*), yellow (*golden beryl*), pink (*rose beryl, morganite*), colorless. Streak white. Luster vitreous. Transparent to translucent. (See pp. 180, 194.)

In pegmatite; less common in granite, mica schist, slate; in bituminous limestone; with topaz, tourmaline, garnet, chrysoberyl, rutile.

$7\frac{1}{2}$ G. 3.6–4.6 SPINEL, $MgAl_2O_4$; also Fe, Mn, Cr, Zn—see varieties below.

$8\frac{1}{2}$ Struct.—Isometric crystals (octahedrons, Fig. 1); granular, compact, disseminated. Cleavage indistinct; brittle; fracture conchoidal.

Color red, yellow, green, blue, brown, black (see varieties below). Streak white. Luster vitreous, dull. Transparent to opaque. (See p. 196.)

Ruby spinel, $MgAl_2O_4$, includes the red and reddish transparent to translucent varieties: *spinel ruby*, deep red; *balas ruby*, rose-red; yellow to orange red; violet; sp. gr. 3.5–3.6. In gem placers with zircon, garnet, magnetite; sometimes in crystalline limestone.

9 G. 3.9–4.1 CORUNDUM. (See p. 44.)

SECTION 21

Streak yellow, red, or brown; mineral black or nearly so.

$1\frac{1}{2}$ G. 2.0–2.1 SULPHUR. (See p. 67.)
$2\frac{1}{2}$

$2\frac{1}{2}$ G. 5.8–5.9 PYRARGYRITE (*Dark Ruby Silver*), Ag_3SbS_3; Ag 59.9%.
3

Struct.—Disseminated, incrusting, compact; small hexagonal-rhombohedral crystals rare. Cleavage indistinct; brittle; fracture conchoidal, uneven.

Color dark red to black. Streak purplish red, cherry-red. Luster adamantine, metallic. Transparent to opaque. (See pp. 142, 156.)

In veins with proustite, other silver minerals, galena.

3 G. 4.4–5.1 TETRAHEDRITE. (See p. 25.)
4

$3\frac{1}{2}$ G. 5.9–6.2 *Descloizite*. (See p. 88.)

$3\frac{1}{2}$ G. 3.8–3.9 SIDERITE. (See p. 41.)
4

$3\frac{1}{2}$ G. 3.9–4.1 SPHALERITE. (See p. 64.)
4

$3\frac{1}{2}$ G. 5.8–6.1 CUPRITE. (See p. 88.)
4

H.

3½　G. 4.2–4.4　MANGANITE, MnO·OH; Mn 62.4%; H₂O 10.3%.

4　　**Struct.**—Prismatic orthorhombic crystals striated lengthwise; often groups or bundles. **Cleavage** perfect, one direction lengthwise (010); rarely granular stalactitic; brittle; fracture uneven.

Color steel-gray to iron-black. **Streak** reddish brown to black. **Luster** metallic, submetallic. Opaque. (See p. 150.)

Often altered to pyrolusite. With ores of manganese and iron; barite; calcite, siderite.

5　G. 3.6–4.0　LIMONITE (*Bog Iron Ore, Brown Hematite, Brown Clay*
5½　　　　　*Ironstone, Brown Ocher, Yellow Ocher*), FeO·OH, with capillary and adsorbed water (compare *Goethite* below). Fe 55–60%; H₂O 12–14%.

Struct.—Amorphous, earthy, fibrous, botryoidal, stalactitic; crystals pseudomorphous after pyrite, marcasite, siderite, etc. **Cleavage** none; brittle; fracture conchoidal, splintery, uneven, earthy.

Color yellow, brown, black. **Streak** yellowish brown. **Luster** metallic; silky, dull; often varnish-like surface. Opaque. (See pp. 146, 150, 158, 186.)

In gossan; replacing limestone; nodules in clays; impure in *bog iron ore* and earthy *ocher* deposits.

5　G. 4.0–4.4　GOETHITE. (See p. 89.)
5½

5　G. 7.2–7.5　WOLFRAMITE. (See p. 26.)
5½

5　G. 4.7–4.9　*Hausmannite*, MnMn₂O₄; Mn 72%.
5½　　**Struct.**—Granular, compact; simple and twinned acute tetragonal pyramids, striated crosswise. **Cleavage** perfect, one direction crosswise (001); brittle; fracture uneven.

Color black, brownish black. **Streak** chestnut-brown. **Luster** submetallic, greasy. Opaque. (See pp. 26, 178.)

With manganese ores, magnetite, hematite, barite.

5　G. 2.9–3.4　HORNBLENDE. (See p. 54.)
6

5　G. 3.2–3.6　PYROXENE. (See p. 74.)
6

5　G. 3.3–3.5　HYPERSTHENE. (See p. 53.)
6

5　G. 4.5–5.0　ILMENITE. (See p. 26.)
6

5　G. 3.7–4.7　PSILOMELANE. (See p. 26.)
6

H.

5½ G. 4.3–4.6 CHROMITE (*Chromic Irone Ore*), $FeCr_2O_4$; Cr_2O_3 68%; some Mg and Al.

Struct.—Disseminated, granular, compact; isometric crystals (octahedrons, Fig. 1) small and rare. Cleavage none; indistinct parting four directions at 70½° and 109½° (111); brittle; fracture conchoidal, uneven. Color iron-black, brownish black. Streak dark brown. Luster metallic, submetallic, dull. Opaque. May be slightly magnetic. (See pp. 150, 152, 192, 194.)

In peridotites and serpentine with olivine, enstatite, talc, chlorite, magnetite; in black sands and platinum placers.

5½ G. 9.0–9.7 URANINITE. (See p. 27.)

5½ G. 4.2–4.7 TURGITE. (See p. 85.)
6

5½ G. 4.9–5.3 HEMATITE (*Red Iron Ore, Specular Iron, Kidney Ore, Red*
6½   *Ocher, Martite*), Fe_2O_3; Fe 70%.

Struct.—Compact, granular, radiated, reniform, botryoidal, columnar; micaceous (*specular*); earthy (*red ocher*); thin tabular hexagonal rhombohedral crystals. *Martite*, octahedral crystals, pseudomorphous after magnetite. Cleavage none; brittle; sometimes parting; fracture uneven, splintery. Color steel-gray, red, reddish brown, black. Streak dark red, cherry-red, brownish red. Luster metallic, submetallic, dull. Opaque. (See pp. 146, 150, 158, 186.)

Ore deposits in sedimentary and metamorphic rocks; igneous contacts.

5½ G. 5.1–5.2 FRANKLINITE. (See p. 27.)
6½

6 G. 5.3–7.3 COLUMBITE, $(Fe,Mn)Cb_2O_6$; with Ta, grading into *Tantalite*, $(Fe,Mn)Ta_2O_6$; Ta_2O_5 up to 86%.

Struct.—Orthorhombic crystals, short, square, prismatic; granular, disseminated. Cleavage indistinct, one direction (100); brittle; fracture conchoidal, uneven. Color iron-black, grayish and brownish black; may be iridescent. Streak dark red, brownish black, black. Luster submetallic, greasy, dull. Opaque. (See pp. 148, 152, 178.)

In pegmatite with beryl, lepidolite, tourmaline, spodumene, cassiterite.

6 G. 4.7–4.8 *Braunite*. (See p. 28.)
6½

6 G. 4.1–4.3 RUTILE. (See p. 58.)
7

6 G. 6.8–7.1 CASSITERITE. (See p. 70.)
7

SECTION 22

Streak yellow. red, or brown; mineral yellow. red. or brown.

H.

0 G. 3.6–4.0   LIMONITE (*Bog Iron Ore, Yellow Ocher*), FeO·OH with
1   capillary and adsorbed water; Fe 55–60%; H_2O 12–14%.
                   Yellow, yellowish brown, earthy. (See p. 83.)

0 G. 4.0–4.4   GOETHITE (*Yellow Ocher*), FeO·OH; Fe 62.9%; H_2O 10.1%.
1   Yellow, yellowish brown, earthy. (See p. 89.)

0 G. 4.9–5.0   GREENOCKITE (*Cadmium Blende*), CdS; Cd 77.7%. Bright
1   yellow powder on zinc ores, calcite, etc.   (See p. 184.)

0   CARNOTITE, approx. $(K_2,Ca)O \cdot 2U_2O_3 \cdot V_2O_5 \cdot nH_2O$; V_2O_5
1   20%; U_2O_3 63%.

Dull opaque canary yellow powder, minute waxy scales; rarely solid
masses; greasy feel; cuts like paraffin. Affects photographic plate in one
to seven days.

In cracks and pores of sandstone with roscoelite and other uranium and
vanadium minerals. (See p. 166.)

0 G. 4.9–5.3   HEMATITE (*Red Iron Ore, Red Ocher*), Fe_2O_3; Fe 70%.
1   Red powdery or earthy masses.   (See p. 84.)

0 G. 4.2–4.7   TURGITE, hydrous ferric oxide; Fe 65–66%. Red powdery
1   or earthy masses.   (See pp. 146, 150, 158.)

0 G. 8.0–8.2   CINNABAR.   (See p. 86.)
1

1   G. 5.6–5.7   *Iodyrite (Iodargyrite)*, AgI; Ag 46%.
1½

1   G. 4.5   *Molybdite (Molybdic Ocher)*, $Fe_2(MoO_4)_3 \cdot 7\frac{1}{2}H_2O$; MoO_3
                   59.4%.

2   **Struct.**—Earthy powder, crusts; rarely fibrous, radiating, or hair-like
orthorhombic crystals. **Cleavage** distinct, one direction crosswise (001);
brittle.

Color and **streak** straw-yellow, yellowish white. **Luster** dull, silky.
Translucent to opaque.

With molybdenite, of which it is an alteration product.

1½ G. 3.5–3.6   REALGAR, AsS; As 70.1%.

2   **Struct.**—Granular, earthy incrustations, disseminated; **rarely** short
monoclinic prisms, striated lengthwise. **Cleavage** distinct, one direction
lengthwise (010); slightly sectile; fracture conchoidal.

H.

Color deep red to orange, becoming yellow (*orpiment*) on long exposure to light. Streak orange-yellow. Luster resinous, adamantine, dull. Transparent to translucent. (See p. 152.)

In veins with orpiment, stibnite, native arsenic, pyrite; disseminated in clay, dolomite, etc.

$1\frac{1}{2}$ G. 3.4–3.5 ORPIMENT, As_2S_3; As 61%.

2 Struct.—Foliated, granular, earthy incrustations; rarely small monoclinic crystals. Cleavage distinct, one direction (010); thin flakes flexible; slightly sectile.

Color and streak lemon-yellow. Luster resinous, greasy; pearly on cleavage. Translucent to nearly opaque. (See p. 152.)

In veins with realgar, stibnite, barite, calcite, pyrite; forms from realgar on long exposure to light.

$1\frac{1}{2}$ G. 2.0–2.1 SULPHUR. (See p. 67.)
$2\frac{1}{2}$

$1\frac{1}{2}$ G. 2.9–3.0 ERYTHRITE (*Cobalt Bloom*), $Co_3(AsO_4)_2 \cdot 8H_2O$; CoO 37.5%;
$2\frac{1}{2}$ sometimes Ni, Fe, Ca.

$1\frac{1}{2}$ G. 2.1 COPIAPITE. (See p. 60.)
$2\frac{1}{2}$

2 G. 8.0–8.2 CINNABAR, HgS; Hg 86.2%.

$2\frac{1}{2}$ Struct.—Granular, earthy, incrusting; small thick tabular hexagonal-rhombohedral crystals rare. Cleavage indistinct, three directions at 60° and 120° ($10\bar{1}0$); brittle to sectile; fracture uneven.

Color purplish red to brownish red. Streak scarlet to brownish red. Luster adamantine, dull. Transparent to opaque. (See pp. 144, 154.)

Veins and disseminated in sandstone and limestone with pyrite, marcasite, realgar, stibnite, barite, opal, quartz, sulphur, mercury.

2 G. 5.5–5.6 PROUSTITE (*Light Ruby Silver*), Ag_3AsS_3; Ag 65.4%.

$2\frac{1}{2}$ Struct.—Compact, disseminated, incrusting; small hexagonal-rhombohedral crystals rare. Cleavage three directions at 72° and 108° ($10\bar{1}1$), not conspicuous; brittle; fracture conchoidal.

Color and streak scarlet to brownish red. Luster adamantine, dull. Transparent to translucent. (See pp. 140, 156.)

In veins with pyrargyrite and other silver minerals and galena.

2 G. 3.1–3.2 *Autunite*, $Ca(UO_2)_2(PO_4)_2 \cdot 8H_2O$; UO_3 62.7%.

$2\frac{1}{2}$ Struct.—Thin tabular orthornombic (pseudotetragonal) crystals; foliated and scaly micaceous aggregates. Cleavage perfect, one direction (001); flakes brittle.

H.

Color lemon to sulphur-yellow. Streak yellowish. Luster pearly, sub-adamantine. Transparent to translucent. (See p. 166.)

With uraninite and other uranium minerals; with silver, tin and iron ores. Commonly in pegmatite.

$2\frac{1}{2}$ G. 9.0   Calaverite. (See p. 30.)

$2\frac{1}{2}$ G. 8.8–8.9 COPPER (Native Copper), Cu; often some Ag, Bi, Hg, etc.

3   Struct.—Scales, plates, lumps, branching aggregates; isometric crystals, commonly distorted. Cleavage none; ductile and malleable; fracture hackly.

Color copper-red, tarnish black, blue, green. Streak copper-red, shiny. Luster metallic. Opaque. (See p. 146.)

In amygdules and veins in basic lavas and in accompanying conglomerate, sandstone, shale, etc., with silver, zeolites, datolite, epidote, quartz, calcite; in oxidized zone of other copper ores.

$2\frac{1}{2}$ G. 15.6–19.3 GOLD (Native Gold), Au; commonly some Ag, sometimes
3   Cu, Bi, etc.; Ag 20% or more, Electrum.

Struct.—Grains, scales, lumps; rarely small isometric crystals, commonly distorted. Cleavage none; ductile and malleable; fracture hackly.

Color gold-yellow, brass-yellow, pale yellow; does not tarnish. Streak gold-yellow, shiny. Luster metallic. Opaque. (See p. 146.)

In veins with quartz, pyrite, galena, sphalerite, and other sulphides; in sands and gravels (placers).

$2\frac{1}{2}$ G. 5.8–5.9 Pyrargyrite. (See p. 82.)
3

$2\frac{1}{2}$ G. 5.9–6.1 Crocoite, $PbCrO_4$; Pb 63.9%.

3   Struct.—Monoclinic prismatic crystals; acicular, granular, columnar, incrusting. Cleavage distinct, two directions at 86° and 104° (110), less distinct two other directions (100)(001); sectile; fracture conchoidal, uneven.

Color bright red. Streak orange-yellow. Luster adamantine, vitreous. Translucent. (See p. 154.)

In veins with galena, quartz, pyrite, vanadinite, wulfenite.

$2\frac{1}{2}$ G. 2.7–2.8 Polyhalite. (See p. 60.)
3

3   G. 6.6–7.2 Vanadinite. (See p. 67.)

3   G. 4.1–4.6 Olivenite. (See p. 90.)

3   G. 4.9–5.0 Greenockite. CdS: Cd 77.7%.

H.

$3\frac{1}{2}$ **Struct.**—Earthy coatings, powdery; rarely small hexagonal crystals. **Cleavage** inconspicuous, three directions at 60° and 120° ($11\bar{2}0$); brittle; fracture conchoidal.

Color yellow, orange-yellow, greenish yellow. **Streak** orange-yellow. **Luster** resinous, adamantine, dull. Translucent to opaque. (See p. 85.) With sphalerite, smithsonite, galena, calcite.

$3\frac{1}{2}$ G. 5.9–6.2 *Descloizite*, $Pb_2Zn(OH)VO_4$; PbO 55.4%; ZnO 19.7%; V_2O_5 22.7%.

Struct.—Small orthorhombic crystals forming drusy crusts. (See p. 154.)

$3\frac{1}{2}$ G. 3.8–3.9 SIDERITE. (See p. 41.)
4

$3\frac{1}{2}$ G. 3.9–4.1 SPHALERITE. (See p. 64.)
4

$3\frac{1}{2}$ G. 5.8–6.1 CUPRITE (*Ruby Copper, Red Oxide of Copper*), Cu_2O; Cu
4   88.8%; with OH in *Hydrocuprite*.

Struct.—Compact, granular, earthy, capillary (*chalcotrichite*): isometric crystals. **Cleavage** indistinct; brittle; fracture uneven.

Color ruby-red, reddish black; orange (*hydrocuprite*). **Streak** brownish red. **Luster** submetallic, adamantine, dull. Transparent to opaque.

With native copper, malachite, azurite, chrysocolla, limonite, tenorite, chalcocite, chalcopyrite. (See pp. 146, 156.)

$3\frac{1}{2}$ G. 6.5–7.1 PYROMORPHITE. (See p. 79.)
4

4 G. 5.4–5.7 ZINCITE (*Red Zinc Ore*), ZnO; Zn 80.3%; commonly Mn.
$4\frac{1}{2}$ **Struct.**—Lamellar, granular; rarely hemimorphic hexagonal crystals. **Cleavage** distinct, one direction (0001); sometimes distinct 3 other directions at 60° (1010); brittle; fracture uneven.

Color deep red to orange. **Streak** orange-yellow. **Luster** adamantine. Translucent to opaque. (See p. 186.)

In crystalline limestone with franklinite, willemite, rhodonite.

$4\frac{1}{2}$ G. 5.9–6.2 SCHEELITE. (See p. 65.)
5

5 G. 3.6–4.0 LIMONITE. (See p. 83.)
$5\frac{1}{2}$

H.

5   G. 4.0–4.4 Goethite, FeO·OH; Fe 62.9%; H_2O 10.1%.

5½   **Struct.**—Small tabular, scaly (*lepidocrosite*), or acicular orthorhombic crystals; compact, granular, foliated, fibrous. **Cleavage** distinct, one direction lengthwise (010); brittle; fracture uneven, splintery.

Color yellow, reddish brown, dark brown, black. **Streak** yellow, yellowish brown. **Luster** submetallic, adamantine, dull. Translucent to opaque. (See pp. 146, 150, 158, 186.)

In amorphous and fibrous form the essential mineral of *limonite*, above. With other iron ores; in cavities in hematite and limonite; inclusions giving color to some feldspars and quartz.

5   G. 7.2–7.5 WOLFRAMITE.   (See p. 26.)
5½

5   G. 7.3–7.7 Niccolite.   (See p. 29.)
5½

5   G. 4.7–4.9 *Hausmannite*.   (See p. 83.)
5½

5   G. 2.9–3.4 HORNBLENDE.   (See p. 54.)
6

5   G. 3.2–3.6 PYROXENE.   (See p. 74.)
6

5   G. 3.3–3.5 Hypersthene.   (See p. 53.)
6

5½   G. 4.3–4.6 CHROMITE.   (See p. 84.)

5½   G. 4.2–4.7 Turgite.   (See p. 85.)
6

5½   G. 4.9–5.3 HEMATITE.   (See p. 84.)
6½

6   G. 4.1–4.3 RUTILE.   (See p. 58.)
7

6   G. 6.8–7.1 CASSITERITE.   (See p. 70.)
7

SECTION 23

Streak blue or green.

H.

1   G. 3.2–3.3   BLUE ASBESTOS (*Crocidolite*).

2   **Struct.**—Long delicate flexible fibers, easily separable.
Color and **streak** lavender-blue. (See. p. 91.)

1   G. 2.2–2.4   GLAUCONITE.   (See p. 78.)
2

1   G. 2.6–3.0   CHLORITE.   (See p. 72.)
2½

1   G. 3.0–3.1   ANNABERGITE.   (See p. 78.)
2½

1   G. 2.3–2.8   GARNIERITE.   (See p. 78.)
4

1½   G. 2.6–2.7   VIVIANITE.   (See p. 72.)
2

2   G. 2.0–2.2   CHRYSOCOLLA.   (See p. 78.)
3

3   G. 4.1–4.6   *Olivenite* (*Wood Copper*). $Cu_2(OH)AsO_4$; Cu 49.8%; As_2O_5
40.7%.

3   G. 2.6–2.7   *Zaratite.*

3   G. 3.7–3.8   ATACAMITE, $Cu_2(OH)_3Cl$; Cu 59.5%; Cl 16.6%; H_2O
12.7%.

3½   **Struct.**—Crystalline aggregates, fibrous, granular, incrusting; slender
prismatic orthorhombic crystals, striated lengthwise. **Cleavage** distinct,
one direction lengthwise (010); brittle; fracture conchoidal.
Color emerald-green, blackish green. **Streak** apple-green. **Luster** vitreous, adamantine. Transparent to opaque. (See p. 156.)
With malachite and other secondary copper minerals, also sulphides,
limonite, hematite.

3½   G. 3.9–4.0   MALACHITE (*Green Carbonate of Copper*), $Cu_2(OH)_2CO_3$;
4   Cu 57.4%.

Struct.—Radial fibrous, botryoidal, stalactitic, incrusting, earthy; slender
monoclinic crystals in tufts. **Cleavage** one direction crosswise (001); brittle;
fracture conchoidal, splintery.

H.

Color emerald-green, grass-green, dark green. Streak light green. Luster adamantine, silky, dull. Translucent to opaque. (See p. 156.)
With other oxidized copper minerals, sulphides, native copper.

$3\frac{1}{2}$ G. 3.7–3.8 AZURITE (*Blue Carbonate of Copper*), $Cu_3(OH)_2(CO_3)_2$;
4   Cu 55.2%.

Struct.—Short prismatic or tabular monoclinic crystals; radiating, botryoidal, incrusting, earthy. Cleavage distinct, two directions at 121° (021); brittle; fracture conchoidal.
Color azure-blue, dark blue. Streak blue. Luster vitreous, dull. Translucent to opaque. (See p. 156.)
With other oxidized copper minerals, sulphides, native copper.

$3\frac{1}{2}$ G. 3.9   BROCHANTITE, $Cu_4(OH)_6SO_4$; Cu 56.2%. (See p. 156.)
4

$3\frac{1}{2}$ G. 3.9–4.0 ALABANDITE, MnS.

4   Struct.—Granular, compact; isometric-tetrahedral crystals rare. Cleav-age distinct, three directions at 90° (100); brittle; fracture uneven.
Color iron-black, tarnish brownish black. Streak olive-green. Luster submetallic, dull. Opaque. (See p. 144.)
In veins with rhodochrosite and metallic sulphides.

$3\frac{1}{2}$ G. 3.1–3.3 SCORODITE. (See p. 80.)
4

4   G. 3.2–3.3 CROCIDOLITE (*Blue Asbestos*), approx. $NaFe''Fe'''(SiO_3)_3$.

Struct.—Asbestos-like; long delicate flexible fibers, easily separable; compact, earthy.
Color and streak lavender-blue, leek-green; grayish-white (*amosite*). Luster silky, dull. Opaque. (See p. 162.)
Cross-fiber veins in banded ferruginous shales.

5   G. 3.3–3.4 DIOPTASE, H_2CuSiO_4; Cu 40.3%. (See p. 188.)

5   G. 2.4–2.5 LAZURITE (*Lapis Lazuli*), $Na_5Al_3S_3(SiO_4)_3$.

$5\frac{1}{2}$ Struct.—Compact; isometric crystals (dodecahedrons, Fig. 7) rare. Cleavage inconspicuous, six directions at 60°, 90°, and 120° (110); brittle; fracture uneven.
Color azure-blue, violet-blue, greenish blue. Streak pale blue. Luster vitreous. Translucent to opaque. (See p. 168.)
At contacts in crystalline limestone, with pyrite, calcite, pyroxene. Often intimately mixed with calcite, pyrite, muscovite, pyroxene, etc.

5   G. 2.9–3.4 HORNBLENDE. (See p. 54.)
6

H.
5   G. 3.2–3.6   PYROXENE. (See p. 74.)
6

$5\frac{1}{2}$ G. 9.0–9.7   Uraninite. (See p. 27.)

$5\frac{1}{2}$ G. 2.6–2.8   Turquois. (See p. 81.)
6

6   G. 3.5–3.6   *Chloritoid.* (See p. 54.)
7

DETERMINATION OF MINERALS BY MEANS OF BLOWPIPE AND CHEMICAL TESTS

APPARATUS

Blowpipe. The ordinary jeweler's blowpipe of brass, 10 or 12 inches long, or the cheaper one of japanned iron, serves very well. The more expensive instrument with a platinum tip is more durable (Figs. 55, 56, 57, 58). In any case it is essential that the tip shall be perforated with a very small, smooth hole.

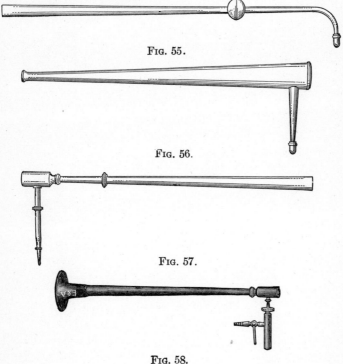

FIG. 55.

FIG. 56.

FIG. 57.

FIG. 58.

Types of Blowpipes.

The gas blowpipe (Fig. 58) which requires no Bunsen burner, is most convenient; it may also be fed by compressed air.

The hard rubber mouthpiece, shown in same figure, is advantageously used with any type of blowpipe.

Lamp. Many types of lamp, or even a candle, may be successfully used with the blowpipe. (*a*) The ordinary Bunsen gas burner (Fig. 59), or a low form, more convenient for blowpiping (Fig. 60), with a tube to be inserted or slipped over the top. The tube is flattened to a narrow slit at the top and cut off slanting, generally with projecting points left to form a rest for the blowpipe

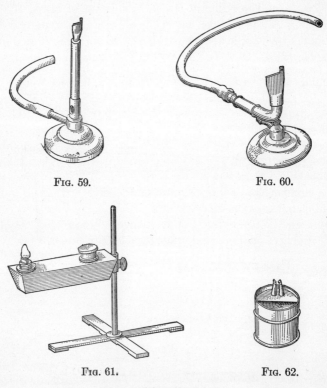

Fig. 59.   Fig. 60.

Fig. 61.   Fig. 62.

Types of Blowpipe Lamps.

tip. (*b*) A lamp to use olive oil or other vegetable oil (Fig. 61), or (*c*) one using tallow, paraffin, or other solid fuel (Fig. 62). The last is most convenient for portable use. It is lighted with a match and the flame is then blown steeply downward for a few seconds in order to melt some of the fuel next to the wick. The heat of the flame then keeps it going. (*d*) Ordinary candles (preferably large and of tallow) serve very well.

Forceps. For most purposes plain iron forceps, 4 or 5 inches long and filed down to small points, are satisfactory. Those with platinum points are better but very expensive (Fig. 63). Points made of metallic alloys are also used satisfactorily. The points of the " cross-legged " forms close automatically and hold the fragment to be tested.

Charcoal. Best from soft wood (willow, pine, etc.). Convenient sizes, about $\frac{1}{2}\times1\times4$ inches, may be purchased. Used as a

Fig. 63. Forceps, or Tweezers to be used in Blowpipe Work.

support in many operations with the blowpipe (Figs. 70, 71, 76), and in making reductions the carbon assists the flame.

Platinum Wire. A thin platinum wire, 26 B. & S. gage, about 0.4 mm. diameter and 3 inches long, sealed in a small glass tube for a handle (Fig. 74), or in a holder made for the purpose. Most used with a circular loop, $\frac{1}{8}$ inch (3 mm.) in diameter, at the end to hold a bead of borax, soda, or other flux.

Open and Closed Tubes. To be made of " hard," or " combustion " tubing 4 or 5 mm. internal diameter for closed tubes and 7

Fig. 64.—Hammer and Anvil.

Fig. 65.—Test Tube Holder.

or 8 mm. diameter for open tubes. For open tubes cut with a file into 4-inch lengths and use either straight, or better, with a bend near one end (Fig. 73), which may be made by heating until the glass is soft. For closed tubes (Fig. 72), cut into 5-inch lengths, heat the middle in the Bunsen flame or blast lamp, turning slowly in order to heat all sides alike; when soft pull quickly apart. Hold the tapering part of each tube thus formed in the flame and pull away the slender glass tip.

Hammer. Any small hammer will serve. For the special hammer, a wire handle is best (Fig. 64).

Anvil. Any smooth flat block of iron or steel (Fig. 64). The flat side of a geologist's hammer or prospector's pick is good.

Magnet. A magnetized knife blade or chisel or a small horseshoe magnet.

Test Tubes. Good sizes are $4 \times \frac{1}{2}$ and $5 \times \frac{5}{8}$ inches.

In addition to the above the following articles will be found convenient in the laboratory. For portable outfits they may be dispensed with.

Test Tube Holder. Of brass wire (Fig. 65) or wood—for holding hot tubes (or a strip of paper is wrapped around the tube, the loose ends of paper being held in the fingers).

Streak Plate. Unglazed porcelain; a convenient size is $1\frac{1}{2} \times 3$ inches. A clean, fine-grained whetstone serves very well.

Blue Glass. A piece 2 or 3 inches square, for observing flame colors. The Merwin Color Screen, of celluloid, is also useful.

Watch Glasses. Shallow, 2 inches in diameter.

Test Tube Support. Wood, with several holes larger than the tubes. Easily made.

Agate Mortar. $1\frac{1}{4}$ inches diameter or larger, with agate pestle. Fragments can be ground under the hammer, and if the anvil is placed in a paper tray of sufficient depth (Fig. 64), the particles that fly will be caught.

Diamond Mortar. Of steel; two-piece form is best. Useful when only small particles of a mineral are obtainable or when the hardness of the mineral is over 6, when grinding in the agate mortar would damage the latter.

Glass Funnel. Two inches in diameter or larger.

Filter Paper. Round and twice the diameter of the funnel.

Plaster Tablets. Thin paste of plaster of Paris is spread about $\frac{1}{4}$ inch thick on a sheet of glass that has been slightly oiled. While still soft cut the paste with a knife into rectangles about $1\frac{1}{2} \times 4$ inches. These are readily removed after the plaster hardens. Used for support, like charcoal, and show some sublimates better.

REAGENTS

To be used dry:

Sodium Carbonate, or soda, Na_2CO_3; or sodium bicarbonate, common baking soda, $NaHCO_3$. For fusion in chlorine test, it must be free from Cl.

Sodium Tetraborate, or borax, $Na_2B_4O_7 \cdot 10H_2O$.

Borax Glass may be prepared as required by making borax beads (p. 112) and pulverizing them for use as a flux.

Sodium Ammonium Phosphate, also called " phosphorus salt " and " microcosmic salt," $HNaNH_4PO_4 \cdot 4H_2O$. Loses NH_4OH and $4H_2O$ on heating, becoming *sodium metaphosphate* ($NaPO_3$), abbreviated s.ph.

Test Papers, small strips of blue and red litmus paper and yellow turmeric paper.

Occasional use will also be found for the following:

Potassium Bisulphate, $KHSO_4$.

Turner's Flux, 1 part finely powdered fluorite (CaF_2) with 3 parts potassium bisulphate ($KHSO_4$).

Von Kobell's Flux, 1 part potassium iodide (KI), 2 parts sulphur (S), and 1 part potassium bisulphate ($KHSO_4$).

Tin, foil or granulated. Scraps of tin cans or other tin plate will serve. Also *Zinc,* either granulated or scraps of sheet metal; *Potassium Nitrate,* KNO_3; and powdered *Galena,* PbS, *Gypsum,* $CaSO_4 \cdot 2H_2O$, and *Fluorite,* CaF_2.

To be used in liquid form:

Water, H_2O, distilled or rain water is best; for most purposes any clear water that is not " hard " will serve.

Hydrochloric Acid, HCl (" muriatic acid "), for most purposes the concentrated acid as obtained from the supply houses (sp. gr. 1.20) is diluted with an equal quantity of water, giving a solution a little stronger than 5/N.

Other mineral acids are more dangerous to handle and less useful than hydrochloric. Many of the reagents that follow are rarely needed; on the other hand, most of those used in a chemical laboratory will occasionally be found useful.

Nitric Acid, HNO_3 (" aqua fortis "). To dilute the concentrated acid (sq. gr. 1.42) to approximately 5/N, add two volumes of water.

Nitrohydrochloric Acid (" aqua regia "), 3 parts hydrochloric and 1 part nitric acid.

Sulphuric Acid, H_2SO_4 (" oil of vitriol "). In diluting add the concentrated acid (sq. gr. 1.84) very slowly to 6 volumes of water, for approximately 5/N.

Ammonium Hydroxide, or ammonia, NH_4OH. Add to the concentrated solution (sp. gr. .90) three volumes of water, for approximately 5/N. This solution will neutralize an equal volume of the dilute acids.

Potassium Hydroxide, KOH (" caustic potash "). Best kept as sticks broken to short bits and placed in a well-stoppered bottle— to be dissolved in a little water as needed.

Ammonium Molybdate, $(NH_4)_2MoO_4$. Dissolve the crystals in water that has been made alkaline with ammonia. For use acidify a little of this solution in a test tube with HNO_3; the ppt. that forms is quickly cleared up by further addition of acid.

Cobalt Nitrate, $Co(NO_3)_2$. Dissolve the crystals in 10 parts of water. A dropping bottle holding one or two ounces is convenient for laboratory use.

BLOWPIPE OPERATIONS AND CHEMICAL TESTS

Blast. The blast of the blowpipe should not be blown from the lungs and should not interfere with regular breathing. Distend the cheeks fully and, while breathing through the nose, allow the air to escape from the mouth through the blowpipe without making any effort to blow. Before the supply is exhausted distend the cheeks again from the lungs. In this way the blast may be continued for several minutes, when necessary, without fatigue. If the blowpipe tip is in good condition the flame will be smooth, steady, and silent (Figs. 67–69).

Flames. A candle flame or luminous gas flame consists of 3 concentric parts (Fig. 66): (*a*) an inner cone of unburned gases; (*b*) a mantle of unburned gas or vapor, full of glowing particles of carbon, where carbon monoxide (CO) and water (H_2O) are forming by combustion; (*c*) a hot, non-luminous mantle of the products of complete combustion, carbon dioxide (CO_2) and water (H_2O) mingling with the surrounding air, and hence with an excess of oxygen. Hot fuel is in excess in (b), hence it is reducing in its action; but the temperature is too low for vigorous reduction. The excess of oxygen makes (c) oxidizing, and it is also hotter. A non-luminous Bunsen or alcohol flame differs only in lacking the incandescent carbon in (b). An alcohol lamp, an oil lamp (for vegetable oil), or even a candle, may be used, when gas and laboratory appliances are not available.

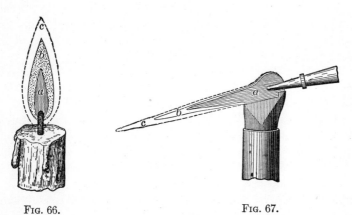

FIG. 66.   FIG. 67.

FIG. 66.—Candle flame: (a) Unburned gases; (b) burning gases, forming H_2O, CO, and luminous C; (c) hot combustion products, H_2O, CO_2, mingled with O from surrounding air. The luminous gas flame is the same.

FIG. 67.—Blowpipe flame: (a) Mixture of unburned gas and air from the blowpipe; (b) burning gas gives intense heat and slight reducing action; (c) and beyond, hot combustion products with excess of O from the air— *oxidizing flame* (o.f.). A candle or kerosene flame may be used in the absence of gas or alcohol.

In determinative mineralogy these flames are often directed laterally or inclined downward by the use of the blowpipe. For *oxidizing* effects the tip should be inserted slightly into the flame, as in Fig. 67, thereby mixing more oxygen with the gases at the base. The best *reducing* effect is obtained by withdrawing the tip a little from the flame and blowing very gently (Fig. 68). The flame should not be sooty, but a little luminous carbon should extend down the whole length of it.

Ignition: Fusion. The application of intense heat is commonly called *ignition*. The hottest flame is entirely non-luminous and the hottest part of it is just beyond the visible blue tip. The fusibility of a mineral is tested at this point by strongly heating an elongated fragment not more than 1.5 mm. ($\frac{1}{16}$ of an inch) in thickness; that is, thinner than the "lead" of an ordinary pencil. This is held in the forceps so that it projects into the flame (Fig. 69). The

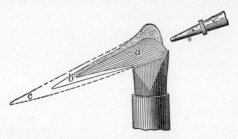

Fig. 68.—Blowpipe flame: (b) Strong *reducing flame* (r.f.), with gentle blast and more gas than used in o.f.

mineral may fuse *quietly*, or with *intumescence* (bubbling and swelling up), or with *exfoliation* (splitting into leaves or flakes). The result may be fusion to a bead of colored or colorless *glass*, clear or filled with bubbles; or to a white, opaque *enamel*. If infusible the mineral may remain unchanged, or it may change

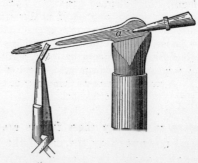

Fig. 69.—Testing fusibility, showing maximum size of fragment, manner of holding it, and position in the flame.

color, or become opaque, etc. All of these properties should be carefully noted.

Decrepitation. The violent breaking away of particles with little crackling explosions owing to sudden unequal heating or to the expansion of minute inclusions of water or liquid carbon dioxide is called decrepitation. This sometimes interferes seriously with the determination of fusibility. By first heating the mineral very gradually and gently in the Bunsen flame this difficulty may sometimes be avoided; otherwise heat a few fragments in a closed tube until decrepitation ceases and select a fragment of suitable size, if such remains. When this fails, make a thin paste of the finely powdered mineral with water, spread a little of this on charcoal and heat, at first very gently, then intensely. The crust thus formed can be taken up carefully in the forceps and tested for fusibility.

Scale of Fusibility. The degree of fusibility of minerals is indicated by numbers referring to the following scale. Comparison should be made on fragments of about the same size. Penfield recommends a standard size of about 1.5 mm. in diameter, as explained above. With the more difficultly fusible minerals, however, a much smaller fragment with a very thin edge or fine point should be tested before deciding that it is infusible.

SCALE OF FUSIBILITY

(Penfield's modification of von Kobell's scale)

(Minerals named in parentheses have about the same fusibility as the standard.)

1. *Stibnite*, Sb_2S_3. Fragments larger than standard size fuse easily in a luminous flame; fuses easily in closed tube below red heat. (Realgar, orpiment, sulphur.)

2. *Chalcopyrite*, $CuFeS_2$. Standard size fragment fuses in luminous flame; small fragment fuses in closed tube at red heat. (Galena, arsenopyrite, apophyllite.)

3. *Almandite* (Garnet), $Fe_3Al_2(SiO_4)_3$. Standard fragment fuses readily to globule with blowpipe; only thinnest edges rounded in luminous flame. (Malachite, wernerite, stilbite.)

4. *Actinolite*, $Ca(Mg,Fe)_3(SiO_3)_4$. Edges easily rounded on standard fragment; fine splinter fuses easily to globule. (Tremolite, wollastonite, barite.)

5. *Orthoclase*, $KAlSi_3O_8$. Edges of standard fragment rounded with difficulty; only finest splinters fuse to globule. (Sphalerite, biotite, scheelite.)

6. *Enstatite*, var. *Bronzite* (Mg,Fe)SiO$_3$. Only finest points and thinnest edges can be rounded at all. (Enstatite, calamine, serpentine.)

Quartz may be added as No. 7 to represent minerals that are infusible in the blowpipe flame.

Flame Colors. Some minerals on ignition impart to the blow-pipe flame a distinct color, which is best seen against a dark background. It is often more distinct when a trace of fine powder is introduced into the Bunsen flame with a clean, dry platinum wire. Hold the wire first in the cool edge of the flame, at the base, then raise it gradually into the hottest central part near the tip. If the wire is first moistened with water a larger quantity will adhere, and this is sometimes advantageous. Instead of water dilute HCl is often helpful, and with some minerals concentrated H$_2$SO$_4$.

Absorption-light filters are useful in analyzing mixed flames. Blue and green glass are commonly used for this purpose, but the Merwin flame-color screen is more effective. It consists of strips of transparent blue and violet celluloid that are partly overlapped, forming three color divisions. In use the glass or screen is held close to the eyes and the colored flame viewed through it. The colors imparted by various substances and the effects of absorption-filters are given in the table on the opposite page.

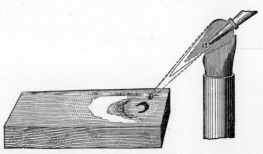

Fig. 70.— Roasting on charcoal; use very small o.f., scarcely red heat, to oxidize S, As, Sb and to drive off volatile constituents.

Roasting on Charcoal. Spread a fine powder of the mineral thinly on charcoal and heat with a small oxidizing flame, a considerable distance beyond the tip of the blue and at no more than a dull red heat (Fig. 70). If the mineral fuses easily heat intensely

FLAME COLORS

(For abbreviations, see page 217)

(Merwin screen: (1) Blue; (2) Overlap; (3) Violet)

Color.	Shade.	Substance.	Absorption-effects. Remarks.
Red	Crimson	Sr	1, 2. Invisible; 3. Crimson. Faint yellow through green glass. Alk. after ign. Sr sol. with few drops $BaCl_2$ sol. gives red flame *after* green.
Red	Crimson	Li	1, 2. Invisible; 3. Crimson. Invisible through green glass. Not alk. after ign. Li sol. with few drops $BaCl_2$ sol. gives red flame *before* green.
Red	Yellowish to orange	Ca	1. Gnh. yel.; 2. Faint grn.; 3. Pale crimson. Invisible through green glass. Improved by HCl. Alk. after ign.
Yellow	Intense	Na	Intense and persistent. 1, 2, 3. Invisible. Invisible through blue glass.
Green	Yellowish	Ba	1. Green; 2, 3. Pale green. Alk. after ign.
Green	Yellowish	B	1. Green; 2, 3. Pale green. Use conc. H_2SO_4; for insol. minerals use 3 parts Turner's flux. (Turmeric test decisive.)
Green	Yellowish	$MnCl_2$	1. Emerald; 2. Pale bluish green; 3. Pale lavender.
Green	Pale yelh.	Mo	From oxide or sulphide.
Green	Emerald	CuO CuI	With HCl blue flame tinged with green.
Green	Pale	Te Sb	
Green	Pale bluish	P	1. Grn.; 2. Pale grn.; 3. Light violet-red. Use conc. H_2SO_4.
Green	Bluish	Zn	Bright streaks in outer part of flame.
Blue	Azure	$CuCl_2$	Outer fringe of emerald green. 1. Bright grn.; 2. Pale grn.; 3. Blue, with green fringe.
Blue	Indigo	Se	Characteristic radish-like odor.
Blue	Pale azure	Pb	Green tinge in outer part of flame.
Blue	Pale	As	Characteristic garlic odor.
Violet	Pale	K	1. Blue-violet; 2. Faint violet-red; 3. Reddish-violet. Purplish-red through blue glass.

till the volatile constituents are driven off, then pulverize with a little powdered charcoal and repeat the roasting with the mixture, using the small oxidizing flame and low temperature again.

Ignition on Charcoal. With the edge of a small coin make a slight depression near one end of the coal and place in it a few grains of the mineral, not larger than pin heads. Hold the length of the coal in line with the flame and tilted toward it (Fig. 71), in order to catch any sublimate that may form.

First heat for only 2 or 3 seconds with a small gentle oxidizing flame, as in roasting (Fig. 70), not allowing the visible flame to come near the mineral. Note reactions, if any: (1) decrepitation,

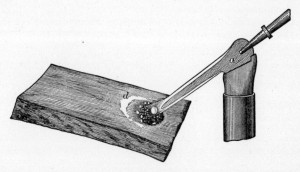

Fig. 71.—Reduction on charcoal, with sublimates, when formed, at (*d*) and beyond. For comparison burn a spot on the coal and observe the color and texture of the ash. Note that the grain shows distinctly in the ash, while sublimates tend to conceal it.

(2) deflagration, (3) visible fumes. The moment the heat is stopped seek for (4) odors, and observe (5) any change in color and (6) color and position of sublimate, if any. (Caution: Do not mistake ash for sublimate.) If the mineral blackens, test when cold for (7) magnetism. Repeat the oxidizing flame with increasing intensity, using fresh material if necessary, until the reactions · are clearly determined. Next use the reducing flame (Fig. 71) on the oxidized material, beginning gently and increasing the intensity. Look for the above reactions and also (8) globules of metal that may be reduced. If the reactions are weak and uncertain mix the powdered mineral with three times its volume of soda and a little borax and charcoal powder, then fuse on charcoal for a full minute with the most intense heat.

SUBLIMATES ON CHARCOAL

(For abbreviations, see page 217)

Near Assay.	Dist. from Assay.	Substance.	Remarks.
White, very volatile	White to grayish	As_2O_3	Mostly far from assay; often strong garlic odor
Dense white, volatile	Gray or slightly brownish	White, TeO_2 Gray, Te	Volatilizes in r.f., coloring flame pale green
Dense white, volatile	Bluish	Sb_2O_3 and $SbSbO_4$	Heavy near the assay
White	White to bluish	Chlorides of Cu, Pb, Hg, NH_4, and alkalis	
Pale yel. to wh. hot; wh. cold; non-vol. in o.f.	Faint white	SnO_2	Moistened with $Co(NO_3)_2$ and ignited, subl. becomes bluish-green
Pale yel. hot; wh. cold; vol. in o.f.	Bluish	MoO_3	Touched with r.f., subl. becomes azure-blue. Cu-red MoO_2 subl. next to assay
Canary-yel. hot; wh. cold; non-vol. in o.f.	Faint white (See p. 134)	ZnO	Moistened with $Co(NO_3)_2$ and ignited the subl. becomes green
Yel. hot; pale yel. cold; vol.in o.f. and r.f.	Dense white with bluish-wh. border	PbO $PbSO_3$ $PbSO_4$	Forms when galena and other Pb sulphides are heated very hot on charcoal
Dark yel. hot; S-yel. cold; vol. in o.f. and r.f.	Bluish-white	PbO	Heated with von Kobell's flux forms volatile yelh.-grn. subl., PbI_2
Dark orange-yel. hot; orange-yel. cold; vol. in o.f. and r.f.	Greenish-white	Bi_2O_3	Fused with von Kobell's flux in small o.f. forms yel. subl. fringed by brilliant red
Nearly blk. to rdh.-brn.; vol. in o.f. and r.f.	Yellow	CdO	Iridescent when very thin
Rdh. to deep lilac		Ag with Pb and Sb	Ag alone gives slight bnh. subl. after long ignition
Copper-red	White	MoO_2 MoO_3	Touched with r.f., white subl. becomes azure-blue
Steel-gray, faint metallic luster; very vol.	White; may be tinged red	White, SeO_2 Red, Se	Subl. colors r.f. azure-blue. Characteristic radish - like odor

Reduction of Metals. Mix equal volumes of finely powdered mineral,* charcoal, and borax with 3 volumes of soda. Moisten slightly with water and place a mass the size of a small pea in a shallow depression on the charcoal. Fuse in a strong reducing flame for two or three minutes without interruption, unless a bead of metal becomes distinctly visible in a shorter time. If no metal is visible pry off the assay with a chisel or knife, removing with it a little of the charcoal on which it rests; grind to a fine powder in an agate mortar, and while continuing the grinding, allow water to flow gently from the tap upon the hand and into the mortar. The surplus soda dissolves and the powdered charcoal is floated away by the overflow. Globules of metal, flattened by the grinding, will appear as bright scales on the pestle and in the mortar. (See Fig. 71.)

Transfer the metal to a watch glass, add a drop or two of HNO_3, warm gently and add an equal amount of water.

White Metal. Sn changes to white insoluble oxide; Pb soluble and gives white precipitate with a drop of H_2SO_4; Ag soluble and gives with a drop of HCl a white precipitate which is soluble in ammonia; Pt insoluble in HNO_3, soluble in aqua regia. Evaporate to dryness, add water and KCl. A yellow precipitate confirms Pt.

Yellow or Red Metal. Cu soluble in HNO_3 and gives reddish-brown precipitate with potass. ferrocyanide; Au insoluble in HNO_3, soluble in aqua regia. Evaporate to dryness, add a drop or two of water and a drop of dilute solution of $SnCl_2$. A violet-brown precipitate confirms Au.

On Plaster Tablets. The tablet may be placed on charcoal as a support. A little of the pulverized mineral is mixed with von Kobell's flux and fused near one end of the tablet. Volatile iodides are formed, many of which produce characteristic sublimates on the cool part of the plaster. The same process may be used on charcoal, and in the accompanying table the results are compared with those on plaster.

In Closed Tube. The object is to heat the mineral with little air, and hence with little oxidation. Use small *fragments;* fine powder adheres to the side of the tube and may interfere with sublimates. Volatile emanations that give an odor or condense as a

---

* If the mineral yields S, As, or Sb in o.f. on charcoal, it must first be thoroughly roasted in order to convert it into oxides. (See Fig. 70.)

IODIDE SUBLIMATES ON PLASTER AND CHARCOAL

(For abbreviations, see page 217)

On Plaster.	Substance.	On Charcoal.
Chrome-yellow, volatile	PbI_2	Chrome-yel.; gnh. if thin; volatile
Yellow to orange; very volatile	AsI_3	Faint yellow
Orange to red; disappears in strong ammonia fumes	SbI_3	Faint yellow
Scarlet with yel.; if strongly heated is dull yel. and blk.	HgI	Faint yellow
Rdh.-brn., nearly scarlet	SeI_4	Does not show on charcoal
Chocolate-brn., with underlying scarlet; in ammonia fumes becomes orange and then cherry-red	BiI_3	Bright red; yellow near assay
Purplish-brn., darker border	TeI_4	Does not show on charcoal
Ultramarine-blue, deep	MoI_4	Does not show on charcoal

sublimate or a liquid on the side of the tube are to be specially noted; also decrepitation, phosphorescence, fusion, change in form or color, or magnetism. The upper end of the tube must be kept cool, and this is best assured by holding it with the fingers only and keeping it nearly horizontal (Fig. 72).

In Open Tube. The object is to heat the mineral with a good supply of air for oxidation. Place *finely powdered* mineral near one end of the tube (at the elbow if the tube is bent). Hold the tube steeply inclined, with the powder at the lower end, using a holder, since the whole tube must become hot. An edge of the flame should play constantly (or very frequently) on the upright portion of the tube in order to insure an active draft. This may be facilitated also by blowing into the lower end of the tube with the blowpipe. Use but little of the mineral, in order to avoid choking the tube and reducing the draft; also, with a large amount, volatilization may exceed oxidation and the results will be mixed and indecisive. (See Fig. 73.)

Observe odors, visible fumes, and sublimates.

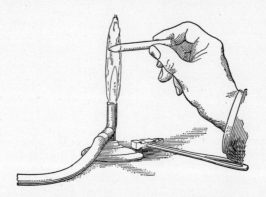

FIG. 72.—Heating in closed tube (c.t.): Hold the tube with the fingers only, and hold it in nearly horizontal position.

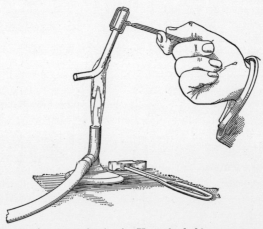

FIG. 73.—Heating in open tube (o.t.): Use tube holder and allow part of the flame to play up the steeply inclined arm of the tube, in order to insure a sufficient draft, or blow into the lower end with the blowpipe.

In Borax Bead. A round loop ($\frac{1}{8}$ inch diameter) of platinum wire may be made conveniently by bending it around the tapering part of a pencil near the point (Fig. 74a). The loop is heated in the

SUBLIMATES IN CLOSED TUBE

(For abbreviations, see page 217.)

Hot.	Cold.	Substance.	Remarks.
Colorless liquid; easily volatile	Cols. liquid	H_2O	Neutral or acid; rarely alkaline
White solid	White solid	$PbCl_2$, $SbCl_3$, As_2O_3, Sb_2O_3, NH_4 salts	
Gray metallic liquid globules		Hg	Unite by rubbing with strip of paper
Pale yel. to cols. liquid; difficultly volatile	Cols. to wh. globules	TeO_2	From Te and some compounds
Dark yellow to red liquid; easily volatile	Yel. xln. solid; pale in small amount	S	From S and some sulphides
Dark red liquid, nearly blk.; easily volatile	Rdh.-yel. transparent solid	AsS As_2S_3	From sulphides and sulpharsenites
Black solid; difficultly volatilized	Rdh.-brown	Sb_2OS_2	Sulphides and sulphantimonites
Brilliant blk., solid; often gry. and xln. near heated end		As	From As and arsenides. Break off closed end and heat subl. for garlic odor
Brilliant blk., solid		HgS	Subl. rubbed gives red powder
Blk. fusible globules		Te	Te and tellurides; usually some TeO_2 formed (see above)
Blk. fusible globules; smallest deep red by transmitted light		Se	Often also wh. xln. SeO_2

Bunsen or blowpipe flame and dipped into the powdered borax. The part that adheres is fused to a clear globule (Fig. 75); this is again dipped into the borax, and the process is repeated until a spherical bead is obtained. The hot bead is touched lightly to a fine powder of the mineral * and is then heated thoroughly in the

SUBLIMATES IN OPEN TUBE

(For abbreviation, see page 217)

Color and Character.	Substance.	Remarks.
White xln., readily volatile	As_2O_3	Xln. (octahedrons) on the warm glass
White xln., readily volatile	SeO_2	Usually radiating xls.; often a little red Se
White xln., slowly volatile	Sb_2O_3	Xls. are octahedrons and prisms
White non-vol., infusible	$PbSO_3$ $PbSO_4$	Slight deposit; mostly on lower side of tube near assay
Pale yel. globules; slowly vol.	TeO_2	Globules white or colorless when cold
Pale yel. hot; wh. cold; amorph., infus., non-vol.	$SbSbO_4$	Dense wh. smoke; subl. mostly on under side of tube; usually some volatile Sb_2O_3
Pale yel. hot; wh. cold; fus. and vol. at red heat	MoO_3	Network of delicate xls. near assay
Yel. to orange; easily vol.	S,AsS	These sublimates result from too rapid heating; will not form with proper draft and oxidation. Heat tube above assay first, then directly under it
Blk. hot; brn. cold; dif. volatile	Sb_2OS_2	
Brilliant blk.; volatile	As,HgS	
Gry. metallic globules; volatile	Hg	Unite by rubbing with strip of paper
Red, volatile	Se	Often with white SeO_2 (see above)

* Sulphides, arsenides, antimonides, etc., must first be roasted thoroughly at a dull red heat (Fig. 70), in order to convert them into oxides; otherwise no characteristic reaction will occur.

oxidizing blowpipe flame.* The degree of solubility of the particles and the colors, if any, imparted to the bead are carefully noted. It is then heated continuously for some time in the reducing flame and any change noted. The quantity of the powdered mineral in the bead is gradually increased until a distinct reaction is obtained or until the bead is saturated with it.

A bead about half the size described above may be made on the end of the wire without a loop by holding it horizontally or pointed somewhat downward in the flame. Moisten the bead with the tongue and touch the finely powdered mineral. After reducing, cool the bead in the inner cone of the Bunsen flame in order to avoid oxidation.

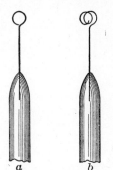

In Sodium Metaphosphate Bead. The bead is made by heating sodium ammonium phosphate on a loop of platinum wire in the same manner as previously described for the borax bead; but when first fused it is much more liquid than borax and the greatest care must be exercised in order to avoid dropping it. It is best to tilt the burner at a considerable angle (Fig. 75), so that beads cannot drop into it and clog it. Hold the wire over the center of the flame, with the circular loop horizontal. Do not undertake to fuse much of the salt at a time, but build up the bead by small additions, heating each time until all bubbling stops.

Fig. 74. — Platinum wire loops: (a) single loop ⅛ inch, for bead tests; (b) double loop, holding larger quantity, for decomposing insoluble minerals in fluxes.

The salt fuses to sodium metaphosphate, $NaPO_3$, and is used in exactly the same manner as the borax bead.

In Sodium Carbonate (Soda) Bead. The soda bead on platinum wire is opaque white when cold. It is prepared in the same manner as borax or s.ph. beads (see preceding sections), and is useful for the following reactions:

Manganese: in o.f., green when hot, blue when cold; in r.f., colorless.

Chromium: in o.f., yellow.

Quartz, chalcedony, or opal: in fine powder fused with about

---

* A minute grain of KNO_3 added to the hot bead after the mineral is dissolved gives instant oxidation.

equal volume of soda gives vigorous effervescence of CO_2 and forms a clear glass.

With Aids.   For most purposes dilute hydrochloric acid is used; but for sulphides and arsenides, which require oxidation, nitric acid is best.

Usually the object of the first test with an acid is to determine whether or not the mineral is decomposed or dissolved by it.   This is best done as follows:

(1) Using the small blade of a knife (say less than one-fourth inch wide) for a spatula, put into the test tube as much of the *finely*

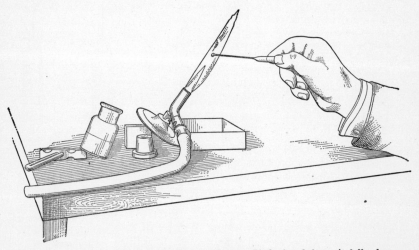

FIG. 75.—Making a bead in the Bunsen flame.   If the bead drops it falls clear of the burner instead of clogging it.   This position is specially important for sodium metaphosphate (s.ph.) beads.   A metal tray should be so placed as to catch the fused fluxes that drop.

pulverized mineral (*not* lumps or grains) as will lie on one-half inch of the tapering point.   Pure homogeneous material should be used, or allowance made for any known impurity.

(2) Add acid (dilute HCl unless otherwise specified) to a depth of one-half to three-quarters of an inch.

(3) Shake up the powder in the acid and note carefully its behavior—how much it roils the liquid and how slowly or rapidly it settles out and clears.

(4) If no immediate reaction occurs in the cold acid, heat to the

BORAX BEAD REACTIONS

(For abbreviations, see page 217)

(M indicates medium amount; + indicates much; − indicates little)

Oxidizing Flame.		Reducing Flame.		Amount.	Oxide of
Hot.	Cold.	Hot.	Cold.		
Colorless	Colorless	Colorless	Colorless	+ or −	Si, Al, Sn
Colorless	Cols. or opaq. wh.	Colorless	Cols. or opaq. wh.	+ or −	Ca, Sr, Ba, Mg, Zn, Zr, Cb
Pale yel.	Cols. or wh.	Pale yel.	Colorless	+	Pb, Sb, Cd
Pale yel.	Cols. or wh.	Gray	Gray	+	Bi
Pale yel.	Cols. or wh.	Brown	Brown	+	Mo
Pale yel.	Cols. or wh.	Yellow	Yel. to yelh.-brn.	M	W
Pale yel.	Cols. or wh.	Grayish	Bnh.-violet	M	Ti
Yellow	Nearly cols.	Pale green	Nearly cols.	−	Fe, U
Yellow	Yelh.-green	Green	Green	−	Cr
Yellow	Pale yelh.-grn.	Dirty grn.	Fine green	−	V
Yel. to orange	Yellow	Pale green	Pale grn. to nearly cols.	M to +	U
Yel. to orange	Yellow	Bottle grn.	Pale green	M to +	Fe
Yel. to orange	Yelh.-grn.	Green	Green	M to +	Cr
Green	Blue	Cols. to grn.	Opaq. red (+)	− to M	Cu
Blue	Blue	Blue	Blue	− to M	Co
Violet	Rdh.-brn.	Opaq. gray	Opaq. gray	− to M	Ni
Violet	Rdh.-violet	Colorless	Colorless	−	Mn

boiling point over the Bunsen flame * and note any change, particularly whether any of the mineral powder has disappeared.

(5) If the mineral seems unchanged continue the boiling until two-thirds of the acid has been evaporated.

(6) If the result still seems to be negative, filter the acid into a clean test tube and evaorate to dryness. The residue, if any, is the measure of the reaction that has taken place.

(7) If solution or other reaction occurs the results should be carefully noted, as follows:

(a) Solution *with effervescence* in cold acid, or only on heating (and this point should be carefully observed), with the evolution of CO_2, colorless and odorless, from carbonates (test with $Ba(OH)_2$ on glass rod); H_2S, colorless and disagreeable odor, from some sulphides; Cl, nearly colorless, pungent odor (bleaches moist litmus paper), from some higher oxides in HCl; NO_2, dark red vapors, from oxidation of sulphides, etc., in HNO_3.

(b) Solution *without effervescence*, giving a clear colorless solution, *without residue*. When slow this reaction is sometimes difficult to detect. Filtration and evaporation to dryness may be resorted to in case of doubt, or a drop of perfectly clear liquid, after settling, may be removed with a pipette and evaporated on a watch glass, a piece of platinum foil, or a flake of mica. A residue shows that some solution has taken place.

(c) Solution may occur without effervescence and without residue, as described in the preceding paragraph, but with a *colored solution—yellowish* to *brownish red* from ferric iron minerals in HCl; *green* from nickel and from mixtures of copper and iron (add ammonia and the solution becomes blue with copper or nickel, more intense with copper); *blue* from copper minerals, intensified by the addition of an excess of ammonia; *pink* or *pale rosé* from cobalt minerals.

(d) Solution may occur without effervescence, leaving an *insoluble residue—gelatinous silica*, from some silicates, appears on evaporation of the acid and remains insoluble when diluted with water or more acid; *powdery* or *flaky silica* separates from some silicates—it is white and more translucent than the fine powder of the mineral;

* An alcohol lamp is a good substitute, and an ordinary kerosene lamp serves very well if the tube is held in the top of the chimney. A test tube may even be heated over a candle flame by holding it just high enough to avoid blackening it with soot.

SODIUM METAPHOSPHATE BEAD REACTIONS

(For abbreviations, see page 217)

(M indicates medium amount; + indicates much; − indicates little)

Oxidizing Flame.		Reducing Flame.		Amount.	Oxide of
Hot.	Cold.	Hot.	Cold.		
Colorless	Cols. or opaq. white	Colorless	Cols. or opaq. white	− or +	Ca, Sr, Ba, Mg, Zn, Al, Zr, Sn, Si (Si nearly insol.)
Pale yel.	Colorless	Pale yel.	Colorless	+	Cd
Pale yel.	Colorless	Gray	Gray	+	Pb, Sb, Bi
Pale yel.	Colorless	Brown	Brown	+	Cb
Pale yel.	Colorless	Dirty blue	Fine blue	M	W
Pale yel.	Colorless	Yellow	Violet	− to +	Ti
Yellow	Colorless	Pale yelh.-grn.	Colorless	−	Fe
Yellow	Pale grnh.-yel.	Pale grn.	Fine grn.	M	U
Yelh.-grn.	Colorless	Dirty grn.	Fine grn.	M	Mo
Yel. to bnh.-red	Yel. to cols.	Red, yel., to yelh.-grn.	Nearly cols. to pale violet	M to +	Fe
Yel. to deep yel.	Yellow	Dirty grn.	Fine grn.	− to M	V
Red to bnh.-red	Yel. to redh.-yel.	Red to bnh.-red	Yel. to redh.-yel.	− to M	Ni
Green	Pale blue	Pale yelh.-grn.	Pale blue, nearly cols.; at times ruby red	−	Cu
Dark green	Blue	Bnh.-grn.	Opaq. red	M	Cu
Dirty grn.	Fine grn.	Dirty grn.	Fine grn.	− to M	Cr
Blue	Blue	Blue	Blue	− to M	Co
Gryh.-violet	Violet	Colorless	Colorless	M	Mn

white opaque metallic oxides, espcially from tin, antimony, and lead minerals in HNO_3; *yellow powder,* WO_3, from some tungstates in HCl; *yellow floating mass* of sulphur, often black with particles of the mineral, from many sulphides in HNO_3.

With Cobalt Nitrate.   The solution is useful with light-colored infusible minerals.   Heat a small amount of the fine powder or minute fragments intensely on charcoal in the oxidizing flame; moisten the mineral with the solution, and again ignite to an intense white heat.   Distinct colors may be imparted, as follows:

Blue, aluminum minerals, zinc silicates.

Bluish green, tin oxide.

Yellowish green, zinc and titanium oxides.

Dark green, oxides of antimony and cobalt.

Pink, usually pale, from magnesium minerals.

Calcite and aragonite are readily distinguished by reaction with $Co(NO_3)_2$ solution.   Place fine powder of calcite and the mineral to be tested in separate test tubes, fill each about one-half inch deep with the solution, and boil both together by holding the tubes side by side over the Bunsen flame.   Aragonite is colored a deep lavender by $CoCO_3$ while calcite remains white, except on long continued boiling.

Precipitates from Solution.   The following reagents are most commonly used.   For distinctions between the various precipitates, see the tests for the elements on succeeding pages.

Ammonia precipitates hydroxides of Al, Be, Bi, chromic Cr, Fe, Pb, Ti, and rare earth metals.   (In the presence of phosphoric, arsenic, silicic, and hydrofluoric acids various other substances are also precipitated.)

Ammonium carbonate and *ammonium oxalate* precipitate Ca, Sr, and Ba from solutions made alkaline with ammonia.

Ammonium sulphide precipitates from neutral or alkaline solutions sulphides of Fe, Zn, Mn, Co, Ni, and hydroxides of Al, Cr, and rare earth metals.

Barium chloride precipitates $BaSO_4$ from acid solutions of a sulphate—a delicate test.

Hydrochloric acid precipitates chlorides of Ag, Pb, and mercurous Hg from solutions in HNO_3.

Silver nitrate precipitates silver chloride, bromide, or iodide from solutions of the corresponding minerals in water or HNO_3.

Carbon dioxide clouds a drop of $Ba(OH)_2$ held on the end of a glass rod, forming $BaCO_3$.

Sodium phosphate precipitates Mg from solutions in which ammonia and ammonium carbonate give no precipitates or in the filtrate after precipitating with these reagents.

Sulphuric acid precipitates sulphates of Pb, Ba, and Sr, and also Ca in concentrated solutions.

REACTIONS FOR THE ELEMENTS

(For list of elements, see page 218, abbreviations, page 217)

ALUMINUM (Al; trivalent; at.wt. 26.97)

(1) **Color with Cobalt Nitrate.** Fine powder of light-colored infus. Al minerals assumes a fine blue color when moistened with the solution and intensely heated either on ch. or in a small loop of Pt wire. Zn silicates also give blue color, but will yield test for Zn.

(2) **Precipitation with Ammonia.** Added in slight excess to acid solutions, gelatinous $Al(OH)_3$ is precipitated. To distinguish from other similar-looking precipitates obtained in the same way, filter, wash the ppt., place part of it in test tube with H_2O and KOH; if it is $Al(OH)_3$ it will go easily into solution. Burn the filter (in crucible or on ch.) and the rest of the ppt. will give foregoing test with cobalt nitrate.

For Al in silicates, see Silicon (2), page 129.

ANTIMONY (Sb; trivalent and pentavalent; at.wt. 121.77)

(1) **Oxide Subl. on ch.** Heat fragments on ch. in o.f. A dense white subl. of Sb_2O_3 forms very near the assay (compare As). Where thin the coating looks bluish. Subl. is volatile and may be driven about readily by the o.f. or r.f. No distinctive odor (compare As) unless S or As is present.

(2) **Antimonate Subl. in o.t.** When heated in o.t. most Sb sulphides yield a heavy white subl., $SbSbO_4$, along the under side of the tube, which is non-vol. (compare As), straw-yel. when hot and white on cooling.

(3) **Oxysulphide Subl. in c.t.** On intense ign. sulphides yield a black subl. of Sb_2S_2O, rich redh.-brn. on cooling. Volatilizes with difficulty.

(4) **Iodide Subl. on Plaster.** Mixed with von Kobell's flux or moistened with HI and heated in o.f. on plaster tablet, a red subl. of SbI_3, which disappears in fumes of strong ammonia.

(5) **Flame Color.** Sb volatilizes in r.f. and gives a pale greenish color to the flame. Pt forceps must not be used.

(6) **Oxidation with HNO₃.** Sb minerals yield white insol. powder ($HSbO_3$) (metantimonic acid) on heating in HNO_3. Dilute, filter, and test powder as in (1) above.

ARSENIC (As; trivalent and pentavalent; at.wt. 74.93)

(1) **Oxide Subl. on ch.** Metallic As, its sulphides and the arsenides when heated on ch. yield white fumes of a garlic-like odor and a white crystalline subl. of As_2O_3 far from the assay.

(2) **Oxide Subl. in o.t.** Subl. and odor like preceding are produced in the tube. Easily volatile and driven out of the tube.

(3) **Metallic Mirror in c.t.** The metal and some arsenides yield a brilliant black arsenical mirror. When abundant the part nearest the assay crystallizes and looks gray. By breaking off the closed end of tube and heating the subl. the garlic odor is produced. Oxygen compounds require powdered charcoal also in the c.t.

(4) **Iodide Subl. on Plaster.** Powder mixed with von Kobell's flux or moistened with HI and heated in o.f. on plaster tablet, a vol. orange-yel. subl. of AsI_3 forms.

(5) **Flame Color.** In r.f. As volatilizes and colors the flame violet.

(6) **Oxidation with HNO₃.** As minerals in hot HNO_3 yield white insol. arsenic acid (H_3AsO_4). Dilute, filter and apply test as in (3) above.

BARIUM (Ba; bivalent; at.wt. 137.36)

(1) **Flame Color.** A gnh.-yel. color is imparted to the flame, sometimes intensified by moistening with HCl. Silicates do not give the flame color. Must be distinguished carefully from B, $MnCl_2$, and P flame colors.

(2) **Sulphate Precipitate.** A few drops of dilute H_2SO_4 give a white ppt. of $BaSO_4$ from solutions in water and dilute acids. Insol. on addition of water and boiling; disting. from Ca.

A delicate test and distinguishes from B and P. Insoluble silicates require previous fusion of the finely powdered mineral with 3 volumes of soda in a loop of Pt wire, which renders them soluble in HCl. Test ppt. for flame color, using clean Pt wire. If both Ba and Sr are present a mixed flame results.

(3) **Alkaline Reaction.** Like the other alkaline earths and most alkalis, some Ba minerals give alkaline reaction on moist turmeric paper after ignition.

BISMUTH (Bi; trivalent; at.wt. 209.0)

(1) **Metallic Bi and Oxide Subl. on ch.** Heat the mineral with 3 times its volume of soda on ch. Brittle metallic globules of Bi are obtained and a yellow coating of Bi_2O_3 which is white farther away. Subl. much like that of Pb, but metal less malleable; distinguished by the following test.

(2) **Iodide Ppt. on ch. and Plaster.** Mix the powdered mineral with von Kobell's flux or moisten with HI and heat in the o.f. on ch. The subl. is yellow near the assay and bordered by brilliant red BiI_3. On a plaster plate the subl. is chocolate-brown but changes to a brilliant red on exposure to strong ammonia fumes.

BORON (B; trivalent; at.wt. 10.82)

(1) **Flame Color.** A somewhat yellowish-green (siskin-green) flame color. Compare Ba and $MnCl_2$ flame colors. Readily distinguished by other tests. Some B minerals require heating with 3 volumes of Turner's flux; the BF_2 formed gives a momentary color to the flame.

(2) **With Turmeric Paper.** Moisten turmeric paper with a dilute HCl sol. of the mineral and dry it on the outside of a test tube containing boiling water. The paper becomes reddish-brown; on moistening with ammonia it becomes black. Insol. minerals must first be fused in fine powder with 3 volumes of soda on a loop of Pt wire and then dissolved in HCl.

BROMINE (Br; univalent; at.wt. 79.9)

(1) **Precipitation as Bromide.** Solutions of bromides in water or dilute HNO_3 yield a white ppt. of AgBr when $AgNO_3$ sol. is added.

(2) **Pb Bromide Subl. in c.t.** AgBr heated in c.t. with galena (PbS) yields a subl. of $PbBr_2$, which is S-yellow while hot and white when cold.

CADMIUM (Cd; bivalent; at.wt. 112.4)

(1) **Oxide Subl. on ch.**   Heated on ch. with 3 volumes of soda, metallic Cd is volatilized and sublimed as reddish-brown CdO, which is yellow distant from the assay and iridescent if only a little forms.

CAESIUM (Cs; monovalent; at.wt. 132.8)

(1) **Chloride ppt.**   Hydrochloplatinic acid added to HCl solution produces a fine yellow ppt. of Cs_2PtCl_6.

CALCIUM (Ca; bivalent; at.wt. 40.07)

(1) **Flame Color.**   Some Ca minerals give yelh.-red color to the flame (green through green glass), often strengthened by moistening with HCl.   Must not be confused with the much redder Sr and Li flames.

(2) **Sulphate ppt.**   A few drops of dilute H_2SO_4 added to an HCl sol. of a Ca mineral precipitates white $CaSO_4 \cdot 2H_2O$, which goes into solution on addition of water and boiling.   This sol. in water distinguishes it from Sr and Ba.   Avoid large excess of HCl.

(3) **Carbonate or Oxalate ppt.**   Ammonium carbonate or oxalate added to a solution made strongly alkaline with ammonia forms a white ppt. of the corresponding Ca compound.   The oxalate is also formed in slightly acid solutions and this test can be applied in solutions of phosphates, silicates, and borates, which cannot be made alkaline with ammonia without precipitating Ca salts.

(4) **Alkaline Reaction.**   Like other alkaline earths and most of the alkalis, some Ca minerals give an alkaline reaction on moist turmeric paper after ignition.

For Ca in silicates, see Silicon (2), page 129.

CARBON (C; tetravalent; at.wt. 12)

(1) **Odor in c.t.**   The characteristic empyreumatic odor of distilling organic substances is given in c.t. by hydrocarbons and bituminous coal.   Anthracite does not yield it, but is combustible in the o.f.   Anthracite coal and graphite burn, when a small fragment is heated to redness in c.t. on several times its volume of pyrolusite.

(2) **CO_2 from Carbonates.**   Heat fragments of the mineral in the c.t. held horizontally with a drop of $Ba(OH)_2$ in the open end of the tube; the latter is clouded with a white ppt. of $BaCO_3$.

(3) **Effervescence with Acids.** Treat the powdered mineral with dilute HCl, HNO_3, or H_2SO_4, and warm if necessary. Guard against mistaking boiling for effervescence. Tip the test tube gently and pour accumulated CO_2 (gas) into another tube containing $Ba(OH)_2$; on shaking the latter a white ppt. of $BaCO_3$ forms. Concentrated acids do not yield the test unless the salts formed are soluble in the acids.

CHLORINE (Cl; univalent; at.wt. 35.45)

(1) **Flame Color with CuO.** Mix powdered mineral with CuO and moisten with H_2SO_4, dry gently on ch. and ignite; or saturate a small s.ph. bead with CuO, add a fragment of the mineral and heat in the o.f. In either case the azure-blue flame of $CuCl_2$ will appear. Br gives a similar reaction.

(2) **Evolution of Cl.** A powdered chloride heated in a small test tube with a little pyrolusite (MnO_2) and 4 times its volume of $KHSO_4$ gives off Cl gas, which is recognized by its pungent odor and its bleaching effect on a piece of moist litmus paper placed inside the tube. AgCl and silicates containing Cl require fusion first with 3 volumes of soda (C.P., free from Cl).

(3) **AgCl ppt.** From a solution of a chloride in water or dilute HNO_3 a few drops of $AgNO_3$ sol. ppts. white AgCl, curdy if abundant, bluish opalescent if little. Br and I give similar reactions. Light soon changes color of the ppt. to violet. Insoluble minerals must first be fused with 3 volumes of soda.

(4) **Sublimate with Galena.** To distinguish chloride, bromide, and iodide of Ag, heat in c.t. with powdered galena. A subl. of $PbCl_2$ forms colorless globules which are white when cold; $PbBr_2$ is S.-yel. hot and white when cold; PbI_2 is dark orange-red hot and lemon-yellow cold. The presence of Br obscures that of Cl, and I obscures both of the others.

CHROMIUM (Cr; trivalent and sexivalent; at.wt. 52)

(1) **Borax Bead Reac.** In o.f. yellow hot (red with much), yel.-grn. cold. In r.f. green hot and cold.

(2) **S.ph. Bead Reac.** In o.f. dirty green hot, clear green cold. In r.f. similar colors but weaker. V differs in giving yellow color to s.ph. bead in o.f.

(3) **Soda Bead Reac.** In o.f. dark yellow while hot, light yellow and opaque cold; in r.f. yelh.-green opaque when cold.

COBALT (Co; bivalent; at.wt. 58.94)

(1) **In Borax and s.ph. Beads.** Fine blue in both o.f. and r.f. When Cu or Ni interferes remove the bead from the Pt wire and fuse it on ch. with a granule of Sn and the Co color will appear.

(2) **HNO$_3$ Sol.** Strong sol. in HNO$_3$ is rose-red, becoming brown with excess of ammonia, and again becoming red on standing.

COLUMBIUM (Niobium) (Cb; pentavalent; at.wt. 93.1)

(1) **Reduction in Solution.** Mix powdered mineral with 5 volumes of borax, moisten to a paste with water and fuse in a double loop of Pt wire (Fig. 74b). Crush 2 or 3 such beads to powder and boil with HCl to a clear solution. Add Sn and boil and the sol. becomes blue, which changes slowly to brown on continued boiling and disappears on dilution. With Zn instead of Sn the blue color changes quickly to brown. If much Ti is present a violet color forms before the Cb blue.

W gives similar tests, but other tests for that element will distinguish.

COPPER (Cu; bivalent and univalent; at.wt. 63.57)

(1) **Flame Color.** The oxide and oxidized sulphides give an emerald-green color. When moistened with HCl the flame is azure-blue. The same result is obtained by adding a grain of common salt, NaCl, to a s.ph. bead saturated with the substance.

Metallic Cu on ch. Oxides and sulphides that have been previously roasted yield globules of red malleable Cu when fused in r.f. on ch. with 3 volumes of a flux of equal parts of soda and borax.

(3) **Borax and s.ph. Bead Reactions.** In o.f. green hot and blue cold; in r.f. pale with little Cu, red and opaque with much (Cu$_2$O +Cu).

A *ruby red transparent bead* is obtained by adding a little tin or tin-bearing substance to a borax bead made pale blue with Cu in o.f. Dissolve thoroughly in o.f. and reduce slightly. If too much reduced the bead is colorless. A delicate test for either Cu or Sn.

(4) **Color in Solution.** Blue or green sol. in HNO$_3$ or HCl made deep blue by adding ammonia in excess. Ni gives a much fainter blue by similar treatment.

(5) **Cuprous Cu.** Dissolve mineral in a little HCl and add water. A white ppt. of cuprous chloride (CuCl) appears.

FLUORINE (F; univalent; at.wt. 19)

(1) **HF in c.t.** Mix the finely powdered mineral with an equal volume of powdered glass and 3 volumes of $KHSO_4$ and heat gently in c.t. The HF liberated attacks the glass and forms SiF_4, which decomposes to H_2SiF_6 with separation of SiO_2; this forms a volatile white subl. in the tube. Break off bottom of tube, wash subl. with water and dry; the remaining subl., SiO_2, is non-vol.

(2) **Etching Glass.** Mix powdered mineral with a few drops of conc. H_2SO_4 and spread over a glass that has been previously coated with paraffin and scratched with a pointed instrument. Let stand 5 minutes or longer. Wash off the acid, warm the glass, and wipe off paraffin to observe etching.

(3) **With $NaPO_3$ in c.t.** Mix the powdered mineral with 5 times the volume of powdered s.ph. beads and heat very hot in c.t. A subl. forms as in (1) and may be tested as there described.

GOLD (Au; univalent and trivalent; at.wt. 197.2)

(1) **Metal with Soda on ch.** The color, fusibility, malleability, and insolubility in any single acid serve to distinguish it from other metals when present in visible particles.

(2) **Purple of Cassius.** Carefully evaporate the solution in aqua regia to dryness, add a little water and dilute solution of stannous chloride $(SnCl_2)$. The purple ppt. of colloidal Au and $Sn(OH)_2$ are soluble in ammonia to a reddish liquid.

HYDROGEN (H; univalent; at.wt. 1)

(1) **Water in c.t.** Minerals containing hydroxyl, acid hydrogen, or water of crystallization, when heated in c.t. give off water which condenses in the cold part of the tube. Hygroscopic water alone will give a slight test. Hydroxyl and acid H require high temperature. Some salts of weak bases yield acid water and from some ammonia compounds it is alkaline. Readily tested by a strip of litmus paper inserted in the tube.

IODINE (I; univalent; at.wt. 126.9)

(1) **Iodide Subl. with Galena.** Heat the powdered mineral with powdered galena in c.t.; a subl. of PbI_2 is formed which is dark orange-red while hot and lemon-yellow when cold.

(2) **Ppt. with AgNO₃.** From dil. HNO_3 solution $AgNO_3$ ppts. white AgI, which differs from AgCl and AgBr in being nearly insoluble in ammonia.

(3) **I with KHSO₄.** Violet I vapor is formed when iodides are heated in c.t. with $KHSO_4$.

IRIDIUM (Ir; trivalent and tetravalent; at.wt. 193.1)

One of the rare Pt metals. See Platinum, page 128.

IRON (Fe; bivalent and trivalent; at.wt. 55.8)

(1) **Magnetism.** A few Fe minerals are magnetic and many become so on heating in r.f. (or roasting and then heating in r.f. in case of sulphides and arsenides). The test is more delicate if the powder is fused with a little soda, giving a magnetic slag. In all cases only the cold material is magnetic.

(2) **Borax Bead Reac.** With small amount of mineral the bead in o.f. is yellow hot and nearly colorless cold; in r.f. it becomes pale green hot and colorless cold. With much of the mineral it is bnh.-red hot and yellow cold; in r.f. it becomes bottle-green hot and paler when cold. With sulphides and arsenides the bead test can be made only after roasting.

(3) **Hydroxide ppt.** When ammonia is added to a dil. HNO_3 sol. or to HCl sol. which has been boiled with a few drops of HNO_3, a bnh.-red ppt. of $Fe(OH)_3$ is formed. In ferrous HCl sol. ammonia gives a dirty green $Fe(OH)_2$ ppt. which slowly turns brown by oxidation.

(4) **Ferrous and Ferric Fe.** In cold dilute acid solutions potassium ferricyanide, $K_6Fe_2(CN)_{12}$, gives a dark blue ppt. with ferrous Fe; in ferric solutions it deepens the color but gives no ppt. Potassium ferrocyanide, $K_4Fe(CN)_4$, gives a dark blue ppt. with ferric solutions; from ferrous sol. it gives a pale bluish-white ppt. which rapidly becomes blue. Put a drop of each reagent on a porcelain plate and near each of these place a drop of the solution to be tested. With a clean platinum wire or the tip of a closed tube bring the edges of each pair of drops together.

A few drops of HNO_3 in a boiling ferrous solution changes the iron to the ferric state. An HCl solution of a ferric mineral is reduced to the ferrous state by boiling with metallic Sn or Zn.

Minerals insol. in acids must first be fused in c.t. with 3 volumes of borax glass (powdered borax beads). Break off lower end of tube and boil in a little HCl for a minute; dilute the sol., divide it into two parts, and test as above for ferrous and ferric Fe.

For Fe in silicates, see Silicon (2), page 129.

LEAD (Pb; bivalent and tetravalent; at.wt. 207.22)

(1) **Metal and Subl. on ch.** Mix 1 part powdered mineral, 1 part powdered charcoal, and 3 parts soda, moisten and fuse in r.f. on ch. Globules of soft, malleable, and sectile metal form, bright in. r.f. and dull on cooling; also subl. of PbO, yellow near assay, bluish-white further away.

(2) **Iodide Subl. on ch.** Heat powdered mineral with 3 volumes of von Kobell's flux in o.f. on ch. A chrome-yel. subl. of PbI_2 forms near and greenish-yellow far from assay.

(3) **Ppts. from Solution.** From solution in dil. HNO_3 either H_2SO_4 or HCl forms a white ppt. ($PbSO_4$ or $PbCl_2$). From a boiling solution of the mineral in HCl white $PbCl_2$ crystallizes out on cooling.

(4) **Flame Color.** Pale azure blue tinged with green.

LITHIUM (Li; univalent; at.wt. 6.9)

(1) **Flame Color.** Crimson flame when heated in Pt forceps or from powdered mineral on clean Pt wire (invisible through green glass). For silicates better results are obtained by mixing the mineral with equal parts of powdered gypsum. Flame color is much like that of Sr, but redder than that of Ca. Compare Sr and Ca.

No alkaline reaction after ignition.

MAGNESIUM (Mg; bivalent; at.wt. 24.3)

(1) **Color with Cobalt Nitrate.** Some light-colored Mg minerals become pale pink when strongly ignited after moistening with $Co(NO_3)_2$ sol.

(2) **Alkaline Reac.** Some Mg minerals give alkaline reac. on moist turmeric paper after ignition, like the alkalis and alkaline earths, but weaker, and less decisive.

(3) **Ppt. from Solution.** Use HNO_3 sol. or HCl sol. that has been boiled with a drop of nitric acid, make strongly alkaline with ammonia, and remove Fe, Al, and Ca by successive precipitation

with ammonia and ammonium oxalate, filtering each time a precipitate appears. To the clear filtrate add sodium phosphate. A crystalline ppt. of $NH_4MgPO_4 \cdot 6H_2O$ appears after standing and cooling.

For Mg in silicates, see Silicon (2), page 129.

MANGANESE (Mn; bivalent, trivalent, tetravalent; at.wt. 54.9)

(1) **Soda Bead Reac.** In o.f. green while hot, bluish-green cold, (Na_2MnO_4); in r.f. white.

(2) **Borax Bead Reac.** In o.f. opaque while hot, reddish-violet when cold, black if too much is used. In r.f. colorless. Similar results in s.ph. but not so delicate.

(3) **Evolution of Cl.** Higher oxides of Mn decompose HCl with evolution of Cl gas.

(4) **Flame Color.** HCl solution gives yellowish green color to flame. Compare Ba and B flames. (See pp. 118, 119.)

MERCURY (Hg; univalent and bivalent; at.wt. 200.61)

(1) **Metal in c.t.** Mix the powdered mineral with 4 volumes of soda that has been dried by heating nearly to redness on clean metal or in a porcelain crucible; put mixture in c.t., cover with dry soda, and heat gradually. Hg appears as gray subl. or as globules on the walls of the tube. Alone in c.t. most Hg compounds volatilize without decomposing. Cinnabar gives a black subl. like the As mirror.

(2) **Hg Ppt. on Cu.** Clean Cu in a Hg sol. receives a coating of metallic Hg, giving the appearance of silver plating.

(3) **Subl. in o.t.** Slowly heated in o.t., cinnabar gives a gray subl. of metallic Hg.

MOLYBDENUM (Mo; tetravalent and sexivalent; at.wt. 96)

(1) **Subl. in o.t.** Thin flakes of molybdenite at a high temperature in o.t. give a yellow subl. of MoO_3, frequently also delicate crystals.

(2) **Flame Color.** At tip of blue flame gives a pale yelh.-green color.

(3) **S.ph. Bead Reac.** With a small amount of the oxide in o.f. the bead is yelh.-green while hot, paler cold; in r.f. dirty green hot, fine green on cooling.

(4) **Color in Sol.**   Place finely powdered mineral with a minute scrap of paper (about 1 mm. square) in a test tube with a few drops of water and an equal quantity of conc. H_2SO_4; heat till copious acid fumes form, let cool, and add water, one drop at a time. A deep blue color appears and quickly disappears with much dilution. Using HCl instead of H_2SO_4, evaporate almost to dryness, cool, add water and metallic Sn, and warm, and a deep blue color appears.

NICKEL (Ni; bivalent; at.wt. 58.69)

(1) **Borax Bead Reac.**   In o.f. violet while hot, redh.-brown cold; opaque by long heating in r.f.   On ch. with Sn the bead becomes colorless.   Co in small amt. obscures the bead test for Ni.

(2) **Color of Sol. and Ppt.**   Sol in HNO_3 is apple-green; becomes blue with ammonia.   Compare the much deeper blue with Cu from this treatment.

(3) **Dimethylglyoxime Test.**   To a solution of the mineral add ammonia in slight excess and a few drops of the reagent.   A scarlet crystalline ppt. forms.   If Fe is present add tartaric acid before ammonia.   If very little Ni is present, boil, and red needles form on cooling.   A very delicate test.

NITROGEN (N; trivalent and pentavalent; at.wt. 14)

(1) **Deflagration on ch.**   Nitrates deflagrate (flash somewhat like gunpowder) upon ignition on ch.

(2) **Fumes in c.t.**   Heat mineral powder in c.t. with $KHSO_4$. NO_2 fumes given off are recognized by red color on looking into the end of the tube.

OSMIUM (Os; bivalent, tetravalent, etc.; at. wt. 190.8)

One of the rare platinum metals.   See Platinum, page 128.

OXYGEN (O; bivalent; at.wt. 16)

(1) **O gas in c.t.**   Some higher oxides give off O when heated in c.t.   A glowing stick inserted will burn brightly.

(2) **Cl Gas with HCl.**   Some higher oxides decompose HCl with the liberation of free Cl, which has a pungent odor and bleaches moist litmus paper inserted in the tube.

PALLADIUM (Pd; bivalent and tetravalent; at.wt. 106.7)

One of the rare platinum metals.   See Platinum, page 128.

PHOSPHORUS (P; pentavalent; at.wt. 31.02)

(1) **Ppt. with Ammonium Molybdate.** Dissolve the powdered mineral in HNO_3, previously fusing in soda bead if insol. Add a few drops of the cold sol. to a test tube containing ammonium molybdate that has been made acid with HNO_3 and let stand a few minutes; a yellow ppt. forms. As gives similar ppt. in hot sol.

(2) **Flame Color.** Pale bluish-green; moistening with H_2SO_4 is required with some minerals.

(3) **PH_3 Test.** Heat intensely in c.t. a small roll of Mg ribbon surrounded by powd. mineral; crack hot tube by touching drop of water. Moisten contents. Phosphine, PH_3, recognized by disagreeable odor.

PLATINUM (Pt; bivalent and tetravalent; at.wt. 195.2)

(1) **Platinum** is recognized by its grayish-white color, infusibility, insolubility in any single acid, and reddish-yellow solution in aqua regia. It usually contains iron and traces of the other metals of the platinum group. These require special methods for identification. When pure or nearly so the following may be recognized:

(2) **Osmium** gives the very penetrating and disagreeable odor of OsO_4 when the fine powder is heated in c.t. with $NaNO_3$ or KNO_3.

(3) **Iridium** and **Iridosmium** are hard (H = 6 − 7), insoluble even in aqua regia. Fusion with $NaNO_3$ in c.t. oxidizes some Ir; break off the lower end of the tube and boil the mass in aqua regia. The solution becomes deep red to reddish-black.

(4) **Palladium** has a bluish tarnish, which is removed and a Pt-like color restored in r.f. The tarnish is renewed by moderate heat in o.f.

POTASSIUM (K; univalent; at.wt. 39.1)

(1) **Flame Color.** Pale violet, obscured by Na; violet or purplish-red through blue glass, which eliminates the yellow of Na. For silicates mix with an equal volume of powdered gypsum and heat on a Pt wire the end of which has been moistened to make the powder adhere.

(2) **Alkaline Reaction.** Some K minerals, like those containing some other alkalis and the alkaline earths, give an alkaline reac. on moist turmeric paper after intense ignition.

For K in silicates, see Silicon (2), page 129.

SELENIUM (Se; bivalent and sexivalent; at.wt. 79.2)

(1) **Odor and Subl. on ch.** Radish-like odor. If abundant, brownish fumes form and a silvery SeO_2 coating, which may have a border of red from admixture of Se.

(2) **Flame Color.** The subl. obtained in (1) is volatile in **r.f.** and imparts a fine azure-blue color to the flame.

(3) **Subl. in o.t.** White crystalline SeO_2 subl. reddened by admixture of Se; volatile and gives a beautiful blue color to flame if the end of the tube is held so that the fumes enter the reducing part of the Bunsen flame.

(4) **Subl. in c.t.** Fused black globules of Se, the smallest deep red to brown by transmitted light. Some white SeO_2 may form above the Se.

SILICON (Si; tetravalent; at.wt. 28.06)

(1) **Gelatinization.** Many silicates are completely soluble in acids and give on continued boiling and evaporation a jelly of H_2SiO_3. HNO_3 is best, but HCl will serve in most cases. All silicates, when first fused with 5 parts of soda and dissolved in dilute HCl and evaporated, yield gelatinous silica. It is convenient to use the double loop (Fig. 74b) and prepare 2 or 3 large beads, in order to provide a sufficient quantity for distinct reactions. This is especially important in the tests under the next section.

(2) **Insol. Residue in Acids.** Insol. silica in powdery form remains after solution of the bases of some minerals. In suspension it makes the solution translucent and not so white and milky as the powder of an insol. mineral. Verify solution by evaporating a drop of the clear liquid on Pt foil or a watch glass (or a flake of mica if HCl or HNO_3 is used) and note considerable residue if solution has occurred.

Evaporate the solution obtained in (1) or (2) to dryness, moisten with conc. HCl, and heat to boiling, then add 2 parts water and boil again. The bases go into sol. but the silica remains and is removed by filtering. For insol. silicates first fuse with soda, as directed in the preceding section.

Detection of Bases in Silicates. (a) To the filtrate from the preceding operations if not a nitric acid solution, add a little HNO_3, heat to boiling and add ammonia in slight excess. Al and Fe are precipitated as hydroxides, $Al(OH)_3$ and $Fe(OH)_3$. If the ppt. is light colored there is little or no Fe:

if it is reddish brown there is considerable Fe and further test must be made for Al as follows: (b) Filter; place the ppt. in a test tube with a little water and a small fragment of stick potash (KOH) and boil. Al(OH)₃ goes into solution and is separated from insoluble Fe(OH)₃ by filtering. Make the filtrate acid with HCl, boil, and add ammonia in excess to precipitate Al(OH)₃ again.

(c) Heat filtrate from (a) to boiling and add a little ammonium oxalate to precipitate Ca. Let stand ten minutes and filter. If filtrate is turbid, pass it repeatedly through the same filter till it comes through clear.

(d) Add to the filtrate from (c) a little more ammonium oxalate to make sure that all Ca has been removed. If no ppt. forms add sodium phosphate and strong ammonia to precipitate Mg. It may have to stand for some time after cooling before the precipitate forms.

(e) If alkalis are to be tested for, filter off the Mg ppt. of (d), evaporate the filtrate to dryness and heat to redness to drive off ammonia salts. Test the residue for K and Na flame colors with a Pt wire.

(3) **In s.ph. Bead.** Silica dissolves very slowly in s.ph., hence a "skeleton" of translucent silica remains after treating a powdered silicate in s.ph. bead.

(4) **In Soda Bead.** Quartz and other forms of SiO_2 effervesce vigorously with Na_2CO_3, when equal volumes of mineral and reagent are used, forming a clear glass.

SILVER (Ag; univalent; at.wt. 107.9)

(1) **Metal on ch.** Fuse powdered mineral with 3 volumes of soda on ch.; a malleable metal globule is obtained which is bright both in the flame and after cooling. Test according to (2) below. Compounds with S, As, and Sb on roasting in o.f. on ch. yield Ag globule which is brittle with Sb.

(2) **Subl. on ch.** When Pb and Sb are present or have been added, the subl. of PbO and Sb_2O_3 on ch. is colored reddish to deep lilac by Ag.

(3) **AgCl ppt.** Dissolve the mineral in conc. HNO_3 and dilute the sol.; add a few drops of HCl or a little common salt and a white ppt. of AgCl forms. Darkens on exposure to light and is sol. in ammonia. Collect ppt. on filter paper and test according to (1) above.

SODIUM (Na; univalent; at.wt. 23)

(1) **Flame Color.** Deep pure yellow, invisible through dark blue glass. For non-vol. silicates mix powdered mineral with equal

volume of powdered gypsum and heat on the point of a Pt wire which has been previously moistened so that powder will adhere.

Everything that is touched by the hands gives a distinct Na flame, so delicate is the test; hence it is of diagnostic value only when the flame color is deep and persistent.

(2) **Alkaline Reac.** Some Na minerals, like those containing most other alkalis and the alkaline earths, give alkaline reac. on moist turmeric paper after ignition.

For Na in silicates, see Silicon (2), page 129.

STRONTIUM (Sr; bivalent; at.wt. 87.6)

(1) **Flame Color.** Crimson, from fragment in forceps or from powder on Pt wire moistened with HCl (faint yellow through green glass). Much like the Li flame; redder than the Ca flame and more persistent.

(2) **Alkaline Reac.** Like many minerals containing alkalis and other alkaline earths, some Sr minerals give alkaline reac. on moist turmeric paper after ignition. No Li minerals give this reaction.

(3) **Sulphate ppt.** A sol. of a Sr mineral gives a white ppt. of $SrSO_4$ on addition of a few drops of dil. H_2SO_4 (dif. from Li) if sol. is not very dilute or too much acid. Ppt. does not dissolve on addition of water and boiling, as does $CaSO_4$. This test is useful for silicates and phosphates, which do not yield tests (1) and (2).

Avoid large excess of HCl.

SULPHUR (S; bivalent and sexivalent; at.wt. 32.1)

Sulphides:

(1) **Fumes in o.t. and on ch.** Finely powdered sulphides in o.t. give sharp pungent SO_2 fumes, which give acid reac. on moist litmus paper in upper end of tube. With Fe and Cu some white fumes of SO_3 appear and H_2SO_4 condenses in the tube. Similar results on ch. in o.f., but less delicate. Some sulphides give blue flame from burning S on ch.

(2) **Subl. in c.t.** Some sulphides yield in c.t. a subl. of S, which is a reddish liquid while hot and a yellow solid when cold.

(3) **Reac. with Soda.** Fuse powdered mineral b.b. on Pt foil, ch., or a flake of mica, with 3 volumes of soda, place the mass on clean Ag and moisten with water; a black stain of Ag_2S forms. The fused mass moistened with HCl yields H_2S, as in (5) below. This

test is not reliable in the presence of Se and Te. Also the gas or ch. may give a slight reac. for S.

(4) **Sol. in HNO₃.** In hot conc. HNO_3 sulphides are oxidized with the formation of H_2SO_4 and red NO_2 fumes. Dilute part of the sol. and add $BaCl_2$; a white ppt. of $BaSO_4$ forms. Free S may also float on the solution, either yellow or blackened with particles of the mineral.

(5) **H₂S with HCl.** Some sulphides dissolve in HCl with the evolution of H_2S gas, which is recognized by its offensive odor.

Sulphates:

(1) **BaSO₄ ppt.** $BaCl_2$ added to a dil. HCl sol. of a sulphate gives a white ppt. of $BaSO_4$, wich does not dissolve on addition of water and boiling, as does $CaSO_4$.

(2) **Reac. with Soda.** Fuse the powdered mineral with equal volume of powdered ch. and 2 volumes of soda on ch., Pt foil, or a flake of mica till effervescence ceases; then test on Ag or with HCl as in (3) for sulphides.

(3) **Decomposition by Heat.** Sulphates of Fe, Al, etc. (weak bases), yield SO_3 on heating in c.t., and if H_2O is present, it is acid water.

TELLURIUM (Te; bivalent; at.wt. 127.5)

(1) **Color of Sol.** Finely powdered mineral heated gently in conc. H_2SO_4 gives reddish violet sol. After cooling add H_2O; color disappears and grayish black ppt. of Te forms. Similar color from Mn minerals with conc. H_2SO_4 does not disappear on dilution.

(2) **Subl. on ch.** Heated in o.f. on ch. a white subl. of TeO_2 forms near assay, resembling Sb_2O_3. Subl. is vol. in r.f. and gives a pale greenish color to the flame. Similar results in o.t. Generally a brownish coat beyond the oxide.

(3) **Subl. in c.t.** Metallic globules of Te and white subl.

TIN (Sn; tetravalent; at.wt. 118.70)

(1) **Reduction by H.** With dil. HCl and fragments of Zn cassiterite develops a dull gray coating of metallic Sn, which becomes bright and gives the characteristic odor of Sn on flesh when rubbed between the fingers.

(2) **Metal and Subl. on ch.** The powdered mineral fused on ch. in r.f. with equal volume of powdered ch. and 2 volumes of soda gives globules of white malleable Sn, which are bright in r.f. and become

dull in the air. Long-continued ignition gives a white subl. of SnO_2 on ch. In somewhat conc. warm HNO_3 the metal does not dissolve but forms white H_2SnO_3, (metastannic acid), as do also the sulphides. Distinguished from Pb and Bi by accompanying subl. on ch. and from Ag by subl. and dull surface of globule in air.

For a delicate borax bead test, see Copper (3), page 122.

Titanium (Ti; trivalent and tetravalent; at.wt. 47.90)

(1) **Color of Sol.** After fusion with borax or soda and solution in HCl, the sol. assumes a delicate violet color on boiling with Sn, if 3% or more Ti is present.

(2) **S.ph. Bead Reac.** In o.f. yellow while hot, colorless cold; in r.f. yellow hot, delicate violet cold. Best reduced with a granule of Sn on ch. When other coloring elements are present use test (1), above.

(3) **Test with H_2O_2.** Fuse the mineral with soda, boil in a small amount of conc. H_2SO_4 and an equal volume of water till clear. Dilute and add H_2O_2; the sol. becomes yellow to amber, according to the quantity of Ti. A delicate test.

Tungsten (W; sexivalent; at.wt. 184)

(1) **S.ph. Bead Reac.** In o.f. colorless; in r.f. green hot, fine blue cold.

(2) **Residue in HCl.** When decomposed by HCl a yellow residue of WO_3 is obtained. Add Sn and continue boiling; a blue color is produced, which finally changes to brown. If insol. in HCl, fuse powder on Pt wire with 6 volumes of soda, pulverize and dissolve in water, filter, acidify with HCl, and boil with Sn. The sol. becomes blue. A delicate test.

(3) **Reduction on Al.** To a drop of water on Al add the finely powdered mineral and a small drop of HCl. A blue color develops on standing.

Uranium (U; tetravalent and sexivalent; at.wt. 238.14)

(1) **S.ph. Bead Reac.** In o.f. yellow while hot, yelh.-green cold; in r.f. a fine green.

Vanadium (V; pentavalent; at.wt. 50.96)

(1) **S.ph. Bead Reac.** In o.f. yellow to deep amber, fading a little on cooling; in r.f. dirty greenish while hot, fine green cold.

(2) **Color of Sol.**   To an acid sol. add a few drops of H_2O_2. The sol. becomes reddish-brown from pervanadic acid, HVO_4. A very delicate test.

ZINC (Zn; bivalent; at.wt. 65.38)

(1) **Subl. on Ch.**   Make a paste of the finely powdered mineral, half its volume of soda, and a little water. The mineral must first

FIG. 76.—Method for Zinc Sublimate.

be thoroughly roasted if S, As, or Sb is present. Heat some of the paste in a small loop of Pt wire, which is held about half an inch from the surface of charcoal (Fig. 76), so that volatilized products are carried by the flame directly against the coal. Using a small bead and an intensely hot reducing flame, Zn is reduced to the metallic state, volatilized, and then, uniting with O at the outside of the flame, is deposited as a circular coating, which is canary-yellow while hot and white when cold. If a spot has previously been moistened with $Co(NO_3)_2$ sol., the sublimate is grass-green at that point.

(2) **Flame Color.**   A large fragment heated near the tip of the blue flame colors it in streaks a vivid pale bluish-green.

(3) **Change of Color.**   Many Zn minerals are straw-yellow or canary-yellow while hot and white when cold.

(4) **Color with $Co(NO_3)_2$.**   Infusible, light colored Zn minerals, when powdered, moistened with $Co(NO_3)_2$, and intensely heated, become green, except silicates, which assume a blue color, generally with some green also.

ZIRCONIUM (Zr; tetravalent; at.wt. 90.6)

(1) **Turmeric Paper Test.**   Fuse the powdered mineral with soda in a loop of Pt wire and dissolve the bead in a small amount of HCl. Turmeric paper placed in the solution assumes an orange color, which is detected by comparing with a piece of turmeric paper in another tube containing only acid.

TABLES FOR THE DETERMINATION OF MINERALS BY MEANS OF THE BLOWPIPE AND CHEMICAL TESTS

PRELIMINARY INSTRUCTIONS AND PRECAUTIONS

The tables are constructed on the plan of eliminating one group of minerals after another until the proper species is found; hence the order as given *must be followed strictly*, both in the general table and in the sections to which it refers.

Each test should be recorded as soon as made, whether results are negative or positive. This may be done in systematic order in a notebook, as suggested on the next page.

If the *crystal system* can be determined, either from crystals or from cleavage, comparison with the crystal tables, pages 198 to 205, will often prove the most convenient means of identification.

Whenever possible, tests should be made only upon fresh, homogeneous material, preferably crystalline. If an impurity can be detected its effect must be carefully allowed for and not attributed to the mineral. For example, surface stains of iron oxide and thin films or small amounts of intermingled calcite or other carbonate are often present and may mislead by discoloring the acid or yielding a temporary effervescence. In case of doubt, decant after boiling and note whether or not the same results are obtained with fresh acid.

The powdered mineral required for many of the tests should be prepared by crushing and grinding (not pounding) small grains of pure material under a hammer on any clean surface of iron or steel. (Fig. 64.) If the mineral is rare and but little can be had for determination, fragments may be wrapped in two or three folds of paper and pounded with a hammer.

All tests must be made with care, and only clear, decided reactions taken into account. Weak uncertain results may be due to the presence of a small amount of some impurity, but often they are the results of careless or hasty manipulation. In every test follow closely the detailed instructions, pages 98 to 117.

The importance of scrupulous care in making acid tests and critical observation of the results cannot be over-emphasized. The student should be thoroughly familiar with the instructions on pages 108 to 117.

Dilute HCl (that is, conc. HCl with an equal volume of water) is always understood in acid tests, unless otherwise specified. In many tests the concentrated acid will not yield as good results.

Do not fill a test tube with acid or other reagent to a depth much greater than its diameter, if it is to be boiled.

When igniting a mineral alone on charcoal, use small particles— about the size of a pin head—and use only as many as can be thoroughly heated in the blowpipe flame.

Do not use the Pt-tipped forceps with a mineral of metallic luster nor with one that yields a metal on charcoal.

Many of the "Instructions and Precautions" given in connection with the physical tables, page 18, also apply equally here.

LABORATORY RECORDS

For each mineral determined record should be made of tests and diagnostic characters, *in the order in which they are met in the tables.* Small loose-leaf note-books, with paper about 3½ by 5½ inches, furnish ample space and have been found most convenient for this purpose.

Such records are particularly useful in case of error, and the separation into two parts, belonging to the general and the special tables, respectively, is also an advantage. The condensed skeleton form saves much of the student's and instructor's time without sacrificing clearness.

Emphasis should be placed on the necessity of recording each test immediately upon its completion.

The following records of the determination of pyrite and orthoclase will serve as illustrations.

No. 37

Luster metallic
Fus. 3; SO_2 *fumes*
No As *nor* Sb

   (Sec. 3, p. 144)
No Ag, Pb, *nor* Cu
Becomes mag. in o. f.
Color brass-yellow
Soluble in cold conc. HNO_3
No S *residue*

   PYRITE, FeS_2

Use: Mfr. H_2SO_4

         J. R. Brown

May 20, 1931

No. 38

Luster vitreous; cl. pearly
Fus. 4–5; no flame color
No metal w. ch. and soda
Not mag. nor alk. after ign.
Insoluble in HCl
Cl. 2 direc. about 90°

   (Sec. 23, p. 174)
G. 2.57; Feldspar Group
K flame w. gypsum
Cl. faces not striated

ORTHOCLASE $KAlSi_3O_8$

  Use: Pottery mfr.

         J. R. Brown.

May 20, 1931

GENERAL TABLE

Caution.—In all chemical tests follow carefully the metho ls outlined on pages 98 to 136.

(For glossary and abbreviations, see pages 207–217.)

I. METALLIC OR SUBMETALLIC LUSTER

A. Fusible, at least on thin edges (fus. 1–5), or volatile: SEC. PAGE

  1. As minerals. White subl. on ch. far from assay; commonly also garlic odor 1   140

  2. Sb minerals.—Dense white subl. on ch. near assay 2   140

  3. Sulphides, no As nor Sb.—Use soda test (p. 132) if SO_2 fumes not observed on ch. 3   142

  4. Not previously included 4   146

B. Infusible or nearly so (fus. above 5):

  1. Fe minerals.—Strongly magnetic or become so after heating in r.f. and cooling 5   148

  2. Mn minerals.—Minute quantity gives Mn reaction in soda or borax bead; sol. in HCl with evolution of Cl gas 6   150

  3. Not previously included 7   152

II. LUSTER NOT METALLIC

A. Easily volatile or combustible 8   152

B. Fusible, at least on thin edges (fus. 1–5), or slowly or partially volatile:

Part I. Metal globules when fused on ch. with equal volume of powdered ch. and 3 volumes of soda:

  1. Pb minerals.—Yellow subl. and Pb globules on ch.; with von Kobell's flux a chrome-yellow coat, darker while hot 9   154

  2. Cu minerals.—Cu globules; Cu reactions with acids.... 10   156

  3. Ag and Bi minerals.—Ag–white metallic globules 11   156

Part II.—Magnetic after heating in r.f. and cooling; Fe, Ni, and Co minerals:

  1. Fine powder sol. in HCl without residue or formation of gel. silica upon evaporation 12   158

2. Fine powder sol. in HCl with gel. silica, or decomposed SEC. PAGE
with separation of silica (latter more translucent and
settles more slowly than mineral powder)........... 13 160
3. Fine powder insol. in HCl or nearly so................ 14 160

Part III. Not included in the foregoing Parts I and II:
    1. Alkaline reaction on moist turmeric paper after intense
        ignition:
        a. Fine powder easily and completely soluble in water.. 15 162
        b. Fine powder insol. in water or only slowly or partially
            soluble....................................... 16 164
    2. Fine powder sol. in HCl without residue or formation of
        gel. silica upon evaporation...................... 17 166
    3. Fine powder sol. in HCl with gel. silica:
        a. Give water in closed tube 18 166
        b. Little or no water given in closed tube.............. 19 168
    4. Fine powder decomposed by HCl with separation of flaky
        or granular silica (more translucent and settles more
        slowly than mineral powder) or yellow WO_3 powder:
        a. Give water in closed tube........................ 20 170
        b. Little or no water given in closed tube............. 21 172
    5. Fine powder insoluble in HCl or nearly so:
        a. Micaceous, scaly, or foliated...................... 22 172
        b. Distinct cleavage 2 directions—feldspars, amphiboles,
            pyroxenes.................................... 23 174
        c. Mn reaction in soda bead......................... 24 176
        d. Not previously included.......................... 25 178

C. Infusible or nearly so (fus. above 5):
    1. Alkaline reaction on moist turmeric paper after intense
        ignition....................................... 26 182
    2. Fine powder sol. in HCl without residue or formation of
        gel. silica upon evaporation..................... 27 184
    3. Fine powder sol. in HCl with gel. silica.............. 28 186
    4. Fine powder decomposed by HCl with separation of flaky
        or granular silica (more translucent and settles more
        slowly than mineral powder) or yellow WO_3 powder. 29 188
    5. Fine powder insol. in HCl or nearly so:
        a. Can be scratched with knife blade (H below 6)...... 30 190
        b. Cannot be scratched with knife (H 6 or harder)..... 31 192

		Name.	Composition.
Vol. on ch. without fusion	As subl. in c.t.	ARSENIC (See p. 31)	As (Sb iso. w. As)
Mag. globule on ch. (Compare Co and Ni minerals below.)	As and S reac. in o.t. As in c.t.; red subl. precedes	ARSENOPYRITE (Mispickel) (See p. 22)	FeAsS (Co iso. w. Fe)
Cu flame on ch. after roasting and moistening with HCl. SO₂ fumes in o.t.	Disting. by phys. properties (Cp. tetrahedrite, p. 140)	ENARGITE (See p. 25)	Cu_3AsS_4 (Some Sb)
Cu flame on ch. as above; no SO₂ fumes in o.t.	Tar. to bnh. color	Algodonite	Cu_6As
Rose col. sol. in conc. HNO₃; Co in borax bd. after roasting (Compare Ni minerals, below)	As subl. in c.t.	SMALTITE (See p. 22)	$CoAs_2$ (Fe, Ni iso. w. Co)
	As and S reac. in o.t., little or none in c.t.	COBALTITE (See p. 21)	CoAsS (Fe iso. w. Co)
Apple-grn. sol. in HNO₃ and dimethylglyoxime test for Ni, abundant ppt.; Ni in borax bd. after roasting. (May be masked by Co)	As subl. in c.t.	CHLOANTHITE (See p. 22)	$NiAs_2$ (Fe, Co iso. w. Ni)
	As in c.t. on intense ign.	NICCOLITE (See p. 29)	NiAs (Fe, Co iso. w. Ni)
	As and S reac. in o.t. S res. in conc. HNO₃	GERSDORFFITE (See p. 21)	NiAsS (Fe, Co iso. w. Ni)
Ag in HNO₃ sol., S set free	Abund. deep red subl. in c.t., rdh.-yel. cold; slight S subl. above it	PROUSTITE (Ruby Silver) (See p. 86)	Ag_3AsS_3 (Somet. Sb)

SECTION 2.   Metallic luster;

Easily and completely vol. on ch.; no Pb reac. Stibnite, slender xls. slightly flexible.	Wh. slowly vol. subl. in o.t.	Antimony (See p. 31)	Sb (Somet. Ag. Fe, As)
	SO₂ and wh. non-vol. subl. in o.t.	STIBNITE (Antimony Glance) (See p. 23)	Sb_2S_3
Cu reac. in HNO₃ sol. No Pb or Ag globule w. soda on ch.	May contain Pb, Ag, Zn, Fe and As	TETRAHEDRITE (Gray Copper) (See p. 25)	Cu_3SbS_3 (Fe, Zn, Pb, Ag iso. w. Cu; As iso. w. Sb)

Color.	Streak.	Hardness.	Specific Gravity.	Fusibility.	Crystallization and Structure.	Cleavage and Fracture.
Sn-wh.; tar. dk. gry.	Gry.	3½	5.6–5.7	Vol.	Hex. rhom.; us. crusts	C. 1, basal, per. F. uneven
Ag-wh. to Fe-gry.	Blk.	5½–6	5.9–6.2	2	Orth.; gran.; comp.	C. 2, prism., 68°, poor F. uneven
Gryh.-blk.	Gryh.-blk.	3	4.4–4.5	1	Orth.; gran.; comp.	C. 2, prism., per., 82° F. uneven
Steel-gry.	Gry.	4	7.6	2	Massive	F. uneven
Sn-wh.	Blk.	5½–6	6.4–6.6	2½	Iso. pyrito.; gran.; comp.	C. 4, oct. 70½°, poor F. uneven
Ag-wh. to gry. w. rdh.-tone	Blk.	5½	6.0–6.3	2–3	Iso. pyrito; Figs. 5, 15, 16	C. 3, cubic, poor F. uneven
Sn-wh.	Gryh.-blk.	5½–6	6.4–6.6	2	Iso. pyrito.; gran.; comp.	C. 4, oct., 70½° F. uneven
Pale Cu-red	Brnh.-blk.	5 –5½	7.3–7.7	2	Hex.; comp.; dissem.	F. uneven
Sn-wh.	Blk.	5½	5.6–6.2	2	Iso. pyrito.; gran.	C. 3, cubic, poor F. uneven
Scarlet to ruby-red	Scarlet	2 –2½	5.5–5.6	1	Hex. rhom., hemimor; compact.	C. 3, rhom. poor F. conch.

fus. 1-5 or vol.; Sb. subl. on ch.

Sn-wh.	Sn-wh.	3 –3½	6.6–6.7	1	Hex. rhom.; us. mass.	C. 1, basal, per. F. uneven
Pb-gry.	Pb-gry.	2	4.5–4.6	1	Orth.; long prism.; xls.	C. 1, pinac. per. F. uneven
Gry. to Fe-blk.	Gry. to Fe-blk.	3–4	4.4–5.1	1½	Iso. tetrh., Figs. 13, 14; comp.	F. uneven

		Name.	Composition.
Ag reac. in HNO₃ sol. w. HCl; no Pb. Ag globule after roasting and fus. w. soda on ch. Subl. red to lilac when only Ag, Sb, and S are present	Cu reac. in HNO₃ sol.; mineral gray	FREIBERGITE (Ag Tetrahedrite) (See p. 25)	$(Cu,Ag)_8Sb_2S_7$ (Fe, Zn iso. w. Cu₂; some As)
	Deep red to blk.; st. Indian-red	PYRARGYRITE (Ruby Silver, Dark Red Silver Ore) (See p. 82)	Ag_3SbS_3 (Somet. As)
	Blk., stout 6-sided (orth.) prisms	STEPHANITE (Brittle Silver Ore) (See p. 24)	Ag_5SbS_4
	Blk., 6-sided (mon.) plates; triangular markings on basal plane	POLYBASITE (See p. 24)	$(Ag,Cu)_9SbS_6$ (As iso. w. Sb)
	Sb and Ag. reac. No S. Sectile	*Dyscrasite* (See p. 31)	Ag_3Sb to Ag_6Sb
Pb reac. after roasting and fus. on ch. w. von Kobell's flux	Cu reac. with HNO₃ sol.; steel-gry.	BOURNONITE (Cogwheel Ore) (See p. 25)	$PbCuSbS_3$
	No Ag or Cu	JAMESONITE (Feather Ore) (See p. 21)	$Pb_2Sb_2S_5$ (Often Fe)

SECTION 3.   Metallic luster;

Ag globule in o.f. on ch.	Contains only Ag and S. Sectile		ARGENTITE (Silver Glance) (See p. 24)	Ag_2S
Pb globule and yel. subl on ch.	No Bi		GALENA (Galenite) (See p. 24)	PbS (Often some Ag)
Cu flame on ch. after roasting and moistening w. HCl	Mag. in o.f. (Stannite only after long ign.) (Millerite, below, may have Cu impurities)	Brass-yel.	CHALCOPYRITE (Copper Pyrites) (See p. 28)	$CuFeS_2$
		Brnh.-bronze, purple tar.	BORNITE (Peacock Ore) (See p. 28)	Cu_5FeS_4
(Continued on next page)		Steel-gray.; wh. subl. in o.f.	*Stannite* (Tin Pyrites) (See p. 21)	Cu_2FeSnS_4 (Zn iso. w. Fe)

Color.	Streak.	Hardness.	Specific Gravity.	Fusibility.	Crystallization and Structure.	Cleavage and Fracture.
Steel-gry.	Blk., often rdh.	3 –4	4.8–5.0	1½	Iso. tetrh.	F. uneven
Deep red to blk.	Purplish red	2½–3	5.8–5.9	1	Hex. rhom.; heminor.; dissem.; comp.	C. 3, rhom., poor, 72° F. conch., uneven
Fe-blk.	Fe-blk.	2 –2½	6.2–6.3	1	Orth.; comp.; dissem.	F. uneven
Fe-blk.	Blk.	2 –3	6.0–6.2	1	Mon., tabular; comp.; dissem.	C. 1, basal, poor F. uneven
Ag-wh.	Ag-wh.	3½	9.4–9.9	1½	Orth.; comp.; gran.	C. 3, basal and prism, 56°, 68°, 124°
Steel-gry.	Fe-gry.	2½–3	5.7–5.9	1	Orth.; gran.; cogwheel twins	F. uneven
Blkh.-gry.	Gryh.-blk.	2 –3	5.5–6.0	1	Orth.; acic., feathery	C. 1, basal, per. F. uneven

fus. 1-5 or vol.; no As nor Sb; SO_2 in o.t.

Color.	Streak.	Hardness.	Specific Gravity.	Fusibility.	Crystallization and Structure.	Cleavage and Fracture.
Blkh.-gry.	Blkh.-gry.	2 –2½	7.2–7.4	1½	Iso., us. comp.	F. hackly, sectile
Pb-gry.	Pb-gry.	2½	7.4–7.6	2	Iso.; us. xls. or gran. Fig. 5	C. 3, cubic, per 90°
Brass-yel.	Grnh.-blk.	3½–4	4.1–4.3	2	Tet. sphenoidal; us. comp.	F. uneven
Brnh.-red, bronze Purplish tar.	Pale gryh.-blk.	3	4.9–5.4	2½	Iso.; us. comp.	F. uneven
Steel-gry. to Fe-blk.	Blkh.	4	4.3–4.5	1½	Tetrag., us. comp.	F. uneven

			Name.	Composition.
Cu flame on ch. after roasting and moisting w. HCl. *Concluded*	Not. mag. in o.f. (unless impure from admixture of bornite, etc.)	Cu in r.f. after roasting. Covellite much S in c.t., Chalcocite none	CHALCOCITE (Copper Glance) (See p. 25)	Cu_2S (Somet. Fe)
			COVELLITE (Indigo Copper) (See p. 23)	CuS
Mag. in o.f.; no Cu. Contains Fe, Co, or Ni	Pale brass-yel. Completely sol. in cold conc. HNO_3		PYRITE (Iron Pyrites; Fool's Gold) (See p. 29)	FeS_2 (Somet. Cu, Au, Ni, Co)
	Pale brass-yel. to wh. S separates from cold conc. HNO_3 sol.		MARCASITE (See p. 29)	FeS_2 (Somet, As)
	Decomposed by HCl with evolution of H_2S	Brnh.-bronze; us. mag.; st. blk.	PYRRHOTITE (Magnetic Pyrites) (See p. 29)	FeS (Ni iso. w. Fe) S in sol. up to $3\frac{1}{2}\%$
		Zn. reac. w. soda; submetallic luster	SPHALERITE (Zinc Blende; Black Jack) (See p. 64)	ZnS (Fe, Mn, Cd, iso. w. Zn)
	HNO_3 sol. grn. Ni in borax bd. after roasting. Millerite capillary xls. or velvety crusts; Pentlandite gives Fe ppt. w. am. from HNO_3 sol.		MILLERITE (Hair Pyrites) (See p. 28)	NiS (Slender xls. elastic)
			PENTLANDITE (See p. 29)	$(Fe,Ni)S$
	HNO_3 sol. rose col. Co in borax bd. after roasting		LINNAEITE (See p. 22)	$(Co,Ni)_3S_4$ (Fe, Cu iso. w. Co)
Hg subl. in c.t. with dry soda	SO_2 and Hg in o.t., blk. subl. in c.t.		CINNABAR (See p. 86)	HgS (Us. w. Fe_2O_3, clay, bitumen)
Mn in borax bd. after roasting	H_2S in HCl		ALABANDITE (See p. 81)	MnS
Rdh.-violet sol. when gently heated in conc. H_2SO_4 (See p. 132)			TELLURIDES (See p. 148)	

Color.	Streak.	Hardness.	Specific Gravity.	Fusibility.	Crystallization and Structure.	Cleavage and Fracture.
Dk. Pb-gry. Blkh. or blue tar.	Dk. Pb-gry.	$2\frac{1}{2}$–3	5.5–5.8	$2\frac{1}{2}$	Orth.; us. mass.	F. conch.
Indigo-blue	Pb-gry. to blk.	$1\frac{1}{2}$–2	4.6	$2\frac{1}{2}$	Hex.; us. comp. or crusts	C. 1, basal, per., thin flakes, flexible
Pale brass-yel.	Grnh.-blk. to brnh.-blk.	6 –$6\frac{1}{2}$	4.9–5.2	$2\frac{1}{2}$–3	Iso. pyrito.; Figs. 1, 5, 15, 16; dissem.	F. uneven
Pale yel. to almost wh.	Gryh. or brnh.-blk.	6 –$6\frac{1}{2}$	4.8–4.9	$2\frac{1}{2}$–3	Orth.; tabular; pyram.; cockscomb xls.	C. 2, prism., 75°, poor F. uneven
Yelh. to bnh. bronze	Blk.	$3\frac{1}{2}$–$4\frac{1}{2}$	4.5–4.6	$2\frac{1}{2}$–3	Hex.; us. comp., gran.	C. 1, basal, poor F. uneven
Dk. brn. to blk.	Lt. to dk. brn.	$3\frac{1}{2}$–4	3.9–4.1	5	Iso. tetr.; us. gran., comp.	C. 6, dodec., per., 60°, 90°, 120° F. conch.
Brass-yel.	Grnh.-blk.	3 –$3\frac{1}{2}$	5.3–5.7	$1\frac{1}{2}$–2	Hex. rhom.; us. capil., fibr., crusts	C. rhom. F. uneven, splintery
Lt. bronze yel.	Blk.	$3\frac{1}{2}$–4	4.6–5.1	$1\frac{1}{2}$–2	Iso., gran., comp.	C. 4, oct., $70\frac{1}{2}$°, $109\frac{1}{2}$° F. uneven
Pale steel-gry.; tar. Cu-red	Gryh.-blk.	$5\frac{1}{2}$	4.8–5.0	2	Iso., xls., Fig. 1	C. cubic, 90°, poor F. uneven
Cochineal-red to bnh.	Scarlet	2–$2\frac{1}{2}$	8.1–8.2	$1\frac{1}{2}$ Vol.	Hex. rhom.; gran., earthy	C. 3, prism., per., 60° F. uneven
Fe-blk. Brn. tar.	Olive-grn.	$3\frac{1}{2}$–4	3.9–4.0	3	Iso. tetr.; comp.	C. 3, cubic, per. 90° F. uneven

		Name.	Composition.
Native metal, malleable	Cu reac. w. HNO$_3$ sol.	COPPER (See p. 87)	Cu (Often Ag, Bi, Hg)
	Ag reac. w. HNO$_3$ sol. (Cp. amalgam below)	SILVER (See p. 30)	Ag (Somet. w. Au, Cu, Hg)
	Insol. in HNO$_3$	GOLD (See p. 87)	Au (Us. w. some Ag)
Native metal, brittle or liquid	Bright red subl. on ch. w. von Kobell's flux	BISMUTH (See p. 30)	Bi (Often S and Te)
	Hg subl. in c.t.; amalgam leaves Ag res.	*Mercury* (Quicksilver) (See p. 30)	Hg (Somet. Ag)
		Amalgam (See p. 31)	(Ag, Hg)
Mag. or becomes so in r.f. Contains Fe Cp. the dark micas (below), which sometimes become magnetic	Little or no H$_2$O in c.t.	Strongly mag. before heating	MAGNETITE (Magnetic Iron Ore; Lodestone) (See p. 27)	FeFe$_2$O$_4$ (Somet. Mg, Mn, Ti)
		Nonmag. or but slightly so before heating	HEMATITE (Specular Iron) (See p. 84)	Fe$_2$O$_3$ (Somet. Ti, Mg)
	Much H$_2$O c.t.	Botryoidal, stalactitic, amorphous	LIMONITE (Brown Hematite; Bog Iron Ore) (See p. 83)	FeO·OH·nH$_2$O
		Prismatic xls.	GOETHITE (See p. 89)	FeO·OH
		Rdh.-blk.; st. dark rdh.-brn. Us. decrep. violently in c.t.	TURGITE (See p. 85)	FeO·OH, Fe$_2$O$_3$, H$_2$O
Cu globule in r.f. on ch.		Cuprite submetallic luster; Melaconite earthy or in scales, (tenorite)	CUPRITE (See p. 88)	Cu$_2$O
			Melaconite (Tenorite) (See p. 26)	CuO

Color.	Streak.	Hard-ness.	Specific. Gravity.	Fusi-bility.	Crystallization and Structure.	Cleavage and Fracture.
Cu-red Tar-blk.	Cu-red shiny	$2\frac{1}{2}$–3	8.8–8.9	3	Iso.; scales, plates	F. hackly Duct. and mall.
Ag-wh.; tar. gry. to blk.	Ag-wh, shiny	$2\frac{1}{2}$–3	10.0–12.0	2	Iso.; scales, wire	F. hackly Duct. and mall.
Au-yel.	Au-yel., shiny	$2\frac{1}{2}$–3	15.6–19.3	$2\frac{1}{2}$–3	Iso.; scales, grains	F. hackly Duct. and mall.
Ag-wh., rdh. hue	Ag-wh., shiny	2 –$2\frac{1}{2}$	9.7–9.8	1	Hex. rhom.; us. gran.	C. 1, basal, per., sectile, slightly mall.
Sn-wh.		0	13.6 liq. 14.4 xls.	Vol.	Iso., oct. xls. at −39° C. Fig. 1	C. 3, cubic, 90°
Ag-wh.	Ag-wh., shiny	3 –$3\frac{1}{2}$	13.7–14.1		Iso., plates, coatings	F. uneven, conch.
Fe-black	Blk.	$5\frac{1}{2}$–$6\frac{1}{2}$	4.9–5.2	5–$5\frac{1}{2}$	Iso.; oct. and dodec. Figs. 1, 7; gran.	P. 4, oct., $70\frac{1}{2}$°, $109\frac{1}{2}$° F. conch., uneven
Steel-gry. to Fe-blk.	Dk. red to brh.-red	$5\frac{1}{2}$–$6\frac{1}{2}$	4.9–5.3	5–$5\frac{1}{2}$	Hex. rhom.; comp., gran.	F. uneven, splint. P. basal or rhom.
Dk. brn., blk., yel.	Yelh.-brn.	5 –$5\frac{1}{2}$	3.6–4.0	5–$5\frac{1}{2}$	Fibr.; comp. botryoidal	F. splintery, uneven
Yelh. or redh.-brn. to blk.	Yelh.-brn.	5 –$5\frac{1}{2}$	4.0–4.4	5–$5\frac{1}{2}$	Orth.; acic. or scaly xls.	C. 1, pinac., per. F. uneven
Redh.-blk.	Dk rdh.-brn.	$5\frac{1}{2}$–6	4.2–4.7	5–$5\frac{1}{2}$	Botry.; stalac., earthy	F. splintery, uneven, earthy
Deep red	Brnh.-red	$3\frac{1}{2}$–4	5.8–6.1	$2\frac{1}{2}$–3	Iso.; comp.	F. uneven
Fe-gry. to blk.	Gryh.-blk.	3 –4	5.8–6.2	3	Mon.; earthy, comp., scaly	F. uneven

		Name.	Composition.
Micaceous or foliated	Decomposed by boiling conc. H_2SO_4 (see p. 172)	BIOTITE (Black Mica) (See p. 53)	$(K,H)_2(Mg,Fe)_2$ $Al_2(SiO_4)_3$ (A little F, often Ti)
		PHLOGOPITE (Amber Mica) (See p. 72)	$H_2KMg_3Al(SiO_4)_3$ (A little F and Fe)
W. reac. after fus. w. soda Mag. w. little soda	Mn in soda bd. (Cp. hübnerite, p, 172)	WOLFRAMITE (See p. 26)	$(Fe,Mn)WO_4$
Cb. reac. after fus. w. borax	Mn in soda bd. Mag. w. little soda	COLUMBITE (See p. 84)	$(Fe,Mn)Cb_2O_6$
Gel. sil. in HCl sol. on evaporation	Fus. w. much intumes. Insol. in HCl after fus.	ALLANITE (Orthite) (See p. 58)	$(Ca,Fe)_2(Al,Fe,Ce)_3$ $OH(SiO_4)_3$ (Also Li, Nd, Pr, Y, etc.)
Te minerals. Gently heated in conc. H_2SO_4 gives rdh.-violet sol. (See p. 132) (Mn minerals distinguished by borax bd. test)	Fusible and wholly vol.	*Tellurium* (See p. 30)	Te (Somet. Se, Au, Fe)
	Ag globule in o.f.	HESSITE (See p. 31)	Ag_2Te (Au iso. w. Ag)
	Au w. soda on Ch. Us. w. some Ag.	PETZITE (See p. 31)	Ag_3AuTe_2
		Very brittle; cleavable. Krennerite decrepitates violently b.b. and fuses to Au button → SYLVANITE (See p. 30)	$AuAgTe_4$
		KRENNERITE (See p. 30)	$AuAgTe_4$
	Fuses to Au button	Very brittle; uneven to conchoidal fract. → CALAVERITE (See p. 30)	$(Au,Ag)Te_2$
	Pb w. soda on ch.	$PbSO_4$ ppt. w. H_2SO_4 in HNO_3 sol. → *Altaite*	PbTe (Some Ag, Au)
		Nagyagite	Au, Pb, Sb, Te, S

SECTION 5.   Metallic luster;

Strongly mag. before heating. (Cp. platinum, which is sometimes mag.)	Completely sol. in HCl; sol. reac. for both ferrous and ferric Fe. (Cp. ilmenite, below)	MAGNETITE (Magnetic Iron Ore; Lodestone) (See p. 27)	$FeFe_2O_4$ (Somet, Mg, Mn, Ti)

Color.	Streak.	Hardness.	Specific Gravity.	Fusibility.	Crystallization and Structure	Cleavage and Fracture
Blk., brn., grn.	Pearly, submet.	2 –3	2.7–3.1	5	Mon., pseudo-hex.; plates, scales	C. 1, basal, per. Thin flakes very elastic
Yelh.-brn., grn.	Pearly, submet.	2 –3	2.8–2.9	$4\frac{1}{2}$–5	Mon., pseudo-hex.; plates, scales	C. 1, basal, per. Thin plates very elastic
Dk. gryh.-blk. to brnh.-blk.	Blk.	5 –$5\frac{1}{2}$	7.2–7.5	3–$3\frac{1}{2}$	Mon.; us. xls.	C. 1, pinac., per. F. uneven
Fe-blk. to brnh.-blk.	Dk. red to blk.	6	5.3–7.3	5–$5\frac{1}{2}$	Orth.; us. short prism.	C. 1, pinac., poor F. uneven, conch.
Brn. to pitch-blk.	Gry.	$5\frac{1}{2}$–6	3.0–4.2	$2\frac{1}{2}$	Mon.; us. comp.	F. uneven, conch.
Sn-wh.	Sn-wh.	2 –$2\frac{1}{2}$	6.1–6.3	1	Hex. rhom.; us. gran., comp.	C. 3, prism., per. Somewhat brittle
Steel-gry. Pb-gry.	Gry.	$2\frac{1}{2}$–3	8.3–8.5	1	Iso.; us. comp.	F. uneven
Steel-gry. to Fe-blk.	Gry.	$2\frac{1}{2}$–3	8.7–9.0	$1\frac{1}{2}$	Comp., gran.	F. uneven
Steel-gry. to Ag-wh.	Gry.	$1\frac{1}{2}$–2	7.9–8.3	1	Mon.; branching aggregates	C. 1, pinac., per. F. uneven
Ag-wh. to brass-yel.	Gry.	$2\frac{1}{2}$	8.3–8.4	1	Orth.; us. prism., striated	C. 1, basal, per. F. uneven
Pale bronze-yel.	Yelh.-gry.	$2\frac{1}{2}$	9.0	1	Monocl; us. comp.	F. uneven, conch.
Sn-wh.; tar. bronze-yel.	Gry.	3	8.1–8.2	$1\frac{1}{2}$	Iso.; us. mass.	C. 3, cubic, 90° F. uneven, sectile
Dk. Pb-gry.	Dk. Pb-gry.	1 –$1\frac{1}{2}$	6.8–7.2	$1\frac{1}{2}$	Orth.; us. fol.	C. pinac., per Laminae flex.

fus. above 5; becomes strongly mag. in r.f.

Color.	Streak.	Hardness.	Specific Gravity.	Fusibility.	Crystallization and Structure	Cleavage and Fracture
Fe-blk.	Blk.	$5\frac{1}{2}$–$6\frac{1}{2}$	4.9–5.2		Iso.; xls., oct., dodec., Figs. 1, 7, 11; gran.	P. 4, oct., $70\frac{1}{2}$°, $109\frac{1}{2}$° F. uneven, conch.

			Name	Composition
H_2O_2 test for Ti		Somet. slightly mag.	ILMENITE (Titanic Iron) (See p. 26)	$FeTiO_3$ (Often also Fe_2O_3; somet. Mg)
Gives H_2S in HCl		Zn test, p. 134	SPHALERITE	See p. 64
Cr in s.ph. bead		Bead shows Fe reac. while hot and Cr on cooling	CHROMITE (Chromic Iron) (See p. 84)	$FeCr_2O_4$ (Mg iso. w. Fe; Al and Fe′′′ iso. w. Cr)
Mn in soda bd.		Wh. ZnO subl. on intense ign. w. soda on Pt wire; grn. w. $Co(NO_3)_2$. (Fig. 76, p. 134)	FRANKLINITE (See p. 27)	(Fe,Zn,Mn) $(Fe,Mn)_2O_4$
Not included above	Little or no H_2O in c.t.	Sometimes slightly mag. before heating. Dif. fus.	HEMATITE (Specular Iron) (See p. 84)	Fe_2O_3 (Somet. Ti, Mg)
	H_2O in c.t. Dif. fus.	Mammillary, botryoidal, stalactitic, amorphous	LIMONITE (Brown Hematite; Bog Iron Ore) (See p. 83)	$FeO \cdot OH \cdot nH_2O$
		Us. prisms.; lepidocrocite scaly	GOETHITE (See p. 89)	$FeO \cdot OH$
		Us. decrepitates violently in c.t.	TURGITE (See p. 85)	$FeO \cdot OH, Fe_2O_3, H_2O$

SECTION 6. Metallic luster;

		Name	Composition
Little or no H_2O in c.t.	O in c.t.	PYROLUSITE (See p. 24)	MnO_2 (A little H_2O)
	Slowly sol. in HCl w. gel. sil.	*Braunite* (See p. 28)	$3MnMnO_3 \cdot MnSiO_3$
	No gel. sil.	*Hausmannite* (See p. 83)	$MnMn_2O_4$
Much H_2O in c.t.	Prismatic xls., us. striated	MANGANITE (See p. 83)	$MnO \cdot OH$
	Amorphous; us. Ba reac. in HCl sol. Botry., reniform, stalactitic	PSILOMELANE (See p. 26)	MnO_2, MnO, H_2O, BaO, K_2O, etc.
	Dull, earthy, frothy, powdery, or reniform and compact	WAD (Bog Manganese) (See p. 26)	MnO, MnO_2, H_2O (Often Fe, Si, Al, Ba)

Color.	Streak.	Hardness.	Specific Gravity.	Crystallization and Structure.	Cleavage and Fracture.
Fe-blk.	Blk. to brnh.-red	5 –6	4.5–5.0	Hex. rhom.; us. plates or mass.	F. conch. P. basal, rhom.
Fe-blk. to brnh.-blk.	Dk.-brn.	$5\frac{1}{2}$	4.3–4.6	Iso.; gran., comp.	F. uneven, conch.
Fe-blk.	Rdh.-brn. to blk.	$5\frac{1}{2}$–$6\frac{1}{2}$	5.1–5.2	Iso.; gran., comp., oct. xls., Fig. 1	P. oct. F. uneven, conch.
Steel-gry. to Fe-blk. Earthy, red	Cherry-red brnh.-red	$5\frac{1}{2}$–$6\frac{1}{2}$	4.9–5.3	Hex. rhom.; comp., gran.	F. uneven, splint. P. basal, rhom.
Brn. to blk. Earthy, yel.	Yelh.-brn. Yel. ocher	5 –$5\frac{1}{2}$	3.6–4.0	No xls.; us. comp. or fibr., botryoidal	F. splintery, uneven
Dk. brn. to blk.	Brnh.-yel. to ocher-yel.	5 –$5\frac{1}{2}$	4.0–4.4	Orth.; acic. or scaly xls.	C. 1, pinac., per. F. uneven, splintery
Blk. to rdh.-blk.	Brnh.-red.	$5\frac{1}{2}$–6	4.2–4.7	Botry., stalac., earthy	F. splintery, uneven, earthy

fus. above 5; not. mag. after r.f.; Mn in borax bead

Color.	Streak.	Hardness.	Specific Gravity.	Crystallization and Structure.	Cleavage and Fracture.
Fe-blk.	Blk.	2 –$2\frac{1}{2}$	4.7–4.8	Pseudm., gran., columnar	F. splintery, uneven
Dk. brnh.-blk. to steel-gry.	Brnh.-black.	6 –$6\frac{1}{2}$	4.7–4.8	Tetr.; us. pyram.	C. pyram., per. F. uneven
Brnh.-blk.	Chestnut-brn.	5 –$5\frac{1}{2}$	4.7–4.9	Tetr.; us. gran.; pyram. xls.	C. 1, basal F. uneven
Steel-gry. to Fe-blk.	Rdh.-brn. to blk.	$3\frac{1}{2}$–4	4.2–4.4	Orth.; prism., striated	C. 1, pinac., per F. uneven
Fe-blk.	Brnh.-blk.	5 –6	3.7–4.7	Amor., comp., botry.	F. uneven, conch.
Bluish or brnh.-blk. to dull blk.	Brnh.-blk. to blk.	1 –6	3.0–4.3	Amorph., earthy, comp.	F. earthy

		Name.	Composition.
Very soft. Soils fingers and marks paper easily. Greasy feel.	S and Mo reac. in o.t. Yel.-grn. flame. Characteristic gnh. streak on porcelain or glazed paper.	MOLYBDENITE (See p. 22)	MoS_2
	No reac. in o.t. Very refractory b.b.	GRAPHITE (Plumbago; Black Lead) (See p. 23)	C (Often Fe, clay, etc.)
Cr in borax or s. ph. bd.	Mag. on intense ign. w. equal amt. of soda on ch. (except varieties with much Mg and Al)	CHROMITE (Chromic Iron) (See p. 84)	$FeCr_2O_4$ (Mg iso. w. Fe; Al and Fe''' iso. w. Cr)
H_2O_2 test for Ti after fus. w. soda	Mag. on intense ign. w. equal of soda on ch.	ILMENITE (Titanic Iron) (See p. 26)	$FeTiO_3$ (Some FeO and Mg)
	Submetallic to adamantine luster; us. prismatic xls.	RUTILE (See p. 58)	TiO_2 (Us. a little Fe)
	Similar to Rutile. Disting. by xl. habit and phys. properties. Brookite us. tabular xls.	*Brookite* (See p. 58)	TiO_2
Cb. reac. after fus. w. soda or borax, dissolving in HCl, and boiling w. Sn.	W. little soda becomes mag.; us. Mn reac. also.	COLUMBITE (See p. 84)	$(Fe,Mn)Cb_2O_6$ (Ta iso. w. Cb; a little Sn. and W)
U in s. ph. bd. Little or no Cb	Very heavy; sol. in dil. H_2SO_4 w. slight evolution of gas (He)	URANINITE (Pitchblende) (See p. 27)	Uranate of Pb and U (Also Th, La, Y, Ca, N, He, A, and us. H_2O)
Pt or metals of the Pt group	Malleable; b.b. unaltered; sometimes mag.	PLATINUM (See p. 31)	Pt (Us. w. Fe, Pd, Rh, Ir, Os)

SECTION 8. Nonmetallic luster;

Burns w. blue flame and SO_2 fumes	Subl. in c.t. is red liquid while hot, yel. solid when cold	SULPHUR (See p. 67)	S (Traces Te, Se, As; often clay, bitumen, etc.)
As_2O_3 subl. on ch.; wh. xln. vol.; far from assay	Subl. in c.t. deep red, nearly blk. when hot; a rdh.-yel. transp. solid when cold	REALGAR (See p. 85)	AsS (Slightly sectile)
	Orpiment, thin flakes flexible	ORPIMENT (See p. 86)	As_2S_3

Color.	Streak.	Hard-ness.	Specific Gravity.	Crystallization and Structure.	Cleavage and Fracture.
Pb-gry.	Gryh.-blk., grnh. on glazed paper	1 –1½	4.7–4.8	Hex. (?); foliated, scaly	C. 1, basal, per.; thin flakes, flex. Sectile
Fe-blk. to dk. steel-gry.	Gryh.-blk.	1 –2	1.9–2.3	Hex. rhom.; foliated, earthy	C. 1, basal, per.; thin flakes, flex.
Fe-blk. to brnh.-blk.	Dk. brn.	5½	4.3–4.6	Iso.; us. gran., comp.	F. uneven, conch.
Fe-blk.	Brnh.-red to blk.	5 –6	4.5–5.0	Hex. rhom.; us. plates or gran.	F. conch. P. basal, rhom. 45° and 135° on (100) (110)
Rdh.-brn. to blk. and yelh.	Pale brn. to gry.	6 –7	4.1–4.3	Tetr.; us. xls.; twins	C. 2, prism F. uneven
Hair-brn. to blk.	Wh. to gryh. or yelh.	5½–6	3.9–4.1	Orth.; us. xls. often pseudo-hex.	F. uneven
Fe-blk. to gryh. and brnh.-blk.	Dk. red to blk.	6	5.3–6.5	Orth.; short prism. xls.	F. uneven, conch. C. 1, pinac., poor
Gryh., grnh., or brnh.-blk.	Brnh.-lbk.	5½	9–9.7	Iso.; us. botry., comp., gran.	F. conch.
Whh. steel-gry.	Gry., shiny	4–4½	14–19	Iso.; us. grains or scales	F. hackly; mall., duct.

easily vol. or combustible

Color.	Streak.	Hard-ness.	Specific Gravity.		Crystallization and Structure.	Cleavage and Fracture.
Pale yel. to brnh. and grnh.-yel.	Resinous	1½–2½	2.0–2.1	1	Orth.; Figs. 38, 40 gran., comp.	F. conch.
Aurora-red and orange-yel.	Resinous	1½–2	3.556	1	Mon.; gran, dissem.	C. 1, pinac. F. conch.
Lemon-yel.	Resinous C. pearly	1½–2	3.4–3.5	1	Mon.; us. fol.	C. pinac., per.; striated; flex.

		Name.	Composition.
Hg subl. in c.t. w. dry soda	SO₂ and Hg in o.t.; blk. subl. in c.t.	CINNABAR (See p. 86)	HgS (Us. w. Fe₂O₃, clay, bitumen)
	Cl reac. w. AgNO₃ after soda fus.	*Calomel* (See p. 45)	Hg₂Cl₂
K or Na flame color; sol in H₂O	Alkaline residue after ign.; wholly vol. only by prolonged heating	See Section 15, (p. 162)	

SECTION 9.   Nonmetallic luster; fus. 1-5;

CO₂ efferv. in warm dil. acids	In c.t. dark yel. while hot; decrepitates	CERUSSITE (See p.) 48	PbCO₃
S. reac. in fus. w. soda; sol. in dil. HCl; PbCl₂ ppt. on cooling	Little or no H₂O in c.t.; decrepitates	ANGLESITE (See p. 40)	PbSO₄
HNO₃ sol. reacts for P w. am. mol.	In c.t. slight wh. subl. PbCl₂	PYROMORPHITE (See p. 79)	Pb₅Cl(PO₄)₃ (Often also Ca and As)
As subl. in c.t. w. ch.	Wh. ppt. AgCl w. AgNO₃ in HNO₃ sol.	MIMETITE (See p. 68)	Pb₅Cl(AsO₄)₃ (Often also Ca and P)
V in s. ph. bead	Wh. ppt. AgCl w. AgNO₃ in HNO₃ sol.	VANADINITE (See p. 67)	Pb₅Cl(VO₄)₃ (Somet. P and As)
	H₂O in c.t. Reacts for Zn. Cuprodescloizite contains Cu	DESCLOIZITE (Cuprodescloizite) (See p. 88)	Pb₂Zn(OH)VO₄ (Somet. Cu, As)
Cr in s. ph. bead	Streak orange-yel. Decrepitates on ign.	CROCOITE (See p. 87)	PbCrO₄
Mo in s. ph. bead	Streak white. Decrepitates on ign.	WULFENITE (See p. 68)	PbMoO₄ (Ca somet. iso. w. Pb)

Color.	Luster.	Hardness.	Specific Gravity.	Fusibility.	Crystallization and Structure.	Cleavage and Fracture.
Cochineal-red to brnh.	Adamantine	2 $-2\frac{1}{2}$	8.0–8.2	Vol. $1\frac{1}{2}$	Hex. rhom.; gran., earthy	C. 3, prism., per., 60°, 120° F. uneven
Cols., wh., or gry.	Adamantine	1 -2	6.4–6.5	Vol. 1	Tetr.; xls., coatings	F. conch. Sectile

Pb globule w. soda and ch. on ch.

Color.	Luster.	Hardness.	Specific Gravity.	Fusibility.	Crystallization and Structure.	Cleavage and Fracture.
Cols. to wh. and gry.	Adamantine	3 $-3\frac{1}{2}$	6.4–6.6	$1\frac{1}{2}$	Orth.; pseudohex.	F. conch.
Cols., wh., yelh., grnh.	Adamantine to vitreous	3	6.1–6.4	$2\frac{1}{2}$	Orth.; us. xls.	C. 3, basal and prism. 76°, 90° F. conch.
Grn., yel., brn. and wh.	Resinous	$3\frac{1}{2}$–4	6.5–7.1	2	Hex.; us. prism.	F. uneven conch.
Cols. yel., orange, brn.	Resinous	$3\frac{1}{2}$	7.0–7.3	$1\frac{1}{2}$	Hex.; prism.; crusts	F. uneven
Ruby-red brn., yel.	Resinous	3	6.6–7.2	$1\frac{1}{2}$	Hex.; us. prism.; Fig. 27	F. uneven, conch.
Brnh.-blk. to red	Greasy	$3\frac{1}{2}$	5.9–6.2	$1\frac{1}{2}$	Orth.; us. xls.; drusy	F. uneven, small conch.
Bright red	Adamantine to vitreous	$2\frac{1}{2}$–3	5.0–6.1	$1\frac{1}{2}$	Mon.; us. prism.	C. 2, prism., 86° F. uneven, conch.
Yel., orange-red, gry., wh.	Resinous to adamantine	3	6.7–7.0	2	Tetr.; square tab.	C. pyram. F. uneven, conch.

		Name.	Composition.
Deep red color Hydrocuprite orange)	Strong. sol. in HCl gives wh. ppt. CuCl when much diluted (a cuprous compound)	CUPRITE (Hydrocuprite) (See p. 88)	Cu_2O (OH in hydrocuprite)
CO_2 efferv. in HCl	H_2O in c.t. Disting. by color	MALACHITE (See p. 90)	$Cu_2(OH)_2CO_3$
		AZURITE (See p. 91)	$Cu_3(OH)_2(CO_3)_2$
Blue flame col.	H_2O in c.t.	ATACAMITE (See p. 90)	$Cu_2(OH)_3Cl$
S reac. in fus. w. soda (Compare *Covellite*, p. 144)	Much H_2O in c.t. Sol. in H_2O. Plates moist Fe with Cu	CHALCANTHITE (See p. 79)	$CuSO_4 \cdot 5H_2O$
	Acid H_2O on intense ign. in c.t. Insol. in H_2O	BROCHANTITE (See p. 91)	$Cu_4(OH)_6SO_4$

SECTION 11. Nonmetallic luster; fus. 1-5;

Ag globule, brittle if containing Sb. SO_2 fumes and wh. subl. of As_2O_3 or Sb_2O_3 in c.t. (Cp. polybasite)	Abund. subl. in c.t., deep red hot, rdh-yel. cold; slight S subl. above it	PROUSTITE (Ruby Silver) (See p. 86)	Ag_3AsS_3 (Somet. Sb)
	Slight subl. in c.t., blk. hot, red-brn. cold; slight S subl. above it	PYRARGYRITE (Ruby Silver; Dark Ruby Silver) (See p. 82)	Ag_3SbS_3 (Somet. As)
Mall. Ag globule: Cl, Br, or I reac. w. powdered galena in c.t.	Subl. wh. both hot and cold. Highly sectile mineral	CERARGYRITE (Horn Silver) (See p. 45)	$AgCl$ (Somet. Hg iso. w. Ag)
	Subl. yel. hot, wh. cold. Not disting. by bp. methods. Sectile	EMBOLITE (See p. 66)	$Ag(Cl,Br)$

Color.	Luster.	Hardness.	Specific Gravity.	Fusibility.	Crystallization and Structure.	Cleavage and Fracture.
Ruby-red to rdh-blk. (Orange)	Adamantine to earthy	$3\frac{1}{2}$–4	5.8–6.1	3	Iso.; comp. (Hydrocuprite earthy)	F. uneven
Bright grn.	Vitreous, silky, or dull	$3\frac{1}{2}$–4	3.9–4.0	3	Mon.; us. botry., incrusting.	C. 1, basal, per. F. conch., splint.
Azure-blue	Vitreous	$3\frac{1}{2}$–4	3.7–3.8	3	Mon.; us. xls.; incrust.	C. 2, domal, 29° F. conch.
Emerald-grn.	Adamantine to vitreous	3 –$3\frac{1}{2}$	3.7–3.8	3–4	Orth.; us. prism.	C. 1, pinac., per F. conch.
Deep-azure-blue	Vitreous	$2\frac{1}{2}$	2.1–2.3	3	Tri.; xls., crusts stalac.	F. conch.
Deep emerald grn.	Vitreous	$3\frac{1}{2}$–4	3.9	$3\frac{1}{2}$	Orth.; us. xls.	C. 1, pinac., per. F. uneven

Ag-wh. globule w. soda and ch. on ch.

Color.	Luster.	Hardness.	Specific Gravity.	Fusibility.	Crystallization and Structure.	Cleavage and Fracture.
Scarlet to ruby-red St. scarlet	Adamantine	2 –$2\frac{1}{2}$	5.5–5.6	1	Hex. rhom. hemimor.; comp.	C. 3, rhom., poor, 72° F. conch.
Dk. red to blk. St. purplish	Metallic adamantine	$2\frac{1}{2}$–3	5.8–5.9	1	Hex. rhom. hemimor.; comp., dissem.	C. 3, rhom., poor, 72° F. conch., uneven
Pearl-gry and grnh. to cols.	Resinous to adamantine	1 –$1\frac{1}{2}$	5.5–5.6	1	Iso.; us. wax-like crusts	F. uneven Sectile
Grn. or yel.	Resinous to adamantine	1 –$1\frac{1}{2}$	5.3–5.8	1	Iso.; us. comp.	F. uneven Sectile

		Name.	Composition.
CO₂ efferv. in hot HCl	Decrepitates; becomes blk. and mag. in c.t.	SIDERITE (Spathic Iron) (See p. 41)	$FeCO_3$ (Mg, Mn, Ca iso. w. Fe)
Dif. fus.; strongly mag. after heating in r.f.	Little or no H_2O in c.t.; st. red	HEMATITE (See p. 84)	Fe_2O_3 (Somet. Ti and Mg)
		Martite (See p. 84)	Fe_2O_3
	H_2O in c.t. Earthy, mammillary, stalactitic	LIMONITE (Brown Hematite) (See p. 83)	$FeO \cdot OH \cdot nH_2O$
	Us. prismatic xls. H_2O in c.t.	GOETHITE (See p. 89)	$FeO \cdot OH$
	Us. decrepitates in c.t. H_2O in c.t.	TURGITE (See p. 85)	$FeO \cdot OH, Fe_2O_3, H_2O$
Sol. in cold H_2O; wh. ppt. $BaSO_4$ w. $BaCl_2$ in HCl sol. Acid H_2O in c.t. The ferric salts give $Fe(OH)_3$ ppt. in boiling water	Ferrous iron only; yelh. on exposure. Sweetish astringent metallic taste	MELANTERITE (Copperas) (See p. 78)	$FeSO_4 \cdot 7H_2O$ Mg and Mn iso. w. Fe)
	Ferric iron only. Disagreeable metallic taste	COPIAPITE (See p. 60)	$Fe_4(OH)_2(SO_4)_5 \cdot 17H_2O$ (Often Al, Mg)
P reac. w. am. mol. Much ferrous Fe	Little or no Mn	Whitens w. gentle heat in c.t.	VIVIANITE (See p. 72)	$Fe_3(PO_4)_2 \cdot 8H_2O$
As subl. in c.t. w. ch. fragment	HCl sol rose-red; Co in borax bd. after roasting (Cp. annabergite, below)	ERYTHRITE	$Co_3(AsO_4)_2 \cdot 8H_2O$ (Ni, Fe, Ca iso. w. Co)
	HCl sol. grn.; Ni in borax bd., after roasting (Co may mask bd. reac. for Ni)	ANNABERGITE (See p. 78)	$Ni_3(AsO_4)_2 \cdot 8H_2O$ (Co iso. w. Ni)
	HCl sol. yel; rdh-brn. ppt. w. am.; ferric but no ferrous Fe	SCORODITE (See p. 80)	$FeAsO_4 \cdot 2H_2O$

Color.	Luster.	Hardness.	Specific Gravity.	Fusibility.	Crystallization and Structure.	Cleavage and Fracture.
Lt. to dk. brn. and gry.	Vitreous; C. pearly	$3\frac{1}{2}$–4	3.8–3.9	$4\frac{1}{2}$–5	Hex. rhom.; gran., comp.	C., 3 rhom., per., 73° F. uneven
Brnh-red to blk.	Dull	$5\frac{1}{2}$–$6\frac{1}{2}$	4.9–5.3	5 –$5\frac{1}{2}$	Hex. rhom.; earthy; reniform	F. uneven to splint.
Fe-blk.	Submetallic to dull	6 –7	4.8–5.3	5 –$5\frac{1}{2}$	Iso.	P. 4 oct., $70\frac{1}{2}$°, $109\frac{1}{2}$° F. conch.
Yelh-brn to dk. brn	Silky or dull	5 –$5\frac{1}{2}$	3.6–4.0	5 –$5\frac{1}{2}$	Fibr., botry., earthy	F. splint., uneven
Yelh- or redh-brn. to blk.	Adamantine to dull	5 –$5\frac{1}{2}$	4.0–4.4	5 –$5\frac{1}{2}$	Orth.; acic. or scaly	C. 1, pinac., per. F. uneven, splint.
Rdh-blk. St. dk. redh-brn.	Dull, silky to sub-metal.	5 –6	4.2–4.7	5 –$5\frac{1}{2}$	Botry., incrust., stalac., earthy	F. splint., uneven, earthy
Apple-grn to wh.	Vitreous	2	1.9	1 $4\frac{1}{2}$–5	Mon.; capil., fibr., comp.	C. 1, basal, poor F. conch., earthy
S-yel.	Pearly	$2\frac{1}{2}$	2.1	$4\frac{1}{2}$–5	Mon.; us. gran, scales	C. 1, pinac. F. uneven
Blue, bluish-grn. to cols.	Vitreous; C. pearly	$1\frac{1}{2}$–2	2.6–2.7	2 –$2\frac{1}{2}$	Mon.; earthy, radial	C. 1, pinac., per. F. splint., earthy
Crimson to peach-red	Dull; vitreous; C. pearly	$1\frac{1}{2}$–$2\frac{1}{2}$	2.9–3.0	2	Mon.; us. earthy, acic.	C. 1, pinac., per.; sectile Thin flakes flex.
Apple-grn.	Vitreous	1 –$2\frac{1}{2}$	3.0–3.1	3	Mon.; us. earthy, capil.	F. uneven
Pale grn or brn.	Vitreous	$3\frac{1}{2}$–4	3.1–3.3	2 –$2\frac{1}{2}$	Orth.; us. xls.	F. uneven conch.

		Name.	Composition.
Micaceous, foliated, or scaly. Thin flakes tough and elastic	Slightly sol. in HCl w. separation of SiO_2	BIOTITE (Black Mica) (See p. 53)	$(K,H)_2(Mg,Fe)_2$ $Al_2(SiO_4)_3$
Gel. imperfectly; iso. xls.	Mostly ferric Fe	ANDRADITE (Ca-Fe Garnet) (See p. 70)	$Ca_3Fe_2(SiO_4)_3$ (Fe, Mn, Mg, iso. w. Ca; Al iso. w. Fe)
Gel. after fus. but not before	Partly decomp. by HCl	GLAUCONITE (Greensand) (See p. 78)	$KFe(SiO_3)_2H_2O$, approx. (Some Al; Mg)
Gel. sil. w. HCl; both ferrous and ferric Fe	Fus. w. intumes	ALLANITE (Orthite) (See p. 58)	$(Ca,Fe)_2(Al,Fe,Ce)_3$ $(OH)(SiO_4)_3$ (Some La, Nd, Pr, Y, etc.)

SECTION 14.   Nonmetallic luster; fus. 1-5;

Micaceous; thin flakes tough and flex. or elastic	Dif. fus.	BIOTITE (Black Mica) (See p. 53)	$(K,H)_2(Mg,Fe)_2$ $Al_2(SiO_4)_3$
Red; isometric	Sol. in HCl w. gel. after fus.	ALMANDITE (Fe-Al Garnet) (See p. 70)	$Fe_3Al_2(SiO_4)_3$ (Mn, Mg, Ca iso. w. Fe)
Fus. quietly or w. little intumes. to shiny blk. glass	Little or no Al. Diallage, lamellar to fibr., w. pearly to metalloidal luster	PYROXENE (Diallage) (See p. 74)	$Ca(Mg,Fe)(SiO_3)_2$
	Often Na flame. Contains Al and ferric Fe	AUGITE (See p. 74)	$Ca(Mg,Fe)(SiO_3)_2$ (Al to 15-20%; somet. Mn, Na)
		HORNBLENDE (See p. 54)	$Ca(Mg,Fe)_3(SiO_3)_4$ (Al to 10-18%, Na, and often H, F)
Quietly and dif. fus.	Us. bronzy, metalloidal luster; prism and cl. angles near 90°	HYPERSTHENE (See p. 53)	$(Mg,Fe)SiO_3$
	Prism and cl. angles 54° and 126°; Fe chiefly ferrous; sometimes fibrous (asbestos)	Anthophyllite (Asbestos in part) (See p. 54)	$(Mg,Fe)SiO_3$ (Somet. also Al)

Color.	Luster.	Hard-ness.	Specific. Gravity.	Fusi-bility.	Crystallization and Structure.	Cleavage and Fracture.
Grn. to grnh. or brnh-blk.	Splendent; C. pearly	2–3	2.8–3.1	5	Mon., often 6-sided	C. 1, basal, per.; elastic
Wine-red, grnh., yel., brn., to blk.	Vitreous to resinous	$6\frac{1}{2}$–$7\frac{1}{2}$	3.8–3.9	$3\frac{1}{2}$	Iso., dodecahedron and trapezohe-dron common	F. uneven to conch.
Yelh-grn to gryh. and blkh-grn.	Vitreous, dull	1–2	2.2–2.4	3–4	Amorph., gran., earthy	F. earthy, uneven
Brn. to pitch-blk.	Resinous to submetallic	$5\frac{1}{2}$–6	3.0–4.2	$2\frac{1}{2}$	Mon.; us. comp.	F. uneven, conch.

no metal on ch.; mag. after r.f.; insol. in HCl

Grn. to grnh. or brnh-blk.	Splendent C. pearly	2–3	2.8–3.1	5	Mon., 6-sided plates	C. 1, basal, per.; elastic
Deep red to brnh-blk.	Vitreous	6.5–7.5	3.9–4.2	3	Iso., dodecahe-drons and trap-ezohedrons common	F. uneven to conch.
Lt. to dk. grn.	Vitreous	5–6	3.2–3.6	4	Mon.; us. xls., Figs. 47, 48	C. 2, prism., poor, 87° F. uneven
Gnh-blk. to blk.	Vitreous	5–6	3.2–3.6	3–4	Mons. xls. Figs. 47, 48 gran. colum.	C. 2, prism., poor, 87° F. uneven
Gnh-blk. to blk.	Vitreous to pearly	5–6	2.9–3.4	3–4	Mon. prism. xls., gran.	C. 2, prism., per. 56° F. uneven, splint.
Grn-blk. to brn. and bronze	Pearly to bronzy	5–6	3.4–3.5	5	Orth.; us. mass.	C. 2, pinac. per. F. uneven
Gry. clove-brn., grn.	Vitreous C. pearly	5.5–6	3.1–3.2	5–6	Orth.; us. fibr. or mass.	C. 2, prism. per.

		Name.	Composition.
Fus. w. intumes.	Fused mass dk. brn. or blk.; gel. w. HCl after fus.	EPIDOTE (Pistacite) (See p. 61)	$Ca_2(AlOH)(Al,Fe)_2(SiO_4)_3$
	Pyroelectric. Prismatic xls. w. curved triangular cross section	TOURMALINE (Schorl) (See p. 59)	$R_9Al_3(BOH)_2(SiO_5)_4$ R = Mg, Fe, Ca, Na, K, Li (often a little F)
Fus. w. intumes.; Na flame	Both ferrous and ferric Fe, us. fibrous	CROCIDOLITE (See p. 91)	$NaFe'''(Fe'',Mg)(SiO_3)_3$
W reac. after fus. w. soda. Very heavy	Mn in soda bd.	WOLFRAMITE (See p. 26)	$(Mn,Fe)WO_4$
	Little or no Mn reac.	FERBERITE (See p. 26)	$FeWO_4$ (Some Mn)

SECTION 15. Nonmetallic luster; fus. 1-5; no

Make flame tests below with Pt wire. Most minerals give some yellow color to the flame after yellow. The violet flame of K is purplish-red.

Wh. AgCl ppt. w. HNO₃ sol. and AgNO₃	Wh. BaSO₄ ppt. in H₂O sol. w. HCl and BaCl₂. Kainite salty, bitter, astringent taste	K flame		KAINITE (See p. 40)	$KMgClSO_4 \cdot 3H_2O$
	Intense Na flame; no S; salty taste			HALITE (Rock Salt; Common Salt) (See p. 39)	$NaCl$ (Us. also Ca and Mg)
	K flame, no S	Little or no H₂O in c.t.; salty, bitter		SYLVITE (See p. 40)	KCl (Na iso. w. K)
		Much H₂O in c.t.; bitter taste; absorbs moisture		CARNALLITE (See p. 45)	$KMgCl_3 \cdot 6H_2O$
Sulphates.—H₂O sol. w. HCl and BaCl₂ gives wh. ppt. BaSO₄	Much H₂O in c.t.; fine powder sol. in 500 parts H₂O; Ca flame			GYPSUM (Selenite) (See p. 32)	$CaSO_4 \cdot 2H_2O$
	Na flame; little or no H₂O in c.t.			THENARDITE (See p. 33)	Na_2SO_4

Color.	Luster.	Hardness.	Specific Gravity.	Fusibility.	Crystallization and Structure.	Cleavage and Fracture.
Yelh. to blkh-grn. and gry.	Vitreous	6–7	3.2–3.5	3–4	Mon.; us. prism.	C. 1, basal, per. F. uneven
Blk., brn., grn.	Vitreous to resinous	7–7½	3.0–3.2	3–5 Us. 3	Hex. rhom. hemimor. Fig. 37	F. conch., uneven
Leek-grn. to deep lavender-blue	Silky, dull	4	3.2–3.3	3½	Fibrous	Fibrous
Gryh. to brnh-blk.; st. blk.	Submetallic	5–5½	7.2–7.5	4	Mon.; us. xls	C. 1, pinac. per. F. uneven
Blk. St. brn-blk.	Submetallic	5	7.5	3½	Mon., us. xls.	C. 1, pinac. per. F. uneven

metal on ch.; not mag. after r.f.; alk. after ign.; sol. in water

being handled, but those containing Na as an essential constituent give an intense and persistent when seen through dark blue glass.

Color.	Luster.	Hardness.	Specific Gravity.	Fusibility.	Crystallization and Structure.	Cleavage and Fracture.
Cols., wh. to redh.	Vitreous	2½–3	2.0–2.2	1½–2	Mon.; comp., gran.	C. 3, pinac. and prism., 39½°, 101°
Cols., wh., redh., bluish	Vitreous	2½	2.1–2.6	1½	Iso.; us. cubic, Fig. 5; gran., comp.	C. 3, cubic, per., 90° F. conch.
Cols., wh., redh., bluish	Vitreous	2	1.9–2.0	1½	Iso.; cubes, Fig. 5; gran.	C. 3, cubic, per., 90° F. conch.
Cols., wh., redh.	Vitreous to greasy	1	1.6	1–1½	Orth.; us. mass.	F. conch.
Cols., wh., yel., red, gray	Vitreous C. pearly	1½–2	2.3–2.4	3	Mon.; Figs. 46, 49; gran., comp.	C. 3, prism. and pinac., per., 90°, 66°, 114° F. splint
Cols., wh., brnh.	Vitreous	2–3	2.7	1.5–2	Orth.; xls.; cross-twins	C. 1, basal F. uneven

		Name.	Composition.
	Mg reac. w. $Co(NO_3)_2$ on ch. Bitter salty taste	EPSOMITE (Epsom Salt) (See p. 47)	$MgSO_4 \cdot 7H_2O$
	Intense Na flame; much H_2O in c.t.	MIRABILITE (Glauber Salt) (See p. 46)	$Na_2SO_4 \cdot 10H_2O$
Nitrates.—Deflagrate on ch.; NO_2 fumes w. $KHSO_4$ in c.t.	Intense Na flame; cooling salty taste	SODA NITER (See p. 46)	$NaNO_3$
	K flame; cooling salty taste	NITER (Saltpeter) (See p. 47)	KNO_3
B reac. w. turmeric paper	Swells and fus. to clear glass; taste sweetish alkaline	BORAX (See p. 33)	$Na_2B_4O_7 \cdot 10H_2O$

SECTION 16.   Nonmetallic luster; fus. 1-5; no metal

Make flame tests below with Pt wire and HCl.

CO_2 efferv. in dil. HCl	No H_2O in c.t.	Ba flame	WITHERITE (See p. 48)	$BaCO_3$
S reac. w. powdered ch. and soda on ch.	Much H_2O in c.t. Readily sol. in hot. dil. HCl (Cp. anhydrite, below)	Sol. in 500 parts H_2O; Ca flame; flakes flex.	GYPSUM (Selenite; Alabaster) (See p. 32)	$CaSO_4 \cdot 2H_2O$
		K flame; Mg reac. w. Na phosphate; slight bitter astringent taste	*Polyhalite* (See p. 60)	$K_2MgCa_2(SO_4)_4 \cdot 2H_2O$
	Little or no H_2O in c.t. Anhydrite somet. much H_2O; distinguish by H	Na flame; sol. in HCl; salty taste	*Glauberite* (See p. 34)	$Na_2Ca(SO_4)_2$
		No flame col.; slowly sol. in hot dil. HCl	ANHYDRITE (See p. 41)	$CaSO_4$
		Sr flame; nearly insol. in HCl	CELESTITE (See p. 41)	$SrSO_4$ (Somet. Ca and Ba)
		Ba flame; nearly insol. in HCl Decrepitates	BARITE (Heavy Spar) (See p. 40)	$BaSO_4$ (Somet. Ca and Sr)

Color.	Luster.	Hard-ness.	Specific Gravity.	Fusi-bility.	Crystallization and Structure.	Cleavage and Fracture.
Cols. or wh.	Vitreous; earthy	2 –2½	1.7–1.8	1	Orth.; us. fibr., gran.	C. 1, pinac., per. F. conch.
Cols. or wh.	Vitreous	1½–2	1.4–1.5	1½	Mon.; us. crusts, **mealy** efflores.	C. 1, pinac., per. F. conch.
Cols. or wh.	Vitreous	1½–2	2.2–2.3	1	Hex. rhom.; us. incrust., gran.	C. 3, rhom., per., 73½° F. conch.
Cols. or wh.	Vitreous silky	2	2.1–2.2	1	Orth.; us. crusts, acic.	C. 2, prism., per., 70° F. uneven
Cols., wh., gryh.	Vitreous to resinous	2 –2½	1.7	1–1½	Mon.; us. comp.	C. 1, pinac., per. F. conch.

on ch.; not mag. after r.f.; alk. after ign.; insol. in water

Color.	Luster.	Hard-ness.	Specific Gravity.	Fusi-bility.	Crystallization and Structure.	Cleavage and Fracture.
Cols., wh., yelh., gryh.	Vitreous	3 –4	4.3–4.4	2	Orth. twinned pseudohex.	F. uneven
Cols. wh., yel., red, gry.	Vitreous C. pearly	1½–2	2.3–2.4	3	Mon., Figs. 46, 49; gran., comp.	C. 3, prism., pinac., per., 90°, 66° F. conch., splint.
Brick-red to yel. and wh.	Vitreous to resinous	2½–3	2.7–2.8	1½	Mon.; fibr., lamel.	C. 1, pinac. F. splint.
Cols., wh., yelh., gryh.	Vitreous	2½	2.7–2.8	1½–2	Mon.; us. tab. and xls.	C. 1, basal, per., F. conch.
Cols., wh., blue, gry., red	Vitreous; basal cl., pearly	3 –3½	2.9–3.0	3	Orth.; us. mass.	C. 3, pinac., per., 90°
Cols., wh., blue, red	Vitreous to pearly	3 –3½	3.9–4.0	3	Orth., Fig. 41 xls., fibers	C. 3, basal, per., and prism., 76°, 90°
Cols., wh., blue, yel., red, brn.	Vitreous to pearly	2½–3½	4.3–4.6	3	Orth., xls., comp. lamellar	C. 3, basal, per., and prism., 78½°,. 90°

			Name.	Composition.
F reac. w. KHSO$_4$ and glass in c.t.	Little or no H$_2$O in c.t.	Na flame; easily fus.	CRYOLITE (See p. 48)	Na$_3$AlF$_6$
		Ca flame; often phosphoresces and decrepitates in c.t.	FLUORITE (Fluor Spar) (See p. 77)	CaF$_2$ (Somet. Cl iso. w. F)

SECTION 17.   Nonmetallic luster; fus. 1-5; no metal on ch.; not

H$_2$S efferv. in hot HCl	Wh. ZnO subl. after intense ign. w. soda on Pt wire; subl. grn. w. Co(NO$_3$)$_2$ (See p. 134)		SPHALERITE (Zinc Blende) (See p. 64)	ZnS (Fe, Mn, Cd iso. w. Zn)
P reac. w. am. mol.	Slight F reac. w. KHSO$_4$ in c.t.	CaSO$_4$ ppt. w. H$_2$SO$_4$ in HCl sol. / No H$_2$O in c.t.	APATITE (See p. 68)	Ca$_5$F(PO$_4$)$_3$ (Cl iso. w. F)
	U in s. ph. bd.	CaSO$_4$ ppt. w. dil. H$_2$SO$_4$ in HCl sol.	*Autunite* (See p. 86)	Ca(UO$_2$)$_2$(PO$_4$)$_2$ · 8H$_2$O
B reac. w. turmeric paper	Na flame	Swells; sol. in H$_2$O	BORAX (See p. 33)	Na$_2$B$_4$O$_7$·10H$_2$O
		Ca reac. w. am. oxalate	ULEXITE (See p. 45)	NaCaB$_5$O$_9$·8HO
	B flame	No H$_2$O in c.t.; Cl reac. after fus. w. soda	BORACITE (See p. 52)	Mg$_7$Cl$_2$B$_{16}$O$_{30}$
		Decrepitates, exfoliates; Ca reac. in dil. sol. w. am. oxalate	COLEMANITE (See p. 36)	HCa(BO$_2$)$_3$·2H$_2$O
Yel. powder or earthy mass; greasy feel; V in s. ph. bd.; H$_2$O in c.t.; fus. easily to blk. non-mag. slag			CARNOTITE (See p. 85)	(K$_2$,Ca)O·2U$_2$O$_3$· V$_2$O$_5$·nH$_2$O

SECTION 18.   Nonmetallic luster; fus. 1-5; no metal on ch.; **not**

Fus. quietly to cols. glass	Whitens in c.t.; Na flame w. gypsum	NATROLITE (See p. 37)	Na$_2$Al(AlO)(SiO$_3$)$_3$· 2H$_2$O

Color.	Luster.	Hard-ness.	Specific Gravity.	Fusi-bility.	Crystallization and Structure.	Cleavage and Fracture.
Cols. wh., brnh.	Vitreous to greasy	$2\frac{1}{2}$	2.9–3	$1\frac{1}{2}$	Mon., us. gran. comp.	F. uneven P. 3, often, 88°, 90°
Cols., violet, blue, grn., yel., pink	Vitreous	4	3.0–3.2	3	Iso.; us. cubes, Fig. 5	C. 4, oct., per., $70\frac{1}{2}$°, $109\frac{1}{2}$° F. uneven

mag. after r.f.; not alk. after ign.; sol. in HCl without res. or gel. sil.

Color.	Luster.	Hard-ness.	Specific Gravity.	Fusi-bility.	Crystallization and Structure.	Cleavage and Fracture.
Wh., grn., yel., red, brn., blk.	Res. to adamant.	$3\frac{1}{2}$–4	3.9–4.1	5	Iso. tetr.; gran., comp.	C. 6, dodec. per., 60°, 90°, 120° F. conch.
Grn., blue, violet, red, brn., cols.	Vitreous to greasy	$4\frac{1}{2}$–5	3.1–3.2	5–$5\frac{1}{2}$	Hex., us. prisms	C. 1, basal, poor to distinct F. uneven conch.
Lemon-yel. to S-yel.	Adamant. C. pearly	2 –$2\frac{1}{2}$	3.1–3.2	$2\frac{1}{2}$	Orth.; tabular pseudotetr.	C. 1, basal, per., flakes brittle
Cols., wh., gryh., bluish, grnh.	Vitreous to resinous	2 –$2\frac{1}{2}$	1.7	1–$1\frac{1}{2}$	Mon.; us. comp.	C. 1, pinac., per. F. conch.
Wh.	Silky	0 –1	1.6–1.7	1	Mon.; fibrous	Very fragile
Cols., wh., yel., gry., grn.	Vitreous	7	2.9–3.0	2	Iso. tetrh.; us. isolated xls.	F. conch., uneven
Cols., wh., yelh., gryh.	Vitreous to adamant.	4 –$4\frac{1}{2}$	2.3–2.5	$1\frac{1}{2}$	Mon.; prism. xls.; gran.	C. 2, pinac., per. 90° F. uneven, conch.
Canary-yel.	Dull	0 –1		$2\frac{1}{2}$	Hex. (?); us. earthy	

mag. after r.f.; not alk. after ign.; sol. in HCl w. gel. sil.; water in c.t.

Color.	Luster.	Hard-ness.	Specific Gravity.	Fusi-bility.	Crystallization and Structure.	Cleavage and Fracture.
Cols., wh., yelh., redh., grnh.	Vitreous to pearly	5 –$5\frac{1}{2}$	2.2–2.3	2	Orth.; prism., pseudotetrag. radial, fibr.	C. 2, prism., per., 89° F. uneven

		Name.	Composition.
Fus. with intumescence	To cols. glass; B-flame	DATOLITE (See p. 49)	$Ca(BOH)SiO_4$
	To blebby glass; CO_2 efferv. in HCl	CANCRINITE (See p. 65)	$H_6Na_6Ca(NaCO_3)_2$ $Al_8(SiO_4)_9$
	To wh. blebby enamel; Na flame w. gypsum; pyroelectric	THOMSONITE (See p. 49)	$(Ca,Na_2)_2Al_4(SiO_4)_4 \cdot$ $5H_2O$
	To white blebby enamel; not pyroelectric	LAUMONTITE (See p. 42)	$H_4Ca(AlO)_2(SiO_3)_4 \cdot$ $2H_2O$

SECTION 19. Nonmetallic luster; fus. 1-5; no metal on ch.; not mag.

		Name.	Composition.
Efferv. of H_2S in HCl	Na flame; $BaSO_4$ ppt. w. $BaCl_2$ in HCl sol.	LAZURITE (Lapis Lazuli) (See p. 91)	$Na_5Al_3S_3(SiO_4)_3$
$AgCl$ ppt. w. $AgNO_3$ in HNO_3 sol.; Na flame	Fus. to cols. glass	SODALITE (See p. 80)	$Na_4Al_3Cl(SiO_4)_3$
Mn in borax bd. (Cp. willemite below)	Wh. ZnO subl. in fine powder w. soda on Pt wire; grn. w. $Co(NO_3)_2$. (See p. 134)	TROOSTITE (See p. 65)	$(Zn,Mn)_2SiO_4$
	Little or no Zn; gel. in cold HCl	TEPHROITE (See p. 55)	Mn_2SiO_4 (Some Mg, Fe)
ZnO subl. w. soda on Pt wire (See p. 134)	May also contain Mn	WILLEMITE (See p. 65)	Zn_2SiO_4 (Often Mn, Fe)
Contain Si, Al, and Ca. See Silicon (2), p. 129	Easily sol. in HCl; Na flame	NEPHELITE (See p. 43)	Approx. $NaAlSiO_4$ (Some K and Ca)
	Dif. sol. in HCl; Na flame w. powdered gypsum; fus. to cols. glass	ANORTHITE (Lime Feldspar) (See p. 38)	$CaAl_2(SiO_4)_2$ (Some Na)
	Fus. w. intumes. to dark slag	ALLANITE (Orthite) (See p. 58)	$(Ca,Fe)_2(Al,Fe,Ce)_3$ $(OH)(SiO_4)_3$ (Also La, Nd, Pr, Y, etc.)

Color.	Luster.	Hardness.	Specific Gravity.	Fusibility.	Crystallization and Structure.	Cleavage and Fracture.
Cols., grnh., yelh., redh.	Vitreous	5 –5½	2.9–3.0	2.2–5	Mon.; us. xls.; gran.	F. conch. to uneven
Yel., pink, grnh., bluish, gry., wh.	Vitreous to greasy	5 –6	2.4–2.5	2	Hex.; us. comp.	C. 3, prism., 60°, 120° F. uneven
Cols., wh., grn., brn., gry.	Vitreous to pearly	5–5½	2.3–2.4	2	Orth.; us. radial, fibr.	C. 2, pinac., per., 90° F. uneven
Wh., yelh., gryh., redh.	Vitreous C. pearly	3.5–4	3.2–3.3	2.5	Mon.; prism., radial	C. 3, pinac. and prism., per., 96°, 94°, 137° F. uneven

after r.f.; not alk. after ign.; sol. in HCl w. gel. sil; little or no water in c.t.

Color.	Luster.	Hardness.	Specific Gravity.	Fusibility.	Crystallization and Structure.	Cleavage and Fracture.
Deep azure to grnh.-blue	Vitreous	5 –5½	2.4–2.5	3	Iso; comp.; xls., Fig. 7, dodec.	C. 6, dodec. 60°, 120°, poor F. uneven
Wh., gry., blue grn., redh.	Vitreous to greasy	5 –6	2.1–2.3	3½–4	Iso.; comp., dissem.	C. 6, dodec., 60°, 90°, 120° F. conch., uneven
Apple-grn., flesh-red brn.	Vitreous	5½	4.1–4.2	4–4½	Hex. rhom.; us. mass.	C. 3, prism., 60°, 120° F. uneven
Smoky-gry., brnh.-red	Vitreous to greasy	5½–6	4.0–4.1	3–3½	Orth.; us. gran., comp.	C. 2, pinac., 90° F. uneven, conch.
Yel., red, grn., brn., wh., cols.	Vitreous	5 –6	3.9–4.2	3½–4	Hex. rhom.; comp., gran., dissem.	C. 3, basal and prism., 60°, 120° F. uneven, conch.
Cols., gry., grnh., redh., yelh.	Vitreous to greasy	5 –6	2.5–2.6	3½	Hex. hemimorph., comp., gran.	C. 3, prism., 60°, 120° F. uneven, conch.
Cols., wh., gry., redh.	Vitreous	6 –6½	2.7–2.8	4½	Tri., prism. xls., cleav., comp.	C. 2, basal., per., and pinac., 87° F. uneven
Brn. to blk.	Res., vitr. to submet.	5½–6	3.0–4.2	2½	Mon.; us. mass.	F. uneven, conch.

		Name.	Composition.
Micaceous; flex., but not elastic, or little so	Exfoliates greatly b.b. Hydrated mica	VERMICULITE (Jefferisite) (See p. 59)	Hydrous Mg-Fe-Al silicate (Somet. Na, K)
Dif. fus.; little or no Al or Ca; much Mg. See Silicon (2), p. 000	Us. compact grnh. mass.; sometimes fibrous (chrysotile, commercial "asbestos") or foliated (marmolite)	SERPENTINE (Chrysotile; Marmolite) (See p. 79)	$H_4Mg_3Si_2O_9$ (Some Fe, somet. Ni)
	Compact, fine earthy texture; when dry floats on H_2O	SEPIOLITE (Meerschaum) (See p. 47)	$H_4Mg_2Si_3O_{10}$ (Somet. Cu and Ni)
Whitens and fus. quietly	To clear glass; Na flame	ANALCITE (See p. 49)	$NaAl(SiO_3)_2 \cdot H_2O$
	To translucent glass; Ba in HCl	HARMOTOME (See p. 36)	$H_2Ba, Al_2(SiO_3)_5 \cdot 4H_2O$
Fus. quietly	To wh. enamel; Na flame; little H_2O. Gmelinite often cracks and splits b.b.	PECTOLITE (See p. 49)	$HNaCa_2(SiO_3)_3$
		Gmelinite	$(Na_2,Ca)Al_2(SiO_3)_4 \cdot 6H_2O$
Fus. with intumes.	To blebby white enamel — K flame	APOPHYLLITE (See p. 34)	$(H,K)_2Ca(SiO_3)_2 \cdot H_2O$ (A little F)
	To blebby white enamel — Slowly and diff. sol. in HCl; little H_2O	PREHNITE (See p. 81)	$H_2Ca_2Al_2(SiO_4)_3$ (Fe iso. w. Al)
	To blebby white enamel — Gives slimy sil. in HCl	CHABAZITE (See p. 42)	$CaAl_2(SiO_3)_4 \ 6H_2O$ (Somet. K, Na, Ba, Sr)
	To white enamel — Exfoliates b.b.	STILBITE (See p. 34)	$H_4(Ca,Na_2)Al_2 (SiO_3)_6 \cdot 4H_2O$
	To white enamel — Pearly cl. faces lozenge-shaped	HEULANDITE (See p. 34)	$H_4(Ca,Na_2)Al_2 (SiO_3)_6 \cdot 3H_2O$

Color.	Luster.	Hardness.	Specific Gravity.	Fusibility.	Crystallization and Structure.	Cleavage and Fracture.
Yel., brn., lt. to dk. grn.	Pearly	$1-1\frac{1}{2}$	2.3–2.8	$3\frac{1}{2}$	Mon.; fol., scaly, flaky	C. 1, basal, per. Thin flakes flex., not elastic
Olive to blkh.-grn., yelh.-grn., wh.	Greasy, wax-like, silky	3 –4	2.5–2.6	$5-5\frac{1}{2}$	Mass.; pseudomorphous, fibrous	F. uneven, splint. Fibers tough
Wh. to gryh.-wh.	Dull	$2 -2\frac{1}{2}$	1.0–2.0	$5-5\frac{1}{2}$	Compact; earthy	F. uneven, conch.
Cols., wh., yelh., redh.	Vitreous	$5 -5\frac{1}{2}$	2.2–2.3	$2\frac{1}{2}$	Iso.; us. xls., Trapazoh., Fig. 3	F. uneven, conch.
Wh., gry., yel., red, brn.	Vitreous	$4\frac{1}{2}$	2.4–2.5	$3\frac{1}{2}$	Mon.; us. twinned or radiated tufts	C. 2, pinac., 90° F. uneven
Cols., wh., gry.	Vitr., silky C. pearly	$4\frac{1}{2}-5$	2.7–2.8	$2\frac{1}{2}$	Mon.; fibr., radiated, comp.	C. 2, pinac., per., 85°, 95° F. splint., uneven
Wh., yel. flesh-red, grnh.	Vitreous	$4\frac{1}{2}$	2.0–2.2	$2\frac{1}{2}$	Hex. rhom.; us. xls.	C. 3, prism., 60°, 120° F. uneven
Wh., grnh., yelh., redh.	Vitreous; C. pearly	$4\frac{1}{2}-5$	2.3–2.4	$1\frac{1}{2}$	Tetr.; us. cube-like xls.	C. 1, basal, per. F. uneven
Apple-grn., gry., wh.	Vitreous	$6 -6\frac{1}{2}$	2.8–3.0	2	Orth.; us. globular; tabular xls.	C. 1, basal, poor F. uneven
Wh., yel., flesh-red	Vitreous	$4\frac{1}{2}-5$	2.0–2.2	3	Hex. rhom.; xls. nearly cubic	C. 3, rhom., 85° F. uneven
Wh., yel., brn., red	Vitreous; C. pearly	$3\frac{1}{2}-4$	2.1–2.2	$2-2\frac{1}{2}$	Mon.; twinned; sheaf-like radiated	C. 1, pinac. per. F. uneven
Wh., yel., gry., red, brn.	Vitreous; C. pearly	$3\frac{1}{2}-4$	2.2	$2-2\frac{1}{2}$	Mon.; tabular xls. look orth.	C. 1, pinac. per. F. uneven

		Name.	Composition.
Yel. WO_3 res. on boiling in HCl	Strong Mn reac. in borax bead	HUEBNERITE (See p. 26)	$MnWO_4$ (Fe iso. w. Mn)
	Ca w. am. oxalate; cupro-scheelite, Cu flame	SCHEELITE (See p. 65)	$CaWO_4$ (Us. also Mo; somet. Cu)
Fus. quietly to glassy globule; slowly sol. in HCl	Us. striated on best cl.; often brilliant play of color	LABRADORITE (Ca-Na Feldspar) (See p. 38)	$n(NaAlSi_3O_8)$ $m(CaAl_2Si_2O_8)$ ($n:m = 1:1$ to $1:3$)
Fus. dif. to wh. globule; rather easily sol. in HCl	HCl sol. gives no Al ppt. w. am.; but Ca reac. w. am. oxalate	WOLLASTONITE (See p. 37)	$CaSiO_3$ (Somet. H, Mg)
Ti reac. w. H_2O_2	Fus. w. intumes. to dk. glass	TITANITE (Sphene) (See p. 62)	$CaSiTiO_5$ (Some Fe; somet. Mn)
Fus. w. intumes. to white mass	Cl reac. w. $AgNO_3$; slowly sol. in acids; Na flame	WERNERITE (Scapolite) (See p. 43)	$n(Ca_4Al_6Si_6O_{25})$ $m(Na_4Al_3Si_9O_{24}Cl)$ $n:m = 3:1$ to $1:2$)

SECTION 22. Nonmetallic luster; fus. 1-5; no metal on ch.; not mag.

Li flame; thin flakes elastic	Easily fus. to wh. or gry. globule; acid H_2O in c.t. on intense ign.	LEPIDOLITE (Lithia Mica) (See p. 33)	$(Li,K)_2Al_2(OH,F)_2$ $(SiO_3)_3$
Decomposed by boiling conc. H_2SO_4. (Flakes lose luster and transp. and acid becomes turbid); thin flakes elastic, except chlorite and kämmererite	Us. dk. col.; often w. quartz and feldspar and in igneous rocks	BIOTITE (Black Mica) (See p. 53)	$(K,H)_2(Mg,Fe)_2$ $Al_2(SiO_4)_3$ (A little F, often Tl)
	Lt. to dk. col; much more readily decomposed than biotite	PHLOGOPITE (See p. 72)	$H_2KMg_3Al(SiO_4)_3$ (Some F, Fe)
	Thin flakes flex. but not elastic; much H_2O	CHLORITE (Clinochlore, etc.) (See p. 72)	H,Fe,Mg,Al silicates
Not decomposed by boiling conc. H_2SO_4. (Flakes retain luster and transp., acid remains clear)	Common lt. colored mica; elastic; us. w. quartz and feldspar	MUSCOVITE (Potash Mica) (See p. 33)	$H_2KAl_3(SiO_4)_3$ (Often some Na, Ca, Mg, Fe, F)
	Soft; greasy feel; thin flakes flex. but not elastic; sectile	TALC (Steatite, Soapstone) (See p. 32)	$H_2Mg_3(SiO_3)_4$
	Thin flakes brittle; harder than true micas	MARGARITE (Brittle Mica) (See p. 34)	$H_2CaAl_4Si_2O_{12}$ (Some Fe, Na, K)

Color.	Luster.	Hardness.	Specific Gravity.	Fusibility.	Crystallization and Structure.	Cleavage and Fracture.
Brn. to brnh.-blk.	Resinous	5–5.5	6.9–7.4	4	Mon., us. xls.	C. 1, pinac. per. F. uneven
Wh., yel., grn., brn., redh.	Vitreous to adamant.	4.5–5	5.9–6.1	5	Tetr.; gran.; xls. like octahedrons	C. 4, pyram., 49½°, 80° F. uneven, conch.
Wh., gry., brn., grn.	Vitreous to pearly	5 –6	2.7	3–4	Tri.; us. mass.	C. 2, basal, per. and pinac., 86° F. uneven
Cols., wh., gry., yel., red, brn.	Vitreous; C. pearly	4½–5	2.8–2.9	4	Mon.; us. gran., fibr., comp.	C. 2, pinac., per., 84½° F. uneven
Gry., brn., yel., grn.	Res. to adamant.	5 –5½	3.4–3.6	3	Mon.; tabular wedge-shaped xls.	C. 2, prism., 66½° F. conch. P. 4, pyram.
Wh., gry., grnh., bluish, redh.	Vitreous to pearly	5 –6	2.6–2.8	3	Tetr.; comp., gran., stout prisms	C. 3, prism. and pinac., poor F. uneven, conch.

after r.f.; not alk. after ign.; insol. in HCl; micaceous, foliated, or scaly

Color.	Luster.	Hardness.	Specific Gravity.	Fusibility.	Crystallization and Structure.	Cleavage and Fracture.
Lilac., gryh-wh., redh., yelh.	Pearly	2 –3	2.8–2.9	2–2½	Mon.; us. scaly, comp.	C. 1, basal, per. Flakes tough, elastic
Grn., yel., brn., blk.	Splendent to pearly and submet.	2 –3	2.7–3.1	5	Mon.; 6-sided plates, scaly	C. 1, basal, per. Flakes tough, elastic
Yelh-brn., grn., wh., cols.	Pearly to submet.	2 –3	2.8–2.9	4½–5	Mon., 6-sided xls., plates, scales	C. 1, basal, per. Flakes tough, elastic
Grn. of various shades	Vitreous to pearly	1 –2½	2.6–3.0	5–5½	Mon.; scaly, foliated	C. 1, basal, per.
Wh., gryh., yelh., grnh., brnh.	Vitreous to pearly	2 –3	2.7–3.0	4½–5	Mon.; foliated, flaky, scaly	C. 1, basal, per. Flakes tough, elastic
Apple-grn., gry., wh.	Greasy; C. pearly	1–2.5 (Somet. 3 –4)	2.5–2.8	5	Mon.; us. foliated, gran., comp.	C. 1, basal, per. Sectile Flakes flex. F. uneven
Pink, gry., wh., yelh.	Vitreous; C. pearly	3½–4½	3.0–3.1	4–4½	Mon.; scaly, micaceous	C. 1, basal, per. Flakes brittle

			Name.	Composition.
FELDSPAR Group. — G. 2.5–2.8. 2 cl. at 90° or nearly so; lt. col. Fus. quietly; H. near 6	K flame, w. gypsum	Microcline may show striations on cl. or xl. faces; adularia transp. or opalescent; sanidine glassy	ORTHOCLASE (Potash Feldspar; adularia; sanidine) (See p. 38)	$KAlSi_3O_8$ (Na iso. w. K) (Sanidine contains Na)
			MICROCLINE (See p. 38)	$KAlSi_3O_8$ (Na iso. w. K)
	Strong Na flame w. gypsum; little or no K	Us. fine striations on best cleavage; these *Plagioclase Feldspars* form a continuous series from albite to anorthite. Labradorite and bytownite slightly sol. in HCl; amorthite slowly sol. giving gel. sil. Distinguished by sp. gr.	ALBITE (Soda Feldspar) (See p. 38)	$NaAlSi_3O_8$ (Us. some Ca; often K)
			OLIGOCLASE (Na-Ca Feldspar) (See p. 38)	$m(NaAlSi_3O_8)$ $n(CaAl_2Si_2O_8)$ ($m: n = 6: 1$ to $3: 1$)
			ANDESINE (Na-Ca Feldspar) (See p. 38)	$m(NaAlSi_3O_8)$ $n(CaAl_2Si_2O_8)$ ($m: n = 3: 1$ to $1: 1$)
			LABRADORITE (Ca-Na Feldspar) (See p. 38)	$m(NaAlSi_3O_8)$ $n(CaAl_2Si_2O_8)$ ($m: n = 1: 1$ to $1: 3$)
			BYTOWNITE (Ca-Na Feldspar) (See p. 38)	$m(NaAlSi_3O_8)$ $n(CaAl_2Si_2O_8)$ ($m: n = 1: 3$ to $1: 6$)
			ANORTHITE (Lime Feldspar) (See p. 38)	$CaAl_2Si_2O_8$ (Us. some Na)
AMPHIBOLE Group.—G. 2.9–3.4. Prism and cl. angles 56° and 124°. Xls. us. prismatic, often divergent or radial-columnar. Separate xls. us. 6-sided, vertically striated, and terminated by 2 planes. Fus. quietly or w. little intumes.	Fus. to dark shiny globule; us. intumes. slightly and gives Na flame		HORNBLENDE (See p. 54)	$Ca(Mg,Fe)_3(SiO_3)_4$ (Also Al, Na; often H, F)
	Fus. to grnh. or brnh. globule; but little Na flame; sometimes asbestiform (fibrous)		ACTINOLITE (Nephrite or Jade in part) (See p. 71)	$Ca(Mg,Fe)_3(SiO_3)_4$
	Fus. to cols. or nearly cols. glass; sometimes asbestiform (fibrous)		TREMOLITE (Asbestos in part; (Nephrite or Jade in part) (See p. 37)	$CaMg_3(SiO_3)_4$ (Somet. Fe)
	Dif. fus. (5–6); sometimes asbestiform (fibrous)		*Anthophyllite* (Asbestos in part) (See p. 54)	$(Mg,Fe)SiO_3$ (Somet. also Al)

Color.	Luster.	Hardness.	Specific Gravity.	Fusibility.	Crystallization and Structure.	Cleavage and Fracture.
Cols., wh., cream, flesh-red, gry., grn.	Vitreous to pearly	6	2.57	5	Mon.; Figs. 50–52	C. 2, basal, per. and pinac. 90°
		6–6½	2.54–2.57	5	Tri.	C. 2, basal, per. and pinac. 89° 30'
Cols., wh., gry., grnh., bluish, redh. Often a beautiful play of colors on (010), most notable in labradorite		6–6½	2.62–2.64	4–4½	Tri.; Fig. 54	C. 2, basal, per. and pinac. 86° 24'
		6–6½	2.65–2.67	3½–4	Tri.; us. comp.	C. 2, basal, per. and pinac. 86° 32'
		5–6	2.68–2.69	3½–4	Tri.; us. comp.	C. 2, basal, per. and pinac. 86° 14'
		5–6	2.70–2.72	3–3½	Tri.; us. comp.	C. 2, basal, per. and pinac. 86° 4'
		5–6	2.73–2.75	3½	Tri.; us. comp.	C. 2, basal, per. and pinac. 85° 58'
		6–6½	2.75–2.76	4½–5	Tri.	C. 2, basal, per. and pinac. 85° 50'
Grn. to blk.	Vitreous to pearly	5–6	2.9–3.4	3–4	Mon.; us. prism. xls.; gran.	C. 2, prism. per., 56° F. uneven, splint.
Grn. of various shades	Vitreous to pearly	5–6	3.0–3.2	4	Mon.; slender prism., radiating	C. 2, prism. per., 56° F. uneven, splint. Fibers flex.
Wh., gry.	Vitreous to pearly	5–6	2.9–3.1	4	Mon., bladed, fibr., comp.	C. 2, prism. per., 56° F. uneven Fibers flex.
Gry., clove-brn., grn.	Vitreous to pearly	5–6	3.1–3.2	5–6	Orth.; us. fibr. or lamellar	C. 2, prism. per., 54½° F. splint. Fibers flex.

		Name.	Composition.
PYROXENE Group. —G. 3.0–3.7. Prism and cleav. angles 87° and 93°; cleav. not very pronounced. Xls. us. nearly square prism w. truncated edges 4- or 8-sided. Basal parting often distinct. Fus. quietly or w. little intumes.	Dif. fus. (6); luster often metalloidal (Cp. hypersthene)	ENSTATITE (Bronzite) (See p. 37)	$(Mg,Fe)SiO_3$ (FeO up to 12%)
	Fus. to cols. or nearly cols. glass	DIOPSIDE (See p. 37)	$CaMg(SiO_3)_2$ (Fe iso. w. Mg)
	Fus. to grnh. or brnh. glass; col. deepens w. increase of Fe. Diallage is lamellar to fibrous w. pearly to metalloidal luster	PYROXENE (Diallage) (See p. 74)	$Ca(Mg,Fe)(SiO_3)_2$
	Fus. to shiny blk. glass; often Na flame; contains Al and ferric Fe	AUGITE (See p. 74)	$Ca(Mg,Fe)(SiO_3)_2$ (Also Al, somet. Mn, Na)
	Fus. readily to transp. blebby glass, Na flame. Us. in very tough compact mass	JADEITE (Jade in part) (See p. 50)	$NaAl(SiO_3)_2$
	Swells and fus. to clear or wh. glass; Li flame (may be obscured by Na)	SPODUMENE (Hidenite; Kunzite) (See p. 39)	$LiAl(SiO_3)_2$ (Some Na)
	Mn in soda bead; fus. to nearly blk. glass	RHODONITE (See p. 62)	$MnSiO_3$ (Some Fe, Ca)
	Mn in soda; Zn w. soda on Pt. wire. (See p. 126)	*Fowlerite* (See p. 62)	Zn-rhodonite
		Jeffersonite	Zn-Mn-Pyroxene

SECTION 24.   Nonmetallic luster; fus. 1-5; no metal on ch.; not

Gel. w. HCl after fus.; iso. xls.; red color		SPESSARTITE (Mn Garnet) (See p. 70)	$Mn_3Al_2(SiO_4)_3$ (Us. also Fe and Ca)
Do not gel. after fus.; 2 cl. nearly 90°	Fus. to nearly blk. glass	RHODONITE (See p. 62)	$MnSiO_3$ (Fe, Ca iso. w. Mn)
	Wh. ZnO subl. w. soda on Pt. wire (slight); grn. w. $Co(NO_3)_2$	*Fowlerite* (Zn Rhodonite) (See p. 62)	$(Mn,Zn)SiO_3$ (Fe, Ca, Mg iso. w. Mn)
		Jeffersonite (Mn-Zn Pyroxene) (See p. 74)	$(Ca,Mn)(Mg,Fe,Zn)$ $(SiO_3)_2$

Color.	Luster.	Hard-ness.	Specific Gravity.	Fusi-bility.	Crystallization and Structure.	Cleavage and Fracture.
Yelh., gry., brn., grn.	Pearly to bronzy	5 –6	3.1–3.3	5–6	Orth.; us. lamellar	C. 2, prism., 88°, poor F. uneven
Cols., wh., pale grn.	Vitreous	5 –6	3.2–3.6	4	Mon.; us. xls., Figs. 47, 48	C. 2, prism, 87°, poor
Lt. to dk. grn.	Vitreous	5 –6	3.2–3.6	4	Mon.; us. xls., Figs. 47, 48	C. 2, prism, 87°, poor F. uneven
Grnh-blk to blk.	Vitreous	5 –6	3.2–3.6	3–4	Mon., gran., columnar	C. 2, prism, 87°, poor F. uneven
Wh., gryh., grnh.	Vitreous; C. pearly	$5\frac{1}{2}$–$6\frac{1}{2}$	3.0–3.3	2.5	Mon.; comp.	F. splint,. tough
Wh., gry., pink, emerald-grn., purple	Vitreous; pearly	6 –7	3.1–3.2	$3\frac{1}{2}$	Mon.; cleavable, comp.	C. 2, prism, per., 87° F. uneven, splint.
Rose-red, pink, brn.	Vitreous	$5\frac{1}{2}$–$6\frac{1}{2}$	3.4–3.7	$2\frac{1}{2}$–3	Tri.; us. gran., comp.	C. 2, prism., per., $87\frac{1}{2}$° F. uneven, conch.
(See below)						
(See below)						

mag. after r.f.; not alk. after ign.; insol. in HCl; Mn reac. in soda bead

Brnh-red to hyacinth-red	Vitreous	$6\frac{1}{2}$–$7\frac{1}{2}$	4.0–4.3	3	Iso.; us. xls.	F. uneven, conch.
Rose-red pink, brn.	Vitreous	$5\frac{1}{2}$–$6\frac{1}{2}$	3.4–3.7	$2\frac{1}{2}$–3	Tri.; us. gran., comp.	C. 2, prism. per., $87\frac{1}{2}$° F. uneven, conch.
Rose-red	Vitreous	$5\frac{1}{2}$–$6\frac{1}{2}$	3.7	$2\frac{1}{2}$–3	Tri.; gran., comp.	C. 2, prism. per., $87\frac{1}{2}$° F. uneven, conch.
Grnh-blk to brn.	Vitreous	5 –6	3.4–3.6	3–$3\frac{1}{2}$	Mon.; xls., gran., comp.	C. 2, prism., 87° F. uneven

	Name.	Composition.
Cb. reac. after fus. w. borax; samarskite gives U reac. in s.ph. bd.	COLUMBITE (See p. 84)	$(Fe,Mn)Cb_2O_6$ (Also Ta, and some Sn and W)
W. reac. after fus. w. soda — W. little soda on ch. becomes mag.	WOLFRAMITE (See p. 26)	$(Fe,Mn)WO_4$
Little or no Fe	HUEBNERITE (See p. 26)	$MnWO_4$ (Some Fe)

SECTION 25.   Nonmetallic luster; fus. 1-5; no metal on ch.; not

		Name.	Composition.
Li flame; may be yelh-red or obscured by Na	Swells and fus. to clear or wh. glass. Hiddenite (emerald-green) and kunzite (lilac) are transp.	SPODUMENE (Hiddenite; Kunzite) (See p. 39)	$LiAl(SiO_3)_2$ (Na iso. w. Li)
	P reac. after fus. w. soda Fus. easily w. intumes. to wh. globule	AMBLYGONITE (See p. 38)	$Li(AlF)PO_4$ (Na iso. w. Li; OH w. F)
B flame (Cp. axinite, below)	Rdh. phosphorescence on heating; fus. to cols. glass	DANBURITE (See p. 71)	$CaB_2(SiO_4)_2$
	Fus. w. intumes. to wh. globule; Cl reac. w. CuO on ch.	BORACITE (See p. 52)	$Mg_7Cl_2B_{16}O_{30}$
B flame w. $KHSO_4$ and fluorite	Fus. w. intumes. and pale B flame	AXINITE (See p. 35)	$HCa_3Al_2B(SiO_4)_4$ (Mn, Fe, Mg iso. w. Ca)
	Fus. w. intumes. to blebby glass or slag. Pyroelectric, especially lighter colored varieties. Achroite cols.; indicolite blue; rubellite red	TOURMALINE (See p. 59)	$R_9Al_3(BOH)_2(SiO_5)_4$ (R = Mg, Fe, Ca, Na, K, Li; often some F)

Color.	Luster.	Hardness.	Specific Gravity.	Fusibility.	Crystallization and Structure.	Cleavage and Fracture.
Fe-blk. to gry. and brnh-blk.	Res. to submet.	6	5.3–6.5	5–5½	Orth.; short prism. xls.	C. 1, pinac., poor F. uneven, conch.
Dk. gryh-blk. to brnh. blk.	Res. to submet.	5 –5½	7.2–7.5	3–3½	Mon.; us. xls., gran.	C. 1, pinac. per. F. uneven
Brn. to bnh-blk.	Resinous	5 –5½	6.9–7.4	4	Mon.; us. xls.	C. 1, pinac. per. F. uneven

mag. after r.f.; not alk. after ign.; insol. in HCl; not previously included

Color.	Luster.	Hardness.	Specific Gravity.	Fusibility.	Crystallization and Structure.	Cleavage and Fracture.
Wh., gry., pink, emerald-grn., purple	Vitreous to pearly	6 –7	3.1–3.2	3½	Mon.; cleavable, comp.	C. 1, prism. per., 87° F. uneven, splint. P. 1, pinac.
Wh. to pale grn., or blue	Vitreous to greasy; C. pearly	6	3.0–3.1	2	Tri.; us. mass.	C. 1, basal, per. F. uneven
Wh. to pale yel., yelh-brn. and cols.	Vitreous	7 –7½	3.0	3½	Orth.; us. xls. like topaz	F. uneven, conch.
Cols., wh., gry., yel., grn.	Vitreous	7	2.9–3.0	2	Iso. tetrh.; us. isolated xls.	F. uneven, conch.
Clove-brn., gry., grn., yel., blk.	Vitreous	6 –7	3.2–3.4	2–2½	Tri. xls., Fig. 53 tabular	C. 1, pinac. F. conch.
Blk., brn., grn., blue, red, pink, wh.	Vitreous to resinous	7 –7½	3.0–3.2	3–5	Hex. rhom. hemimor.; Fig. 58; prism., curved triangular cross-section	F. conch., uneven

		Name.	Composition.
GARNET Group.— Fus. quietly (except uvarovite) and gel. w. HCl after fus. Us. dodecahedrons and trapezohedrons. (Figs. 3, 7, 8). No cleavage; parting somet. distinct 6 directions, 60°, 90°, 120° (110)	Ca (grossularite) or Mg (pyrope) ppt. after fus. w. soda and separating Si and Al (See Silicon (2), p. 129)	GROSSULARITE (Ca-Al Garnet) (See p. 70)	$Ca_3Al_2(SiO_4)_3$ (Often Fe, Mg, Mn)
		PYROPE (Mg-Al Garnet) (See p. 70)	$Mg_3Al_2(SiO_4)_3$ (Often Fe, Ca, Cr)
	Fus. to mag. globule	ALMANDITE (Fe-Al Garnet) (See p. 70)	$Fe_3Al_2(SiO_4)_3$ (Mn, Mg, Ca iso. w. Fe)
	Mn in borax bd. (strong)	SPESSARTITE (Mn Garnet) (See p. 70)	$Mn_3Al_2(SiO_4)_3$ (Fe, Ca iso. w. Mn; Fe iso. w. Al)
	Partially sol. in HCl w. gel. sil.	ANDRADITE (Ca-Fe Garnet) (See p. 70)	$Ca_3Fe_2(SiO_4)_3$ (Fe, Mn, Mg iso. w. Ca; Al iso. w. Fe)
Fus. dif. and quietly	Whitens and fus. to vesic. scoria; varieties with Na, Li, Cs, more fus.	BERYL (Emerald, deep green; Aquamarine, pale) (See p. 81)	$Gl_3Al_2(SiO_3)_6$ (Some H; somet. Na, Li, Cs, Ca)
	A little H_2O on intense ign. of powder in c.t.	CORDIERITE (Iolite) (See p. 73)	$(Mg,Fe)_4Al_8(OH)_2$ $(Si_2O_7)_5$
Fus. w. intumes.	To grnh. or brnh. glass; gel. w. HCl after fus.	VESUVIANITE (See p. 70)	$Ca_6Al_3(OH,F)(SiO_4)_5$ (Mg, Fe, Mn iso. w. Ca)
	To wh. blebby glass; strong Na flame; AgCl ppt. w. $AgNO_3$ in dil. HNO_3 sol. after fus. w. soda	WERNERITE (Scapolite) (See p. 43)	$n(Ca_4Al_6Si_6O_{25})$ $m(Na_4Al_3Si_9O_{24}Cl)$ (n: m = 3: 1 to 1: 2)
	To wh. blebby glass; gel. w. HCl after fus. H_2O in c.t.	PREHNITE (See p. 81)	$H_2Ca_2Al_2(SiO_4)_3$ (Fe iso. w. Al)
	To a slag which gel. w. HCl; a little H_2O on intense ign. in c.t.	Lt. col. slag — ZOISITE (See p. 35)	$Ca_2Al_3(OH)(SiO_4)_3$
(Concluded on next page)		Brn. or blk. slag; us. mag. — EPIDOTE (Pistacite) (See p. 61)	$Ca_2(Al,Fe)_3(OH)$ $(SiO_4)_3$

Color.	Luster.	Hardness.	Specific Gravity.	Fusibility.	Crystallization and Structure.	Cleavage and Fracture.
Pale red, yel., grn., wh.	Vitreous	$6\frac{1}{2}$–$7\frac{1}{2}$	3.5–3.6	3	Iso.; us. xls., Figs. 3, 7, 8	F. uneven to conch.
Deep red to redh-blk., rarely purple	Vitreous	$6\frac{1}{2}$–$7\frac{1}{2}$	3.7–3.8	$3\frac{1}{2}$–4	Iso.; us. xls., Figs. 3, 7, 8	F. uneven to conch.
Deep red to brnh-blk.	Vitreous	$6\frac{1}{2}$–$7\frac{1}{2}$	3.9–4.2	3	Iso.; us. xls., Figs. 3, 7, 8	F. uneven, conch.
Brnh-red to hyacinth-red	Vitreous	$6\frac{1}{2}$–$7\frac{1}{2}$	4.0–4.3	3	Iso.; us. xls., Figs. 3, 7, 8	F. uneven to conch.
Wine-red, grnh., yel., brn. to blk.	Vitreous to resinous	$6\frac{1}{2}$–$7\frac{1}{2}$	3.8–3.9	$3\frac{1}{2}$	Iso.; us. xls., Figs. 3, 7, 8	F. uneven to conch.
Grn., blue, yel., pink, cols.	Vitreous to resinous	$7\frac{1}{2}$–8	2.6–2.8	5–$5\frac{1}{2}$	Hex.; us. prism. xls., Fig. 27	C. indistinct F. conch. to uneven
Blue to violet and cols.	Vitreous	7 –$7\frac{1}{2}$	2.6–2.7	5–$5\frac{1}{2}$	Orth.; pseudohex. xls., gran.	C. 1, pinac. F. conch., uneven P. 1, basal
Grn., brn., yel.	Vitreous to resinous	$6\frac{1}{2}$	3.3–3.5	3	Tetr. Figs. 23, 24; gran.	F. uneven
Wh., gry., grnh., bluish, redh.	Vitreous to pearly	5 –6	2.6–2.8	3	Tetr.; stout prism., comp., gran.	C. 3, prism. and pinac., poor F. uneven, conch.
Apple-grn., gry., wh.	Vitreous	6 –$6\frac{1}{2}$	2.8–3.0	2	Orth.; us. reniform	F. uneven
Gryh-wh., grn., pink, yelh-brn.	Vitreous; C. pearly	6 –$6\frac{1}{2}$	3.2–3.4	3–4	Orth.; columnar, bladed	C. 1, pinac. per. F. uneven
Yelh. to blkh-grn., gry.	Vitreous	6 –7	3.2–3.5	3–4	Mon.; us. prism.	C. 1, basal, per. F. uneven

		Name.	Composition.
Fus. w. slight intumes. to colored glass	Ti reac. w. H_2O_2	TITANITE (Sphene) (See p. 62)	$CaSiTiO_5$ (Some Fe; Somet. Mn)
Exfoliates and fus. w. dif. Greasy feel	Pink col. after ign. w. $Co(NO_3)_2$; us. gives H_2O in c.t. on intense ign.	TALC (Steatite, Soapstone) (See p. 32)	$H_2Mg_3(SiO_3)_4$

SECTION 26.   Nonmetallic luster;

CARBO-NATES.— CO_2 efferv. in dil. HCl.	Sr flame; swells and throws out fine branches on intense ign.	Wh. ppt. $SrSO_4$ w. dil. H_2SO_4 in dil. HC. sol.	STRONTIANITE (See p. 36)	$SrCO_3$ (Somet. Ca iso. w. Sr)
(Cp. also the carbonates on the next page, particularly rhodochrosite and siderite which may contain some Ca and give alkaline reaction after ignition.)	Ca flame w. HCl; dil. H_2SO_4 gives wh. ppt. $CaSO_4$ in conc. HCl sol. but not in very dil. sol., showing presence of Ca and absence of Sr and Ba.(Abundant ppt. w. am. oxalate. See p. 120)	Lumps efferv. freely in cold dil. HCl. Aragonite powder colored lavender on boiling in $Co(NO_3)_2$ sol.; decrepitates b.b.	CALCITE (Calc Spar; Marble Limestone; Chalk.) (See p. 40)	$CaCO_3$ (Mg, Fe, Mn, Pb iso. w. Ca)
			ARAGONITE (See p. 41)	$CaCO_3$ (Sr, Pb iso. w. Ca)
		Lumps efferv. freely in hot but not in cold dil. HCl; sol. reac. for Mg after ppt. of Ca	DOLOMITE (Pearl Spar) (See p. 41)	$CaMg(CO_3)_2$ (Fe, Mn iso. w. Mg)
		Becomes blk. and slightly mag. on ign.	*Ankerite* (Fe Dolomite) (See p. 41)	$Ca(Mg,Fe)(CO_3)_2$ (Mn iso. w. Mg)
		Much H_2O in c.t.; wh. $BaSO_4$ ppt. w. $BaCl_2$ in dil. HCl sol.	*Thaumasite*	$CaCO_3 \cdot CaSiO_3 \cdot$ $CaSO_4 \cdot 15H_2O$
	Contains Mg— Little or no ppt. w. am. oxalate in HCl sol., but much w. Na phosphate. Alkaline reac. w. turmeric paper may be weak	Scarcely affected by cold dil. HCl. Wh. fragments become pale pink on ign. w. $Co(NO_3)_2$. Breunnerite gives much $Fe(OH)_3$ ppt. w. am. after boiling HCl sol. w. a drop of HNO_3, Hydromagnesite gives much H_2O in c.t.	MAGNESITE (See p. 42)	$MgCO_3$ (Somet. Fe, Mn)
			Hydromagnesite (See p. 42)	$Mg_2(MgOH)_2(CO_3)_3 \cdot$ $3H_2O$

Color.	Luster.	Hardness.	Specific Gravity.	Fusibility.	Crystallization and Structure.	Cleavage and Fracture.
Gry., brn., yel., grn.	Resinous to adamant.	$5-5\frac{1}{2}$	3.4–3.6	3	Mon.; us. tabular, wedge-shape xls.	C. 2, prism, $66\frac{1}{2}°$ F. uneven P. 4, pyram.
Apple-grn., gry., wh.	Greasy; C. pearly	$1-2\frac{1}{2}$ (somet. $3-4$)	2.5–2.8	5	Mon.; us. foliated, comp., gran.	C. 1, basal, per. F. uneven; sectile, thin flakes flex.

fus. above 5; alk. after ign.

Color.	Luster.	Hardness.	Specific Gravity.	Fusibility.	Crystallization and Structure.	Cleavage and Fracture.
Wh., gry., yel., grn.	Vitreous	$3\frac{1}{2}-4$	3.7		Orth.; us. columnar; xls. pseudohex.	C. 2, prism., 63° F. uneven
Cols., wh., and variously tinted	Vitreous	3	2.7		Hex. rhom.; Figs. 52–57	C. 3, rhom. per., 75° F. conch., seldom observable
Cols., wh., and variously tinted	Vitreous	$3\frac{1}{2}-4$	2.9–3.0		Orth.; often pseudohex.	C. 3, pinac., poor F. uneven
Cols., wh., and variously tinted	Vitreous to pearly	$3\frac{1}{2}-4$	2.8–2.9		Hex. rhom.; gran., comp.; xl. faces curved	C. 3, rhom. per., 74° F. conch. uneven
Brn., gry., redh., seldom wh.	Vitreous to pearly	$3\frac{1}{2}-4$	2.9–3.1		Hex. rhom.	C. 3, rhom. per., 74°
Wh., cols.	Vitreous to dull	$3\frac{1}{2}$	1.8–1.9		Hex.; fibr. or mass.	F. splint., uneven
Wh., yel., gry., brn.	Vitreous, silky, dull	$3\frac{1}{2}-4\frac{1}{2}$	3.0–3.1		Hex. rhom.; us. comp., gran.	C. 3, rhom. per., $72\frac{1}{2}°$ F. conch.
Wh.	Vitreous to silky	$3\frac{1}{2}$	2.1–2.2		Mon.; us. acic.	

			Name.	Composition.
Sol. quietly in warm HCl	Glows on ign.; becomes pale pink if previously moistened w. $Co(NO_3)_2$		BRUCITE (See p. 32)	$Mg(OH)_2$ (Fe, Mn iso. w. Mg)
Sulphates.— Acid H_2O in c.t. and SO_2 odor after intense ign.	Al reac. w. $Co(NO_3)_2$	Slowly attacked by HCl; decrepitates b.b.	ALUNITE (See p. 49)	$KAl_3(OH)_6(SO_4)_2$ (Na iso. w. K)

SECTION 27. Nonmetallic luster; fus. above 5; not

CARBO-NATES.— CO_2 efferv. in dil. HCl	Mn in borax bd.; decrepitates b.b.	Sometimes enough Fe to make mag. on ch.	RHODOCHROSITE (See p. 64)	$MnCO_3$ (Ca, Fe, Mg, Zn iso. w. Mn)
	Wh. ZnO subl. w. soda on Pt wire; grn. subl. w. $Co(NO_3)_2$ (See p. 134)	Little or no H_2O in c.t.	SMITHSONITE (See p. 43)	$ZnCO_3$ (Often Fe, Mn; somet. Ca, Mg)
		H_2O in c.t.; Cu flame w. HCl	*Aurichalcite*	$(Zn,Cu)_5(OH)_6(CO_3)_2$
		H_2O in c.t.; no Cu	*Hydrozincite* (See p. 47)	$Zn_3(OH)_4CO_3$
	Becomes blk. and mag. on ign.; much ferrous Fe	Decrep. in c. t.; little or no Mg or Ca	SIDERITE (Spathic Iron) (See p. 41)	$FeCO_3$ (Ca, Mg, Mn iso. w. Fe)
	Mg reac. in HCl sol. after removing Fe and Ca (See Magnesium (3), p. 125)	Little or no H_2O in c.t.	MAGNESITE (See p. 42)	$MgCO_3$ (Somet. Fe, Mn)
		Much H_2O in c.t.	*Hydromagnesite* (See p. 42)	$Mg_4(OH)_2(CO_3)_3 \cdot 3H_2O$
SULPHIDES. —H_2S efferv. in hot HCl	Wh. ZnO subl. after intense ign. w. soda on Pt wire; subl. grn. w. $Co(NO_3)_2$. (See p. 134)		SPHALERITE (Zinc Blende) (See p. 64.)	ZnS (Fe, Mn, Cd iso. w. Zn)
	Red-brn. CdO subl. after intense ign. w. soda on ch.		GREENOCKITE (See p. 85)	CdS
SULPHATES. —Wh. ppt. $BaSO_4$ w. $BaCl_2$ in HCl sol.	Al reac. w. $Co(NO_3)_2$ on ch.	Sol. in H_2O; no flame react.; alum taste	*Alunogen*	$Al_2(SO_4)_3 \cdot 18H_2O$

Color.	Luster.	Hardness.	Specific Gravity.	Crystallization and Structure.	Cleavage and Fracture.
Wh., gry., grn., blue	Waxy, vitr.; C. pearly	$2\frac{1}{2}$	2.3–2.4	Hex. rhom.; us. foliated	C. 1, basal, per. Sectile; flakes flex.
Wh., gry., redh.	Vitreous	$3\frac{1}{2}$–4	2.6–2.8	Hex. rhom.	C. 1, basal, poor F. uneven

alk. after ign.; sol. in HCl without res. or gel. sil.

Color.	Luster.	Hardness.	Specific Gravity.	Crystallization and Structure.	Cleavage and Fracture.
Rose-red, dk. red, brn.	Vitreous to pearly	$3\frac{1}{2}$–$4\frac{1}{2}$	3.4–3.6	Hex. rhom.; gran., comp.	C. 3, rhom. per., 73° F. uneven
Brn., grn., blue, pink, wh.	Vitreous	5	4.3–4.5	Hex. rhom.; us. botry., incrust., cellular	C. 3, rhom. per., 72° F. uneven, splint.
Pale grn. to blue	Pearly	2	3.5–3.6	Mon.; us. acic., gran., laminated	F. splint.
Wh., gry., yel.	Dull	2 –$2\frac{1}{2}$	3.6–3.8	Earthy, compact, fibr.	F. uneven, splint.
Gry. and brn. of different shades	Vitreous to pearly	$3\frac{1}{2}$–4	3.8–3.9	Hex. rhom.; gran., comp.	C. 3, rhom. per., 73° F. uneven
Wh., yel., gry., brn.	Vitreous, silky, dull	$3\frac{1}{2}$–$4\frac{1}{2}$	3.0–3.1	Hex. rhom.; gran., comp.	C. 3, rhom. per., $72\frac{1}{2}$° F. conch.
White	Vitreous to silky	$3\frac{1}{2}$	2.1–2.2	Mon.; us. acic., bladed, chalky	F. splint., uneven
Wh., grn., yel., red, brn., blk.	Resinous to adamant.	$3\frac{1}{2}$–4	3.9–4.1	Iso. tetr.; gran., comp.	C. 6 , dodec. per., 60°, 90°, 120° F. conch.
Honey-, citron-, or orange-yel.	Resinous to adamant.	3 –$3\frac{1}{2}$	4.9–5.0	Hex. hemimor.; us. incrust.	C. 3, prism., 60°, poor F. conch.
Wh., yelh., redh.	Vitreous to silky	$1\frac{1}{2}$–2	1.6–1.8	Mon.; us. fibr., incrust.	F. splint.

			Name.	Composition.
Blackens and becomes strongly mag. b.b.; fus. 5–6 in fine splinters; slowly sol. in HCl to yel.sol.which reacts for ferric Fe	St. brnh.-red	Little or no H_2O in c.t.	HEMATITE (See p. 84)	Fe_2O_3 (Somet. Tl, Mg)
		H_2O in c.t.; us. decrepitates	TURGITE (See p. 85)	$FeO \cdot OH, Fe_2O_3, H_2O$
	St. yelh.-brn. H_2O in c.t.	Us. prismatic xls.	GOETHITE (See p. 89)	$FeO \cdot OH$
		Amorphous, mammillary, botryoidal, stalactitic	LIMONITE (Brown Hematite; Bog Iron Ore) (See p. 83)	$FeO \cdot OH \cdot nH_2O$ (Often clay, sand, etc.)
Mn in borax bd.	Wh. ZnO subl. w. soda on Pt wire after intense ign.; subl. grn. w. $Co(NO_3)_2$. (See p. 134)		ZINCITE (Red Zinc Ore) (See p. 88)	ZnO (Mn iso. w. Zn)
	Earthy, powdery, frothy; H_2O in c.t.		WAD (Bog Manganese) (See p. 26)	MnO, MnO_2, H_2O (Often Fe, Si, Al, Ba)
P. reac. w. am. mol.	Cu flame		TURQUOIS (See p. 81)	$Al_2(OH)_3PO_4 \cdot H_2O$ (Some Cu)
	Wh. $CaSO_4$ ppt. w. H_2SO_4 in cold conc. HCl sol. F reac. w. H_2SO_4		APATITE (See p. 68)	$Ca_5F(PO_4)_3$ (Cl iso. w. F)
	Al reac. w. $Co(NO_3)_2$ on ch.		WAVELLITE (See p. 80)	$(AlOH)_3(PO_4)_2 \cdot 5H_2O$ (Some F iso. w. OH)
Much Mg; no Ca. See Magnesium (3), p. 125. Sectile	Brilliant glow on intense ign.; Mg reac. w. $Co(NO_3)_2$ on ch. if mineral is light colored		BRUCITE (See p. 32)	$Mg(OH)_2$ (Fe, Mn iso. w. Mg)

SECTION 28. Nonmetallic luster; fus. above

Wh. ZnO subl. w. soda on Pt wire. Grn. subl. w. $Co(NO_3)_2$ (See p. 134)	Decrep. and gives H_2O in c.t.; pyroelectric; almost infus. (fus. 6)		CALAMINE (Smithsonite) (See pp. 36, 43)	$(ZnOH)_2SiO_3$
	Little or no H_2O in c.t.	No H_2S on sol. in HCl (Cp. troostite, p. 168)	WILLEMITE (See p. 65)	Zn_2SiO_4 (Mn, Fe iso. w. Zn)

Color.	Luster.	Hardness.	Specific Gravity.	Crystallization and Structure.	Cleavage and Fracture.
Red to redh-blk.	Dull to submet.	$5\frac{1}{2}$–$6\frac{1}{2}$	4.9–5.3	Mass.; earthy Hex. rhom.	F. uneven splint.
Red to redh-blk.	Dull to submet.	$5\frac{1}{2}$–6	4.2–4.7	Botry., crusts stalac., earthy	F. uneven, splint., earthy
Yel. or redh-brn. to blk.	Dull to adamant.	5 –$5\frac{1}{2}$	4.0–4.4	Orth.; acic. or scaly	C. 1, pinac. per. F. splint., uneven
Yel., brn. to brnh. blk. blk.	Dull, silky	5 –$5\frac{1}{2}$	3.6–4.0	Mass., fibr., botry., earthy	F. splint., uneven
Deep red to orange-yel. St. yel.	Adamant.	4 –$4\frac{1}{2}$	5.4–5.7	Hex. hemimor.; us. gran., lamellar	C. 1, basal, per. F. uneven
Bluish or brnh-blk. to dull	Dull	1 –6	3.0–4.3	Earthy, amorph., comp.	F. earthy
Blue, bluish-grn., grn.	Waxy	$5\frac{1}{2}$–6	2.6–2.8	Tri.; incrust., comp.	F. conch.
Grn., blue, violet, brn., yelh., cols.	Vitreous to subres.	$4\frac{1}{2}$–5	3.1–3.2	Hex., us. prisms; gran.	C. 1, basal, poor, to distinct F. uneven, conch.
Wh., yel., grn., brn.	Vitreous to pearly	$3\frac{1}{2}$–4	2.3–2.4	Orth; us. radiating	C. 3, pinac., 73°, 90° F. uneven, conch.
Wh., gry., grn., blue	Waxy, vitreous; C. pearly	2 –$2\frac{1}{2}$	2.3–2.4	Hex. rhom.; us. foliated	C. 1, basal, per.; flakes and fibers flex.

5; not alk. after ign.; sol. in HCl w. gel. sil.

Color.	Luster.	Hardness.	Specific Gravity.	Crystallization and Structure.	Cleavage and Fracture.
Wh., pale-grn., blue	Vitreous	$4\frac{1}{2}$–5	3.4–3.5	Orth. hemimor., cockscomb groups, tabular	C. 2, prism. per., 76° F. uneven, conch.
Yel., red., grn., brn., wh., cols.	Vitreous	5 –6	3.9–4.2	Hex. rhom.; comp., gran.	C. 3, prism., 60°, 120° F. uneven, conch.

		Name.	Composition.
Cu globule w. soda on ch.	H_2O in c.t.	DIOPTASE (See p. 91)	H_2CuSiO_4
Fe in borax bd.; little or no H_2O in c.t. (Cp. next two minerals, which often contain a little Fe)	Much Mg but no Al or Ca in HCl sol. (See Magnesium (3), p. 125)	OLIVINE (Chrysolite, Peridot) (See p. 63)	$(Mg,Fe)_2SiO_4$ (Somet. a little Ni, Sn, Ti)
F react. w. KHSO$_4$; may react for Fe	A little H_2O on intense ign. in c.t.	CHONDRODITE (See p. 69)	$Mg_5(F,OH)_2(SiO_4)_2$ (Some Fe)
Al reac. w. Co(NO$_3$)$_2$ on ch.	Much H_2O in c.t.; crumbles on ign.	ALLOPHANE (See p. 48)	$Al_2SiO_5 \cdot 5H_2O$

SECTION 29. Nonmetallic luster; fus. above 5; not alk. after

Yel. WO$_3$ powder in boiling HCl	Ca reac. w. am. oxalate in HCl sol.	SCHEELITE (See p. 65)	$CaWO_4$ (Us. some Mo, somet. Cu)
Darkens and gives H_2O in c.t.	Cu globule w. soda on ch.	CHRYSOCOLLA (See p. 78)	$CuSiO_3 \cdot 2H_2O$
	Ni in borax bd.	GARNIERITE (Genthite) (See p. 78)	$H_2(Ni,Mg)SiO_4 \cdot nH_2O$
H_2O in c.t.; amorphous, fibrous or foliated	Us. compact grnh.; sometimes fibrous (chrysotile, commercial "asbestos") or foliated (marmolite)	SERPENTINE (Chrysotile; Marmolite) (See p. 79)	$H_4Mg_3Si_2O_9$ (Some Fe, somet. Ni)
	Compact; fine earthy texture; Mg reac. w. Co(NO$_3$)$_2$ on ch. Fus. = 5. Adheres to tongue	SEPIOLITE (Meerschaum) (See p. 47)	$H_4Mg_2Si_3O_{10}$ (Somet. Cu and Ni iso. w. Mg)
Al reac. w. Co(NO$_3$)$_2$ on ch.	K flame w. powdered gypsum; us. trapezohedrons	LEUCITE (See p. 50)	$KAl(SiO_3)_2$ (Na iso. w. K)

Color.	Luster.	Hardness.	Specific Gravity.	Crystallization and Structure.	Cleavage and Fracture.
Emerald-grn.	Vitreous	5	3.3–3.4	Hex. rhom.; us. prism.	C. 3, rhom. per. 54° F. conch., uneven
Olive-grn. to gryh-grn., brn.	Vitreous	6½–7	3.2–3.6	Orth.; Fig. 36; gran., dissem.	C. 2, pinac., 90° F. conch., uneven
Brnh-red., yel., wh.	Vitreous	6–6½	3.1–3.2	Mon.; comp., gran.	C. 1, basal F. uneven
Cols., yel., grn., blue	Vitreous to waxy	3	1.8–1.9	Amorph.; us. crusts	F. conch., earthy

ign.; decomposed by HCl w. separation of sil. or yel. WO₃ powder

Color.	Luster.	Hardness.	Specific Gravity.	Crystallization and Structure.	Cleavage and Fracture.
Wh., yel., grn., brn., redh.	Vitreous to adamant.	4½–5	5.9–6.1	Tetr.; xls. like oct., gran.	C. 4, pyram., 49½°, 80° F. uneven, conch.
Bluish-grn., grnh-blue, brn., blk.	Vitreous, earthy	2 –3	2.0–2.2	Amorph., comp.	F. conch. to uneven
Pale to deep grn., yelh.	Dull to resinous	1 –4	2.3–2.8	Amorph., botry., comp.	F. uneven, conch.
Olive-grn., blkh-grn., yelh-grn., wh.	Greasy, waxy, silky	3 –4	2.5–2.6	Comp., fibr.	F. conch., splint. Fibers flex., tough
Wh., to gryh-wh.	Dull	2 –2½	1.0–2.0	Compact; earthy	F. uneven, conch.
Wh., gry., cols.	Vitreous	5½–6	2.4–2.5	Iso.; us. trapezo., Fig. 3	F. uneven, conch.

		Name.	Composition.
Slowly attacked by hot HCl w. evolution of H₂S		Wh. ZnO subl. w. soda on Pt wire; grn. w. Co(NO₃)₂. (See p. 134)	SPHALERITE (Zinc Blende) (See p. 64)	ZnS (Fe, Mn, Cd iso. w. Zn)
Become strongly mag. on ign.		Slowly and dif. sol. in HCl	IRON ORES (See Sec. 12, p. 158)	
Micaceous or foliated	Flakes tough and elastic	Fus. w. dif.	MICA (See Sec. 22, p. 172)	
	Flakes flexible but not elastic (Cp. talc. and pyrophyllite, next page)	Much H₂O in c.t. on intense ign.; varieties rich in Fe become black and mag. (prochlorite)	CHLORITE (Clinochlore; Prochlorite) (See p. 72)	H,Fe,Mg,Al silicates (Often a little Cr)
	Flakes brittle ; H₂O in c.t.	Whitens and fus. w. dif. on thin edges	MARGARITE (Brittle Mica) (See p. 34)	H₂CaAl₄Si₂O₁₂ (Some Fe, Na, K)
Greasy feel ; very soft	A little H₂O in c.t. on intense ign. (Cp. kaolinite and bauxite, below)	Al reac. w. Co(NO₃)₂ on ch.; radiated variety exfoliates greatly b.b.	PYROPHYLLITE (See p. 32)	H₂Al₂(SiO₃)₄
		Mg reac. w. Co(NO₃)₂ on ch.; sectile	TALC (Steatite; Soapstone) (See p. 32)	H₂Mg₃(SiO₃)₄
P reac. w. am. mol. after fus. w. soda; us. pale blue-grn. flame		Monazite us. transp. or transl.; Xenotime is opaque	MONAZITE (See p. 69)	(Ce,La,Nd,Pr)PO₄ (Often Th, Yt)
		Al reac. w. Co(NO₃)₂ on ch.; us. radiated or globular	WAVELLITE (See p. 80)	(Al(OH)₃(PO₄)₂·5H₂O (F iso. w. OH)
		Cu flame; in c.t. decrepitates, yields H₂O, turns brn. or blk.	TURQUOIS (See p. 81)	Al₂(OH)₃PO₄·H₂O (Some Cu)
Fus. to clear glass w. equal amt. of soda on Pt wire		H₂O in c.t. at high temp.	OPAL (See p. 50)	SiO₂·nH₂O
Al reac. w. Co(NO₃)₂ on ch.		Little or no H₂O in c.t. H 4–5 lengthwise; 6–7 crosswise	CYANITE (Disthene) (See pp. 74, 194)	(AlO)₂SiO₃, or Al₂SiO₅
		H₂O in c.t.	Decrep. b.b.; SO₂ and acid H₂O at high temp. in c.t.	ALUNITE (See p. 49)	KAl₃(OH)₆(SO₄)₂ (Na iso. w. K)

Color.	Luster.	Hardness.	Specific Gravity.	Crystallization and Structure.	Cleavage and Fracture.
Wh., grn., yel., red, brn., blk.	Resinous to adamant.	$3\frac{1}{2}$–4	3.9–4.1	Iso. tetrh.; gran., comp.	C. 6, dodec. per., 60°, 90°, 120° F. conch.
Grn. of various shades	Vitreous to pearly	1 –$2\frac{1}{2}$	2.6–3.0	Mon.; scaly, foliated	C. 1, basal, per. Thin flakes flex.
Pink, gry., wh., yelh.	Vitreous; C. pearly	$3\frac{1}{2}$–$4\frac{1}{2}$	3.0–3.1	Mon.; scaly, micac., gran.	C. 1, basal, per.; thin flakes brittle
Wh., apple-grn., gry., yel., brn.	Pearly to dull	1 –2	2.8–2.9	Orth.; fol., fibr., radial	C. 1, basal, per.; thin flakes flexible F. uneven, splint.
Apple-grn., gry., wh.	Greasy; C. pearly	1 –$2\frac{1}{2}$	2.5–2.8	Mon. us.; fol., comp.	C. 1, basal, per.; sectile F. uneven Flakes flexible
Yelh-grn. to yelh- and redh-brn.	Resinous	5 –$5\frac{1}{2}$	4.9–5.3	Mon.; sands, dissem.	P. 1, basal F. uneven, conch.
Wh., yel., grn., brn.	Vitreous to pearly	$3\frac{1}{2}$–4	2.3–2.4	Orth.; us. radial	C. 3, pinac., 73°, 90° F. uneven, conch.
Blue, bluish-grn., grn.	Waxy	$5\frac{1}{2}$–6	2.6–2.8	Tri.; us. comp., incrust.	F. conch.
Cols., red, yel., grn., blue, gry.	Vitreous to resinous	$5\frac{1}{2}$–$6\frac{1}{2}$	2.1–2.2	Amorph., botry.	F. conch.
Blue, grn., gry., wh.; often streaked	Vitreous to pearly	4 –5 6 –7	3.5–3.7	Tri.; us. bladed	C. 2, pinac. per., 74°, 106° P. 1, basal F. splint.
Wh., gryh., redh.	Vitreous	$3\frac{1}{2}$–4	2.6–2.8	Hex. rhom.	C. 1, basal F. uneven

			Name.	Composition.
—*Concluded.*	H_2O in c.t.	Insol. sil. skeleton in s.ph.bd.; us. clay-like, compact, or mealy	KAOLINITE (Kaolin; Porcelain Clay) (See p. 44)	$H_4Al_2Si_2O_9$
		Wholly sol. in s.ph. bd. (Bauxite mark on glass with heavy pressure, adheres firmly)	BAUXITE (See p. 46)	Mixture $AlO \cdot OH$ and $Al(OH)_3$ (Often Fe, Si, Ca, Mg)
			GIBBSITE (See p. 48)	$Al(OH)_3$
Blackens and gives H_2O in c.t.	Ni in borax bd.		GARNIERITE (Genthite) (See p. 78)	$H_2(Ni,Mg)SiO_4 \cdot nH_2O$ (Approx.)
W in s.ph. bd.; yel. WO_3 res. in boiling HCl	Ca reac. w. am. oxalate in HCl sol.		SCHEELITE (See p. 65)	$CaWO_4$ (Us. also Mo; somet. Cu)

SECTION 31.   Nonmetallic luster; fus. above 5; not

		Name.	Composition.
Become mag. on ign.	Slowly and dif. sol. in HCl	IRON ORES (See Sec. 12, p. 158)	
	Cr in s.ph. bd. (Cp. picotite p. 296)	CHROMITE (Chromic Iron) (See p. 84)	$FeCr_2O_4$ (Mg iso. w. Fe; Al and Fe''' iso. w. Cr)
	Cleav. 1 direction, per.; often has a metalloidal luster	HYPERSTHENE (See p. 53)	$(Mg,Fe)SiO_3$ (Somet. Al)
	Cleav. and prism angles 54° and 126°; us. slender prisms, often fibrous (asbestos)	*Anthophyllite* (Asbestos in part) (See p. 54)	$(Mg,Fe)SiO_3$ (Somet. also Al)
Blackens b.b. but does not become mag.	Cleav. and prism angles 88° and 92°; often has bronzy, metalloidal luster. (Cp. turquois, next page; also minerals above, which do not always become mag.)	ENSTSATITE (Bronzite) (See p. 37)	$MgSiO_3$ (FeO up to 12%)
Whitens b.b. and fus. slightly on intense ign.	B flame w. Turner's flux on Pt wire; pyro-electric; often curved triangular cross-section. Achroite cols., indicolite blue, rubellite red	TOURMALINE (See p. 59)	$R_9Al_3(BOH)_2(SiO_5)$ (R = Mg, Fe, Ca, Na, K Li, (often some F)

Color.	Luster.	Hardness.	Specific Gravity.	Crystallization and Structure.	Cleavage and Fracture.
Wh., yelh., redh., brnh.	Pearly, dull	$1-2\frac{1}{2}$	2.6	Mon.; us. clay-like, friable	F. earthy
Why., gry., yel., red	Dull, earthy	$1-3$	2.4–2.6	Mass.: clay-like, pisolitic	F. earthy
Wh., gryh., grnh., redh.	Vitreous, dull; C. pearly	$2\frac{1}{2}-3\frac{1}{2}$	2.3–2.4	Mon.; incrust, stalac., scaly, fibr.	C. 1, basal, per.; thin flakes tough
Pale to deep grn., yelh.	Dull to resinous	$1-4$	2.3–2.8	Amorph.; botry., comp.	F. uneven, conch.
Wh., yel., grn., brn., redh.	Vitreous to adamant.	$4\frac{1}{2}-5$	5.9–6.1	Textr.; xls. like oct.; gran.	C. 4, pyram., $49\frac{1}{2}°$, 80° F. uneven

alk. after ign.; insol. in HCl; not scratched w. knife

Fe-blk to brnh-blk.	Dull to submet.	$5\frac{1}{2}$	4.3–4.6	Iso.; us. comp., gran.	F. uneven, conch.
Grnh-blk. to brn. and bronze	Pearly to bronzy	$5-6$	3.3–3.5	Orth.; fol., gran.	C. 1, pinac. per. F. uneven
Gry., clove-brn., grn.	Vitreous; C. pearly	$5-6$	3.0–3.2	Orth.; us. fibr., lamellar	C. 2, prism. per., $54\frac{1}{2}°$ F. splint.
Yelh., gry., brn., grn.	Pearly to bronzy	$5-6$	3.1–3.3	Orth.; us. lamellar, gran.	C. 2, prism., 88° F. uneven P. 1, pinac.
Brn., grn., blue, red, pink, wh., cols.	Vitreous	$7-7\frac{1}{2}$	3.0–3.2	Hex. rhom. hemimorph. Fig. 37 prism.	F. conch. to uneven

		Name.	Composition.
Whitens b.b. and fus. slightly on intense ign. —*Concluded*	Whitens at red heat; gives a little H_2O in c.t. on intense ign. (Cp. the next 8 minerals, which also give H_2O)	BERYL (Emerald, bright grn.; Aquamarine, pale) (See p. 81)	$Gl_3Al_2(SiO_3)_6$ (A little H; somet. Na, Li, Ca)
H_2O in c.t. on intense ign. if not before. (Cp. beryl, above)	Cu flame; P reac. w. am. mol. after fus. w. soda	TURQUOIS (See p. 81)	$Al_2(OH)_3PO_4 \cdot H_2O$ (Some Cu)
	Al reac. w. $Co(NO_3)_2$ on ch.	DIASPORE (See p. 35)	$AlO \cdot OH$ (Some Fe)
(Turquois and diaspore decrep., and former turns brn. or blk.)	A little H_2O on intense ign. in c.t. Staurolite prismatic and often twinned.	CORDIERITE (Iolite) (See p. 73)	$(Mg,Fe)_4Al_8(OH)_2$ $(Si_2O_7)_5$
		STAUROLITE (See p. 71)	$Fe(AlO)_4(AlOH)$ $(SiO_4)_2$ (Fe iso. w. Al; Mg w. Fe)
	Fus. w. equal amt. of soda on Pt wire to clear glass. Hyalite is cols. and transp.	OPAL (Hyalite) (See p. 50)	$SiO_2 \cdot nH_2O$
Al reac. w. $Co(NO_3)_2$ on ch.	F reac. w. $NaPO_3$ (powdered s.ph. beads) in c.t.	TOPAZ (See p. 61)	$Al_2(F,OH)_2SiO_4$
	Xls. us. stout rectangular	ANDALUSITE (Chiastolite) (See p. 39)	Al_2SiO_5, or $Al(AlO)SiO_4$
	Us. fibrous or slender xls.	SILLIMANITE (Fibrolite) (See p. 35)	Al_2SiO_5, or $Al(AlO)SiO_4$
	Us. bladed xls.; scratched by knife parallel to cleav. but not at right angles to cleav.	CYANITE (Disthene) (See pp. 74, 190)	$(AlO)_2SiO_3$, or Al_2SiO_5
	Extremely hard. Alexandrite is grn. by daylight (and by incandescent gas light); red by lamplight	CHRYSOBERYL (Alexandrite) (See p. 76)	$BeAl_2O_4$
	Extremely hard. Emery contains magnetite, hematite, or spinel intimately mixed w. corundum	CORUNDUM (Sapphire, blue; Ruby, red; Emery, black) (See p. 44)	Al_2O_3
Cr in s.ph. bd.	Col. blk.; st. dk. brn.; bd. shows Fe reac. while hot and Cr on cooling	CHROMITE (Chromic Iron) (See p. 84)	$FeCr_2O_4$ (Mg iso. w. Fe; Al w. Cr)

Color.	Luster.	Hardness.	Specific Gravity.	Crystallization and Structure.	Cleavage and Fracture.
Grn., blue, yel., pink, cols.	Vitreous to resinous	$7\frac{1}{2}$–8	2.6–2.8	Hex.; us. prism. Fig. 27	F. conch. to uneven
Blue, bluish-grn., grn.	Waxy	$5\frac{1}{2}$–6	2.6–2.8	Tri.; us. comp., incrust.	F. conch.
Wh., gry., yelh., grnh., brn.	Pearly to vitreous	6 –7	3.3–3.5	Orth., scaly, bladed	C. 1, pinac. per. F. conch.
Lt. to dk. blue; rarely cols.	Vitreous	7 –$7\frac{1}{2}$	2.6–2.7	Orth.; pseudo hex. xls.; gran.	C. 1, pinac. F. conch., uneven P. 1, basal
Yelh-brn., redh-brn. to brnh-blk.	Resinous to vitreous	7 –$7\frac{1}{2}$	3.6–3.8	Orth.; Figs. 43, 44, 45 prisms, twins	C. 1, pinac., poor F. uneven, conch.
Cols., red, yel., grn., blue, gry.	Vitreous to resinous	$5\frac{1}{2}$–$6\frac{1}{2}$	2.1–2.2	Amorph., botry.	F. conch.
Cols., wh., yel., pink, bluish, grnh.	Vitreous	8	3.4–3.6	Orth.; prism., pebbles, comp.	C. 1, basal, per. F. uneven, conch.
Flesh-red, redh-brn., olive-grn.	Vitreous	$6\frac{1}{2}$–$7\frac{1}{2}$	3.1–3.2	Orth.; us. prism.	C. 2, prism., 89° F. uneven
Hair-brn., gry., gryh.-grn.	Vitreous	6 –7	3.2–3.3	Orth.; fibr., radiating	C. 1, pinac., per. F. uneven, splint.
Blue, grn., gry., wh.	Vitreous to pearly	4 –5 6 –7	3.5–3.7	Tri.; us. bladed	C. 2, pinac. per., 74° P. 1, basal F. splint.
Yelh-grn., asparagus-grn. to emerald-grn.	Vitreous	$8\frac{1}{2}$	3.5–3.8	Orth.; us. tab. or pseudo-hex. twins	C. 2, dome, 60° F. uneven, conch.
Wh., gry., pink, red, yel., grn., blue, brn., blk.	Adamant. to vitreous	9	3.9–4.1	Hex. rhom.; rough xls., gran., comp.	P. basal and rhom., 86°, 94° F. uneven, conch.
Fe-blk. to brnh-blk.	Dull to submet.	$5\frac{1}{2}$	4.3–4.6	Iso.; us. gran., comp.	F. uneven, conch.

		Name.	Composition.
Little or no Cr, but fine powder wholly sol. in s.ph. bd. (no silica)	Xls. us. octahedrons, often twins; dark varieties react for Fe	SPINEL (Spinel Ruby, red) (See p. 82)	$MgAl_2O_4$ (Fe, Mn iso. w. Mg; Fe, Cr iso. w. Al)
	Wh. ZnO subl. w. soda and borax on Pt wire; grn. w. $Co(NO_3)_2$. (See p. 134)	*Gahnite* (Zinc Spinel) (See p. 82)	$ZnAl_2O_4$ (Mn, Fe iso. w. Zn; Fe w. Al)
Ti reac. w. H_2O_2	Xls. us. prismatic, often very slender and twinned	RUTILE (See p. 58)	TiO_2 (Us. a little Fe)
	Xls. often tabular	*Brookite* (See p. 58)	TiO_2
Metallic Sn w. Zn and HCl	Wh. subl. SnO_2 on intense ign. w. soda on ch.	CASSITERITE (Tin Stone) (See p. 70)	SnO_2 (Somet. Fe, Ta)
Sp.gr. above 4; Zr Test w. turmeric	Glows w. wh. light on intense ign. Hyacinth is transp. red or brown	ZIRCON (Hyacinth) (See p. 52)	$ZrSiO_4$ (Us. a little Fe)
Fus. w. equal amt. of soda on Pt wire to clear glass with evolution of CO_2	Xls. us. hex. prisms; amethyst, purple	QUARTZ (Rock Crystal; Amethyst) (See p. 50)	SiO_2
	Dense, botryoidal, mammillary, banded (agate)	CHALCEDONY (Agate, Jasper, Chert, Flint) (See p. 51)	SiO_2
	A little H_2O in c.t. at high temp.	OPAL (See p. 50)	$SiO_2 \cdot nH_2O$
Wh. enamel w. soda; slowly sol. in borax to clear glass	Dull blue w. $Co(NO_3)_2$ on ch.	PHENACITE (See p. 66)	Be_2SiO_4
Distinct cl., 2 direc. at 90° or nearly 90°	Fus. 4–5	FELDSPARS (See Sec. 23, p. 174)	
Cb reac. after fus. w. borax	Us. Mn reac. in soda bd. Str. dk. red to blk.	COLUMBITE (See p. 84)	$(Fe,Mn)Cb_2O_6$ (Also Ta and some Sn and W)
Extremely hard; not affected by acids or alkalis; burns in O	Xls. us. octahedrons w. curved faces and brilliant adamantine luster. Bort, rough rounded forms, confused xln.; carbonado, massive, dark gray to black	DIAMOND (Carbonado; Carbon; Bort) (See p. 44)	C (Slight ash in Carbonado)

Color.	Luster.	Hard-ness.	Specific Gravity.	Crystallization and Structure.	Cleavage and Fracture.
Red, lavender, blue, grn., brn., blk.	Vitreous	$8-8\frac{1}{2}$	3.5–3.6	Iso.; us. oct., Fig. 1; gran.	F. conch.
Dk. grn., brn. to blk.	Vitreous	$7\frac{1}{2}$–8	4.0–4.6	Iso.; us. oct., Fig. 1; gran.	F. conch., uneven
Redh-brn. to blk. and yelh.	Adamant.; submet.	6 –7	4.1–4.3	Tetr.; us. xls., twins	C. 2, prism. F. uneven
Hair-brn to blk.	Adamant.; submet.	$5\frac{1}{2}$–6	3.9–4.1	Orth.; us. xls., pseudohex.	F. uneven
Brn. to blk.; rarely yel., red, gry., wh.	Adamant.	6 –7	6.8–7.1	Tetr., gran.; twins, Fig. 25	F. uneven
Cols., gry., grn., brn., red	Adamant.	$7\frac{1}{2}$	4.5–4.8	Tetr.; us. xls., dissem.	F. conch.
Cols., wh., yel., red, grn., blue, brn., blk.	Vitreous to greasy	7	2.65	Hex. rhom.; us. prism. xls.; gran.	F. conch.
Wh., gryh., bnh., to blk.	Vitreous, waxy, dull	7	2.6–2.64	Cryptocrystalline, dense	F. conch.
Cols., red., yel., grn., blue, gry.	Vitreous to resinous	$5\frac{1}{2}$–$6\frac{1}{2}$	2.1–2.2	Amorph., botry.	F. conch.
Cols., wh., yel., rose, brn.	Vitreous	$7\frac{1}{2}$–8	2.9–3.0	Hex. rhom.; us. xls.	C. 3, prism., 60°, 120° F. conch.
Fe-blk. to gry. and brnh-blk.	Resinous to submet.	6	5.3–6.5	Orth.; short prism. xls.	C. 1, pinac., poor F. uneven, conch.
Cols., yel., red, blue, gry., blk.	Adamant. to greasy	10	3.5	Iso.; us. oct. or hexoct., Figs. 1, 4	C. 4, oct. per., $70\frac{1}{2}$°, $109\frac{1}{2}$° F. conch.

MINERALS CLASSIFIED ACCORDING TO CRYSTALLIZATION, LUSTER, AND HARDNESS

While arranged primarily on the basis of crystallization, these tables may also be used for the rapid determination of minerals by means of their physical properties, even without crystals. Thus the minerals of a given hardness are quickly found in all the groups and their specific gravities compared. In case two or more are found to have approximately the same hardness and specific gravity, their composition will usually suggest a distinctive test; or the references to the preceding tables may be used for fuller comparison of both physical and chemical properties.

ISOMETRIC

Metallic or Submetallic Luster

Hardness.	Name.	Composition.	Specific Gravity.	Physical Tables.	Blowpipe Tables.
0	*Mercury*	Hg	13.6	30	146
2 –2½	ARGENTITE	Ag_2S	7.2–7.4	24	142
2½	GALENA	PbS	7.4–7.6	24	142
2½–3	COPPER	Cu	8.8–8.9	87	146
2½–3	SILVER	Ag	10.0–12.0	30	146
2½–3	GOLD	Au	15.6–19.3	87	146
2½–3	HESSITE	Ag_2Te	8.3–8.5	31	148
3	BORNITE	Cu_5FeS_4	4.9–5.4	28	142
3	*Altaite*	PbTe	8.1–8.2	31	148
3 –3½	*Amalgam*	(Ag,Hg)	13.7–14.1	31	146
3 –4	TETRAHEDRITE	Cu_3SbS_3	4.4–5.1	25	140
3 –4	*Tennantite*	Cu_3AsS_3	4.4–5.1	25	140
3½–4	SPHALERITE	ZnS	3.9–4.1	64	144
3½–4	CUPRITE	Cu_2O	5.8–6.1	88	146
3½–4	PENTLANDITE	(Fe,Ni)S	4.6–5.1	29	144
3½–4	ALABANDITE	MnS	3.9–4.0	91	144
4 –4½	PLATINUM	Pt	14.0–19.0	31	152
5½	CHROMITE	$FeCr_2O_4$	4.3–4.6	84	150
5½	LINNAEITE	$(Ni,Co)_3S_4$	4.8–5.0	22	144
5½	GERSDORFFITE	NiAsS	5.6–6.2	21	140
5½–6	SMALTITE	$CoAs_2$	6.4–6.6	22	140
5½–6	CHLOANTHITE	$NiAs_2$	6.4–6.6	22	...
5½–6½	MAGNETITE	$FeFe_2O_4$	4.9–5.2	27	146
5½–6½	FRANKLINITE	$(Fe,Mn,Zn)(Fe,Mn)_2O_4$	5.1–5.2	27	150
6 –6½	PYRITE	FeS_2	4.9–5.2	29	144
6 –7	*Martite*	Fe_2O_3	4.8–5.3	84	...
6 –7	*Iridium*	Ir	22.6–22.8	31	...

Nonmetallic Luster

1 –1½	CERARGYRITE	AgCl	5.5–5.6	45	156
1 –1½	EMBOLITE	Ag(Cl,Br)	5.3–5.8	66	156
2 –2½	HALITE	NaCl	2.1–2.6	39	162
2 –2½	SYLVITE	KCl	1.9–2.0	40	162

ISOMETRIC

Nonmetallic Luster—*Concluded*

Hardness.	Name.	Composition.	Specific Gravity.	Physical Tables.	Blowpipe Tables.
$3\frac{1}{2}$–4	SPHALERITE	ZnS	3.9–4.1	64	144
$3\frac{1}{2}$–4	CUPRITE	Cu_2O	5.8–6.1	88	146
$3\frac{1}{2}$–4	ALABANDITE	MnS	3.9–4.0	91	144
4	FLUORITE	CaF_2	3.0–3.2	77	166
5 –$5\frac{1}{2}$	ANALCITE	$NaAl(SiO_3)_2 \cdot H_2O$	2.2–2.3	49	170
5 –$5\frac{1}{2}$	LAZURITE	$Na_5Al_3S_3(SiO_4)_3$	2.4–2.5	91	168
5 –6	SODALITE	$Na_4Al_3Cl(SiO_4)_3$	2.1–2.3	80	168
$5\frac{1}{2}$	COBALTITE	$CoAsS$	6.0–6.3	21	140
$5\frac{1}{2}$	URANINITE	$UO_3,UO_2,Pb,Th,$etc.	9.0–9.7	27	152
$5\frac{1}{2}$–6	LEUCITE	$KAl(SiO_3)_2$	2.4–2.5	50	188
$5\frac{1}{2}$–6	*Perovskite*	$CaTiO_3$	4.0	66	...
$6\frac{1}{2}$–$7\frac{1}{2}$	GARNET	$R''_3R'''_2(SiO_4)_3$	3.4–4.3	70	180
	PYROPE	$Mg_3Al_2(SiO_4)_3$	3.7	70	180
	ALMANDITE	$Fe_3Al_2(SiO_4)_3$	3.9–4.2	70	180
	SPESSARTITE	$Mn_3Al_2(SiO_4)_3$	4.0–4.3	70	180
	GROSSULARITE	$Ca_3Al_2(SiO_4)_3$	3.5–3.6	70	180
	ANDRADITE	$Ca_3Fe_2(SiO_4)_3$	3.8–3.9	70	180
7	BORACITE	$Mg_7Cl_2B_{16}O_{30}$	2.9–3.0	52	166
$7\frac{1}{2}$–$8\frac{1}{2}$	SPINEL	$MgAl_2O_4$	3.5–3.6	71	196
	GAHNITE	$ZnAl_2O_4$	4.0–4.6	71	196
10	DIAMOND	C	3.5	44	196

TETRAGONAL

Metallic or Submetallic Luster

$3\frac{1}{2}$–4	CHALCOPYRITE	$CuFeS_2$	4.1–4.3	28	142
4	*Stannite*	Cu_2FeSnS_4	4.3–4.5	21	142
5 –$5\frac{1}{2}$	*Hausmannite*	$MnMn_2O_4$	4.7–4.9	83	150
$5\frac{1}{2}$–6	*Octahedrite*	TiO_2	3.8–3.9	56	...
6 –$6\frac{1}{2}$	*Braunite*	$3Mn_2O_3 \cdot MnSiO_3$	4.7–4.8	28	150
6 –7	RUTILE	TiO_2	4.1–4.3	58	152

Nonmetallic Luster

1 –2	*Calomel*	Hg_2Cl_2	6.4–6.5	45	154
3	WULFENITE	$PbMoO_4$	6.7–7.0	68	154
$4\frac{1}{2}$–5	SCHEELITE	$CaWO_4$	5.9–6.1	65	172
$4\frac{1}{2}$–5	APOPHYLLITE	$(H,K)_2Ca(SiO_3)_2 \cdot H_2O$	2.3–2.4	34	170
		$(SiO_4)_9$	2.9–3.1	...	170
5 –$5\frac{1}{2}$	*Hausmannite*	$MnMn_2O_4$	4.7–4.9	83	150
5 –6	WERNERITE	$\begin{cases} n(Ca_4Al_6Si_6O_{25}) \\ m(Na_4Al_3Si_9O_{24}Cl) \end{cases}$	2.6–2.8	43	172
$5\frac{1}{2}$–6	*Octahedrite*	TiO_2	3.8–3.9	56	...
6 –$6\frac{1}{2}$	*Braunite*	$3Mn_2O_3 \cdot MnSiO_3$	4.7–4.8	28	150
6 –7	RUTILE	TiO_2	4.1–4.3	58	152
6 –7	CASSITERITE	SnO_2	6.8–7.1	70	196
$6\frac{1}{2}$	VESUVIANITE	$Ca_6Al_3(OH,F)(SiO_4)_5$	3.3–3.5	70	180
$7\frac{1}{2}$	ZIRCON	$ZrSiO_4$	4.5–4.8	52	196

ORTHORHOMBIC

Metallic or Submetallic Luster

Hardness.	Name.	Composition.	Specific Gravity.	Physical Tables.	Blowpipe Tables.
2	STIBNITE	Sb_2S_3	4.5–4.6	23	140
2 –2½	PYROLUSITE	MnO_2	4.7–4.8	24	150
2 –2½	STEPHANITE	Ag_5SbS_4	6.2–6.3	24	142
2 –3	JAMESONITE	$Pb_2Sb_2S_5$	5.5–6.0	21	142
2½	KRENNERITE	$AuAgTe_4$	8.3–8.4	30	148
2½–3	CHALCOCITE	Cu_2S	5.5–5.8	25	144
2½–3	BOURNONITE	$PbCuSbS_3$	5.7–5.9	25	142
3	ENARGITE	Cu_3AsS_4	4.4–4.5	25	140
3½	Dyscrasite	Ag_3Sb to Ag_6Sb	9.4–9.9	31	142
3½–4	MANGANITE	$MnO \cdot OH$	4.2–4.4	83	150
5 –5½	GOETHITE	$FeO \cdot OH$	4.0–4.4	89	146
5½–6	ARSENOPYRITE	$FeAsS$	5.9–6.2	22	140
5½–6	Brookite	TiO_2	3.9–4.1	58	152
5½–6	Ilvaite	$CaFe_3(OH)(SiO_4)_2$	4.0–4.1	27	...
6	COLUMBITE	$(Fe,Mn)Cb_2O_6$	5.3–6.5	84	148
6	Tantalite	$(Fe,Mn)Ta_2O_6$	6.5–7.3	84	...
6 –6½	MARCASITE	FeS_2	4.8–4.9	29	144

Nonmetallic Luster

Hardness.	Name.	Composition.	Specific Gravity.	Physical Tables.	Blowpipe Tables.
1 –2	PYROPHYLLITE	$H_2Al_2(SiO_3)_2$	2.8–2.9	32	190
1 –2	CARNALLITE	$KMgCl_3 \cdot 6H_2O$	1.6	45	162
1 –2	Molybdite	$Fe_2(MoO_4)_3 \cdot 7\frac{1}{2}H_2O$	4.5	85	...
1½–2½	SULPHUR	S	2.0–2.1	67	152
2	NITER	KNO_3	2.1–2.2	47	164
2 –2½	EPSOMITE	$MgSO_4 \cdot 7H_2O$	1.7–1.8	47	164
2 –2½	Autunite	$Ca(UO_2)_2(PO_4)_2 \cdot 8H_2O$	3.1–3.2	86	166
2 –3	THENARDITE	Na_2SO_4	2.7	33	162
2½–3½	BARITE	$BaSO_4$	4.3–4.6	40	164
3	ANGLESITE	$PbSO_4$	6.1–6.4	40	164
3	Olivenite	$Cu_2(OH)AsO_4$	4.1–4.6	90	...
3 –3½	CERUSSITE	$PbCO_3$	6.4–6.6	48	154
3 –3½	ANHYDRITE	$CaSO_4$	2.9–3.0	41	164
3 –3½	CELESTITE	$SrSO_4$	3.9–4.0	41	164
3 –3½	ATACAMITE	$Cu_2(OH)_3Cl$	3.7–3.8	90	156
3 –4	WITHERITE	$BaCO_3$	4.3–4.4	48	164
3½	Descloizite	$PbZn(PbOH)VO_4$	5.9–6.2	88	154
3½–4	ARAGONITE	$CaCO_3$	2.9–3.0	41	182
3½–4	STRONTIANITE	$SrCO_3$	3.7	36	182
3½–4	BROCHANTITE	$Cu_4(OH)_6SO_4$	3.9	91	156
3½–4	WAVELLITE	$(AlOH)_3(PO_4)_2 \cdot 5H_2O$	2.3–2.4	80	186
3½–4	SCORODITE	$FeAsO_4 \cdot 2H_2O$	3.1–3.3	80	158
4½–5	CALAMINE	$(ZnOH)_2SiO_3$	3.4–3.5	36	186
5 –5½	NATROLITE	$NaAl(AlO)(SiO_3)_3 \cdot 2H_2O$	2.2–2.3	37	166
5 –5½	GOETHITE	$FeO \cdot OH$	4.0–4.4	89	146
5 –5½	THOMSONITE	$(Ca,Na_2)_2Al_4(SiO_4)_4 \cdot 5H_2O$	2.3–2.4	49	168
5 –6	ENSTATITE	$MgSiO_3$	3.1–3.3	37	176

ORTHORHOMBIC

Nonmetallic Luster—*Concluded*

Hardness.	Name.	Composition.	Specific Gravity.	Physical Tables.	Blowpipe Tables.
5 –6	HYPERSTHENE	$(Fe,Mg)SiO_3$	3.3–3.5	53	160
5 –6	*Anthophyllite*	$(Mg,Fe)SiO_3$	3.0–3.2	54	160
$5\frac{1}{2}$–6	*Tephroite*	Mn_2SiO_4	4.0–4.1	55	168
$5\frac{1}{2}$–6	*Brookite*	TiO_2	3.9–4.1	58	152
$5\frac{1}{2}$–6	*Ilvaite*	$CaFe_3(OH)(SiO_4)_2$	4.0–4.1	27	...
6	COLUMBITE	$(Fe,Mn)Cb_2O_6$	5.3–6.5	84	148
6	*Tantalite*	$(Fe,Mn)Ta_2O_6$	6.5–7.3	84	...
6 –$6\frac{1}{2}$	PREHNITE	$H_2Ca_2Al_2(SiO_4)_3$	2.8–3.0	81	170
6 –$6\frac{1}{2}$	ZOISITE	$Ca_2Al_3(OH)(SiO_4)_3$	3.2–3.4	35	180
6 –7	SILLIMANITE	$Al(AlO)SiO_4$	3.2–3.3	35	194
6 –7	DIASPORE	$AlO \cdot OH$	3.3–3.5	35	194
6 –7	*Forsterite*	Mg_2SiO_4	3.2–3.3	63	...
$6\frac{1}{2}$	*Fayalite*	Fe_2SiO_4	3.9–4.1	63	...
$6\frac{1}{2}$–7	OLIVINE	$(Mg,Fe)_2SiO_4$	3.2–3.6	63	188
$6\frac{1}{2}$–$7\frac{1}{2}$	ANDALUSITE	$Al(AlO)SiO_4$	3.1–3.2	39	194
7 –$7\frac{1}{2}$	STAUROLITE	$Fe(AlO)_4(AlOH)(SiO_4)_2$	3.6–3.8	71	194
7 –$7\frac{1}{2}$	CORDIERITE	$(Mg,Fe)_4Al_8(OH)_2$			
		$(Si_2O_7)_5$	2.6–2.7	73	180
7 –$7\frac{1}{2}$	DANBURITE	$CaB_2(SiO_4)_2$	3.0	71	178
8	TOPAZ	$Al_2(F,OH)_2SiO_4$	3.4–3.6	61	194
$8\frac{1}{2}$	CHRYSOBERYL	$BeAl_2O_4$	3.5–3.8	76	194

MONOCLINIC

Metallic or Submetallic Luster

$1\frac{1}{2}$–2	SYLVANITE	$AuAgTe_4$	7.9–8.3	30	148
2 –3	POLYBASITE	$(Ag,Cu)_9SbS_6$	6.0–6.2	24	142
$2\frac{1}{2}$	CALAVERITE	$(Au,Ag)Te_2$	9.0	30	148
3 –4	*Melaconite*	CuO	5.8–6.2	26	146
5	FERBERITE	$FeWO_4$	7.5	26	162
5 –$5\frac{1}{2}$	WOLFRAMITE	$(Fe,Mn)WO_4$	7.2–7.5	26	148
5 –6	HORNBLENDE	Ca,Mg,Fe,Al silicate.	2.9–3.4	54	160
$5\frac{1}{2}$–6	ALLANITE	$(Ca,Fe)_2(Al,Fe,Ce)_3$			
		$(SiO_4)_3$	3.0–4.2	58	148

MONOCLINIC

Nonmetallic Luster

0 –1	ULEXITE	$NaCaB_5O_9 \cdot H_2O$	1.6–1.7	45	166
1 –$1\frac{1}{2}$	VERMICULITE	Mg,Fe,Al silicates	2.3–2.8	59	170
1 –$1\frac{1}{2}$	ANNABERGITE	$Ni_3(AsO_4)_2 \cdot 8H_2O$	3.0–3.1	78	158
1 –$2\frac{1}{2}$	KAOLINITE	$H_4Al_2Si_2O_9$	2.4–2.6	46	192

MONOCLINIC

Nonmetallic Luster—*Continued*

Hard-ness.	Name.	Composition.	Specific Gravity.	Physical Tables.	Blow-pipe Tables.
1 –2½	TALC	$H_2Mg_3(SiO_3)_4$	2.5–2.8	32	172
1 –2½	CHLORITE	H,Fe,Mg,Al silicate	2.6–3.0	72	172
1½–2	GYPSUM	$CaSO_4 \cdot 2H_2O$	2.3–2.4	32	162
1½–2	ORPIMENT	As_2S_3	3.4–3.5	86	152
1½–2 .	VIVIANITE	$Fe_3(PO_4)_2 \cdot 8H_2O$	2.6–2.7	72	158
1½–2	REALGAR	AsS	3.5–3.6	85	152
1½–2	MIRABILITE	$Na_2SO_4 \cdot 10H_2O$	1.4–1.5	46	164
1½–2	*Alunogen*	$Al_2(SO_4)_3 \cdot 18H_2O$	1.6–1.8	...	184
1½–2½	ERYTHRITE	$Co_3(AsO_4)_2 \cdot 8H_2O$	2.9–3.0	...	158
1½–2½	COPIAPITE	$Fe_2(FeOH)_2(SO_4)_5$			
		$\cdot 18H_2O$	2.1	60	158
2	MELANTERITE	$FeSO_4 \cdot 7H_2O$	1.9	78	158
2	*Aurichalcite*	$(Zn,Cu)_5(OH)_6(CO_3)_2$	3.5–3.6	...	184
2 –2½	BORAX	$Na_2B_4O_7 \cdot 10H_2O$	1.7	33	164
2 –3	MUSCOVITE	$H_2KAl_3(SiO_4)_3$	2.7–3.0	33	172
2 –3	*Paragonite*	$H_2NaAl_3(SiO_4)_3$	2.8–2.9	33	...
2 –3	BIOTITE	$(H,K)_2(Mg,Fe)_2Al_2$			
		$(SiO_4)_3$	2.8–3.1	53	148
2 –3	PHLOGOPITE	$H_2KMg_3Al(SiO_4)_3$	2.8–2.9	72	148
2 –3	LEPIDOLITE	$(Li,K)_2Al_2(OH,F)_2$			
		$(SiO_3)_3$	2.8–2.9	33	172
2½	CRYOLITE	Na_3AlF_6	2.9–3.0	48	166
2½	*Glauberite*	$Na_2Ca(SO_4)_2$	2.7–2.8	33	164
2½–3½	GIBBSITE	$Al(OH)_3$	2.3–2.4	48	192
2½–3	KAINITE	$KMgClSO_4 \cdot 3H_2O$	2.0–2.2	40	162
2½–3	CROCOITE	$PbCrO_4$	5.9–6.1	87	154
2½–3	*Polyhalite*	$K_2MgCa_2(SO_4)_4 \cdot 2H_2O$	2.7–2.8	60	164
3 –4	TALC	$H_2Mg_3(SiO_3)_4$	2.5–2.8	32	172
3½	*Hydromagnesite*	$Mg_4(OH)_2(CO_3)_3 \cdot 3H_2O$	2.1-2.2	...	182
3½–4	MALACHITE	$Cu_2(OH)_2CO_3$	3.9–4.0	90	156
3½–4	AZURITE	$Cu_3(OH)_2(CO_3)_2$	3.7–3.8	91	156
3½–4	STILBITE	$H_4(Ca,Na_2)Al_2(SiO_3)_6$			
		$\cdot 4H_2O$	2.1–2.2	34	170
3½–4	HEULANDITE	$H_4(Ca,Na_2)Al_2(SiO_3)_6$			
		$\cdot 3H_2O$	2.2	34	170
3½–4	LAUMONTITE	$H_4Ca(AlO)_2(SiO_3)_4$			
		$\cdot 2H_2O$	2.2–2.3	42	168
3½–4½	MARGARITE	$H_2CaAl_4Si_2O_{12}$	3.0–3.1	34	172
4 –4½	COLEMANITE	$HCa(BO_2)_3 \cdot 2H_2O$	2.3–2.5	36	166
4 –4½	*Phillipsite*	$(Ca,K_2)Al_2(SiO_3)_4$			
		$\cdot 5H_2O$	2.2	36	...
4½	HARMOTOME	$H_2BaAl_2(SiO_3)_5 \cdot 4H_2O$	2.4–2.5	36	170
4½–5	PECTOLITE	$HNaCa_2(SiO_3)_3$	2.7–2.8	49	170
4½–5	WOLLASTONITE	$CaSiO_3$	2.8–2.9	37	172
5	FERBERITE	$FeWO_4$	7.5	26	162
5 –5½	DATOLITE	$Ca(BOH)SiO_4$	2.9–3.0	49	168
5 –5½	TITANITE	$CaSiTiO_5$	3.4–3.6	62	172
5 –5½	MONAZITE	$(Ce,La,Nd,Pr)PO_4$	4.9–5.3	69	190
5 –5½	HUEBNERITE	$MnWO_4$	6.9–7.4	26	172

MONOCLINIC

Nonmetallic Luster—*Concluded*

Hard-ness.	Name.	Composition.	Specific Gravity.	Physical Tables.	Blow-pipe Tables.
5 –5½	*Scolecite*	CaAl(AlO)(SiO$_3$)$_3$ ·3H$_2$O	2.2–2.4	37	...
5 –6	TREMOLITE	CaMg$_3$(SiO$_3$)$_4$	2.9–3.1	37	174
5 –6	ACTINOLITE	Ca(Mg,Fe)$_3$(SiO$_3$)$_4$	3.0–3.2	74	174
5 –6	HORNBLENDE	Ca,Mg,Fe,Al silicate	2.9–3.4	54	160
5 –6	DIOPSIDE	CaMg(SiO$_3$)$_2$	3.2–3.6	37	176
5 –6	PYROXENE	Ca(Mg,Fe)(SiO$_3$)$_2$	3.2–3.6	74	160
5 –6	AUGITE	Ca,Mg,Fe,Al silicate	3.2–3.6	74	160
5 –6	*Lazulite*	(Fe,Mg)(AlOH)$_2$(PO$_4$)$_2$	3.0–3.1	80	...
5½–6	ALLANITE	(Ca,Fe)$_2$(Al,Fe,Ce)$_3$ (SiO$_4$)$_3$	3.0–4.2	58	148
6 –6½	ORTHOCLASE	KAlSi$_3$O$_8$	2.5–2.6	38	174
6 –6½	CHONDRODITE	Mg$_5$(F,OH)$_2$(SiO$_4$)$_2$	3.1–3.2	69	188
6 –7	EPIDOTE	Ca$_2$(Al,Fe)$_3$(OH)(SiO$_4$)$_3$	3.2–3.5	61	162
6 –7	SPODUMENE	LiAl(SiO$_3$)$_2$	3.1–3.2	39	176

TRICLINIC

Nonmetallic Luster

Hard-ness.	Name.	Composition.	Specific Gravity.	Physical Tables.	Blow-pipe Tables.
0 –1	*Sassolite*	H$_3$BO$_3$	1.4–1.5	32	...
2½	CHALCANTHITE	CuSO$_4$·5H$_2$O	2.1–2.3	79	156
4 –5	CYANITE	(AlO)$_2$SiO$_3$	3.5–3.7	74	190
5½–6	TURQUOIS	Al$_2$(OH)$_3$PO$_4$·H$_2$O	2.6–2.8	81	186
5½–6½	RHODONITE	MnSiO$_3$	3.4–3.7	62	176
6	*Amblygonite*	Li(AlF)PO$_4$	3.0–3.1	38	178
6 –6½	MICROCLINE	KAlSi$_3$O$_8$	2.5–2.6	38	174
6 –6½	PLAGIOCLASE	{ n(NaAlSi$_3$O$_8$) (*ab*) m(CaAl$_2$Si$_2$O$_8$) (*an*) }	2.6–2.8	38	174
	ALBITE	ab–ab$_6$an$_1$	2.62–2.64	38	174
	OLIGOCLASE	ab$_6$an$_1$–ab$_3$an$_1$	2.65–2.67	38	174
	ANDESINE	ab$_3$an$_1$–ab$_1$an$_1$	2.68–2.69	38	174
	LABRADORITE	ab$_1$an$_1$–ab$_1$an$_3$	2.70–2.72	38	174
	BYTOWNITE	ab$_1$an$_3$–ab$_1$an$_6$	2.73–2.75	38	174
	ANORTHITE	ab$_1$an$_6$–an	2.75–2.76	38	174
6 –7	CYANITE	(AlO)$_2$SiO$_3$	3.5–3.7	74	190
6 –7	AXINITE	HCa$_3$Al$_2$B(SiO$_4$)$_4$	3.3–3.4	35	178
6 –7	*Chloritoid*	H$_2$FeAl$_2$SiO$_7$	3.5–3.6	54	...
6 –7	*Ottrelite*	H$_2$(Fe,Mn)(Al,Fe)$_2$Si$_2$O$_9$	3.2–3.3	54	...

HEXAGONAL

Metallic or Submetallic Luster

Hard-ness.	Name.	Composition.	Specific Gravity.	Physical Tables.	Blow-pipe Tables.
1 –1½	MOLYBDENITE	MoS$_2$	4.7–4.8	22	152
1 –2	GRAPHITE	C	1.9–2.3	23	152
1½–2	COVELLITE	CuS	4.6	23	144
2 –2½	BISMUTH	Bi	9.7–9.8	30	146

HEXAGONAL

Metallic or Submetallic Luster—*Concluded.*

Hardness.	Name.	Composition.	Specific Gravity.	Physical Tables.	Blowpipe Tables.
2 –2½	*Tellurium*	Te	6.1–6.3	30	148
2½–3	PYRARGYRITE	Ag_3SbS_3	5.8–5.9	82	142
3 –3½	MILLERITE	NiS	5.3–5.7	28	144
3 –3½	*Antimony*	Sb	6.6–6.7	31	140
3 –4	ARSENIC	As	5.6–5.7	31	140
3½–4½	PYRRHOTITE	FeS	4.5–4.6	29	144
5 –5½	NICCOLITE	NiAs	7.3–7.7	29	140
5 –6	ILMENITE	$FeTiO_3$	4.5–5.0	26	150
5½–6½	HEMATITE	Fe_2O_3	4.9–5.3	84	146
6 –7	*Iridosmium*	Ir,Os	18.9–21.2	31	…

Nonmetallic Luster

Hardness.	Name.	Composition.	Specific Gravity.	Physical Tables.	Blowpipe Tables.
0 –1	CARNOTITE	$(K_2,Ca)O \cdot 2U_2O_3 \cdot V_2O_5$ $\cdot nH_2O$	(?)	85	166
1 –1½	*Iodyrite*	AgI	5.6–5.7	85	…
1½–2	SODA NITER	$NaNO_3$	2.2–2.3	46	164
1½–2	COVELLITE	CuS	4.6	23	144
2 –2½	CINNABAR	HgS	8.0–8.2	86	144
2 –2½	PROUSTITE	Ag_3AsS_3	5.5–5.6	86	140
2 –2½	BRUCITE	$Mg(OH)_2$	2.3–2.4	32	184
2½–3	PYRARGYRITE	Ag_3SbS_3	5.8–5.9	82	142
3	CALCITE	$CaCO_3$	2.7	40	182
3	VANADINITE	$Pb_5Cl(VO_4)_3$	6.6–7.2	67	154
3 –3½	GREENOCKITE	CdS	4.9–5.0	85	184
3½	*Thaumasite*	$Ca_3SCSiO_{10} \cdot 15H_2O$	1.8–1.9	…	182
3½–4	PYROMORPHITE	$Pb_5Cl(PO_4)_3$	6.5–7.1	79	154
3½–4	ALUNITE	$KAl_3(OH)_6(SO_4)_2$	2.6–2.8	49	184
3½–4	DOLOMITE	$CaMg(CO_3)_2$	2.8–2.9	41	182
3½–4	SIDERITE	$FeCO_3$	3.8–3.9	41	158
3½–4	MIMETITE	$Pb_5Cl(AsO_4)_3$	7.0–7.3	68	154
3½–4	*Ankerite*	$Ca(Mg,Fe)(CO_3)_2$	2.9–3.1	41	182
3½–4½	MAGNESITE	$MgCO_3$	3.0–3.1	42	182
3½–4½	RHODOCHROSITE	$MnCO_3$	3.4–3.6	64	184
4 –4½	ZINCITE	ZnO	5.4–5.7	88	186
4 –5	CHABAZITE	$CaAl_2(SiO_3)_4 \cdot 6H_2O$	2.0–2.2	65	170
4½–5	APATITE	$CaF(PO_4)_3$	3.1–3.2	68	166
4½	*Gmelinite*	$(Na_3Ca)Al_2(SiO_3)_4$ $\cdot 6H_2O$	2.0–2.2	…	170
5	SMITHSONITE	$ZnCO_3$	4.3–4.5	43	184
5	DIOPTASE	H_2CuSiO_4	3.3–3.4	91	188
5 –6	WILLEMITE	Zn_2SiO_4	3.9–4.2	65	168
5 –6	NEPHELITE	$(K,Na)AlSiO_4$	2.5–2.6	43	168
5 –6	CANCRINITE	$H_6Na_6Ca(NaCO_3)_2Al_8$ $(SiO_4)_9$	2.4–2.5	65	168
5½–6½	HEMATITE	Fe_2O_3	4.9–5.3	84	146
7	QUARTZ	SiO_2	2.65	50	196

HEXAGONAL

Nonmetallic Luster—*Concluded*

Hardness.	Name.	Composition.	Specific Gravity.	Physical Tables.	Blowpipe Tables
7	*Tridymite*	SiO_2	2.3	51	...
$7-7\frac{1}{2}$	TOURMALINE	$R_9Al_3(BOH)_2(SiO_5)_4$	3.0–3.2	59	162
$7\frac{1}{2}-8$	BERYL	$Be_3Al_2(SiO_3)_6$	2.6–2.8	81	180
$7\frac{1}{2}-8$	PHENACITE	Be_2SiO_4	2.9–3.0	66	196
9	CORUNDUM	Al_2O_3	3.9–4.1	44	194

AMORPHOUS OR CRYSTALLIZATION UNKNOWN

Metallic or Submetallic Luster

Hardness.	Name.	Composition.	Specific Gravity.	Physical Tables.	Blowpipe Tables
$1-3$	WAD	MnO_2,H_2O	3.0–4.3	26	150
$2-2\frac{1}{2}$	PYROLUSITE	MnO_2	4.7–4.8	24	150
$2\frac{1}{2}-3$	PETZITE	Ag_3AuTe_2	8.7–9.0	25	148
$3-5$	WAD	MnO_2,H_2O	3.0–4.3	26	150
4	*Algodonite*	Cu_6As	7.6	...	140
$5-5\frac{1}{2}$	LIMONITE	$FeO\cdot OH\cdot nH_2O$	3.6–4.0	83	146
$5\frac{1}{2}-6$	TURGITE	$FeO\cdot OH,Fe_2O_3,H_2O$	4.2–4.7	85	146
$5-6$	PSILOMELANE	MnO_2,MnO,H_2O, etc.	3.7–4.7	26	150
$5-6$	WAD	MnO_2,H_2O	3.0–4.3	26	150

Nonmetallic Luster

Hardness.	Name.	Composition.	Specific Gravity.	Physical Tables.	Blowpipe Tables
$1-2$	GLAUCONITE	approx.$KFe(SiO_3)_2\cdot H_2O$	2.2–2.4	78	160
$1-2$	*Halloysite*	$H_4Al_2Si_2O_9\cdot nH_2O$	2.0–2.2	46	...
$1-3$	BAUXITE	mixture $AlO\cdot OH$ and $Al(OH)_3$	2.4–2.6	46	192
$1-4$	GARNIERITE	approx. $H_2(Ni,Mg)SiO_4\cdot nH_2O$	2.3–2.8	78	188
$2-3$	CHRYSOCOLLA	approx. $CuSiO_3\cdot 2H_2O$	2.0–2.2	78	188
$2-2\frac{1}{2}$	SEPIOLITE	$H_4Mg_2Si_3O_{10}$	1.0–2.0	47	170
$2-2\frac{1}{2}$	*Hydrozincite*	$Zn_3(OH)_4CO_3$	3.6–3.8	47	184
3	ALLOPHANE	approx. $Al_2SiO_5\cdot 5H_2O$	1.8–1.9	79	188
3	*Zaratite*	$Ni_3(OH)_4CO_3\cdot 4H_2O$	2.6–2.7	90	...
$3-4$	SERPENTINE	$H_4Mg_3Si_2O_9$	2.5–2.6	79	170
$3-5$	WAD	MnO_2,H_2O	3.0–4.3	26	150
4	*Crocidolite*	$NaFe'''(Fe,Mg)(SiO_3)_3$	3.2–3.3	91	162
$5-5\frac{1}{2}$	LIMONITE	$FeO\cdot OH\cdot nH_2O$	3.6–4.0	83	146
$5-6$	WAD	MnO_2,H_2O	3.0–4.3	26	150
$5\frac{1}{2}-6$	TURGITE	$FeO\cdot OH,Fe_2O_3,H_2O$	4.2–4.7	85	146
$5\frac{1}{2}-6\frac{1}{2}$	OPAL	$SiO_2\cdot nH_2O$	2.1–2.2	50	190
7	CHALCEDONY	SiO_2	2.6–2.64	51	196

GLOSSARY

Acicular. In slender, needle-like prisms.

Acid igneous rocks. Those containing much silica, part of which appears as quartz, if crystalline.

Acute. Sharply pointed.

Adamantine luster. Like that of cerussite, diamond, or slightly oiled glass.

Aggregate. A group, cluster, or mass.

Alkaline taste. Resembling the taste of soda.

Alliaceous odor. Garlic-like, the odor of arsenic fumes.

Alluvial. Deposited by streams.

Amorphous. Without crystalline molecular structure.

Amygdaloid. An igneous rock having gas vesicles filled with secondary minerals.

Amygdule. A spheroidal aggregate of secondary minerals formed in a vesicle of igneous rock.

Anhydrous. Not containing hydrogen or water in its composition.

Arborescent. Branching; fern-like or tree-like; dendritic.

Argillaceous. Consisting of or containing clay.

Asterism. The property of showing a six-rayed star of light on polished faces in certain directions.

Astringent. Contracting or puckering the tissues, as the mouth in astringent taste.

Basal. Parallel to the basal pinacoid of a crystal; across the length of a prism.

Basalt. Dense, dark, heavy, igneous rock.

Basic igneous rocks. Those low in silica; heavy and generally dark colored.

Bladed. Having long flattened crystals, resembling knife blades.

Blebby. Containing bubble cavities, or vesicles.

Botryoidal. Like a bunch of grapes; consisting of closely grouped spherical masses.

Brittle. Breaking or crumbling readily under a blow or other strain; opposite of tough.

Capillary.   Hair-like; very thin and greatly elongated prismatic crystals.

Cellular.   Full of small openings; sponge-like.

Chatoyant.   Possessing a changeable luster, like a cat's eye in the dark.

Clastic.   Composed of fragments.

Cleavable.   Capable of being split with smooth faces in definite directions.

Cleavage.   The capacity possessed by many crystalline minerals for being split or broken in certain definite directions with smooth faces.   (See p. 10.)

Columnar.   Having slender prisms in close parallel grouping.

Compact.   Consisting of a firm, closely united aggregate.

Complex crystals.   Those having many crystal forms and faces.

Concentric.   Consisting of spherical layers about a common center, like an onion.

Conchoidal fracture.   Breaking with curved, shell-like surfaces.

Concretion.   A rounded or irregular mass that has been formed by the accumulation of dispersed or scattered material.

Concretionary.   Formed as a concretion; containing or consisting of concretions.

Confused.   In irregular, indistinct aggregate.

Conglomerate.   A rock composed chiefly of pebbles cemented together.

Contact mineral.   One that has been formed under the influence of igneous intrusion.

Contact Twin.   Two crystals of the same mineral attached to one another in definite reversed position.

Crested.   Consisting of groups of tabular crystals forming ridges.

Cruciform.   Forming a cross.

Cryptocrystalline.   Minutely crystalline; composed of crystalline particles of microscopic dimensions.

Crystal.   A crystalline solid bounded by natural plane surfaces.   (See pp. 1–6.)

Crystalline.   Having symmetrical molecular structure which, under favorable conditions, is expressed in the forms of crystals; in the absence of crystals it may be evidenced by cleavage and characteristic optical properties.

Crystallization.   The process of forming crystalline structure, which may result in crystals or in irregular crystalline masses.

Cubic. Having the form of a cube (Fig. 5), as crystals; or the directions of the faces of a cube, as cubic cleavage.

Cyclic. Circular, as in certain types of repeated twinning that tend to produce circular forms.

Decrepitation. Violent breaking away of particles, with crackling sound, on sudden heating. (See p. 100.)

Deflagration. Sudden combustion; flashing like gunpowder.

Dendritic. Branching; fern-like or tree-like; arborescent.

Dense. Having a compact porcelain-like texture; consisting of an aggregate of minute, indistinguishable particles.

Diaphaneity. Power of transmitting light; transparency.

Dichroism. The property of showing different colors when viewed by transmitted light in two directions.

Dimorphism. The occurrence of two minerals having the same composition, but differing in crystallization and other physical properties, and often also in chemical properties. Pleomorphism, or polymorphism, is the broader term, referring to two or more.

Disseminated. Scattered through a rock or other mineral aggregate in the form of grains or particles.

Divergent. Extending in different directions from a point; radiating.

Dodecahedron. A crystal form in the isometric system with twelve faces; the rhombic dodecahedron (Fig. 7).

Double refraction. Separation of a ray of light into two parts, which are refracted at different angles.

Drusy. Covered with minute crystals closely crowded, giving a rough surface with many reflecting faces.

Ductile. Capable of being drawn into wire.

Dull. Not reflecting light; absence of luster.

Earthy. Consisting of minute particles loosely aggregated; clay-like, dull.

Effervescence. Evolution of gas in bubbles from a liquid.

Efflorescence. A surface crust or coating, often powdery, formed by evaporation.

Elastic. The property of springing back to its original form when bent, as in thin sheets of mica.

Eruptive rock. One formed by the solidification of a surface flow of lava; a volcanic rock; sometimes used as a synonym of igneous rock.

Etched. Having the surface roughened by solution or corrosion.

Exfoliation. Splitting apart and expansion of flakes or scales on being heated.

Felted. Composed of matted fibers.

Ferruginous. Containing iron.

Fetid odor. A disagreeable or offensive odor, as of hydrogen disulphide.

Fibrous. Having thread-like or hair-like form.

Fissure. A crack or crevice.

Flexible. Capable of being bent without breaking, but not returning to its original position.

Fluorescence. The property of showing colors by transmitted light that are different from the color of the substance as seen by reflected light.

Folia. Thin flakes or leaves; lamellae.

Foliated. Composed of or easily splitting into thin flakes or plates.

Fossiliferous. Containing fossils, remains of plants or animals.

Fracture. The form of surface produced by breaking other than by cleavage and parting. (See p. 10.)

Friable. Readily broken into grains; crumbling easily.

Furrowed. Having deep grooves or striations.

Fusibility. The capacity for being fused or melted in the blowpipe flame. (See p. 157.)

Gangue. Minerals of little or no value in an ore.

Globular. Having spherical, or rounded, form.

Gneiss. A granite-like rock having more or less definite parallel arrangement of its constituents.

Granite. An igneous rock consisting of distinguishable grains of feldspar, quartz and generally biotite or hornblende.

Granular. Composed of distinguishable grains.

Guano. An accumulation of excrement of sea birds, modified by oxidation and leaching.

Habit. The form or combination of forms commonly developed on the crystals of a mineral.

Hackly fracture. Breaking with a rough surface having many sharp points, like most metals.

Hemimorphic. Having the opposite ends (of crystals) terminated differently, as in Fig. 37.

Hexagonal. Six-sided; the system of crystallization having three equal axes making angles of 60° with each other and a fourth axis unequal and at right angles to these. (Fig. 26-37.)

Hexoctahedron. A form of isometric crystal having 48 faces. (Fig. 4.)

Hydrous. Containing hydrogen or water, and therefore yielding water on heating.

Hygroscopic. Capable of taking moisture from the atmosphere.

Igneous rock. A rock formed by the solidification of a molten magma, either at the surface, as volcanic lava, or within the earth, as plutonic and intrusive igneous rocks.

Ignition. Heating with the blowpipe flame.

Impregnated. Having a substance intimately dispersed or disseminated within it.

Impressed. Indented; marked by pressure.

Inclusion. A foreign material inclosed within a mineral.

Incrustation. A crust or coating.

Inelastic. Not elastic; not returning to its original form after bending.

Interlaced. Confusedly intertwined, as fibers or slender crystals.

Intermediate igneous rocks. Those having neither very high nor very low silica; intermediate between acid and basic types.

Intumescence. The property of swelling and bubbling as it fuses.

Iridescence. A play of colors, as in a soap bubble, due to thin surface film or films of air in minute crevices.

Isometric. The system of crystallization having three equal and interchangeable axes at right angles to each other. (Figs. 1-16.)

Isomorphism. The property possessed by some substances of like molecular structure and crystallization of crystallizing together in variable proportions, forming homogenous mixed crystals. (See p. 16.)

Lamellae. Thin plates or layers; laminae.

Lamellar. Consisting of lamellae, or laminae.

Laminae. Thin plates or layers; lamellae.

Laminated. Consisting of lamellae, or laminae.

Lava. Molten rock or the solid rock resulting from its cooling; applied particularly to surface flows.

Lenticular. Lens-shaped; of tabular form, thick at the middle and thinning toward the edges.

Limestone. A rock composed chiefly of calcium carbonate (calcite).

Lodestone. Magnetite that possesses natural polarity, one part attracting one pole of a magnetic needle, the opposte side or end attracting the other pole. Rarely lodestones of pyrrhotite and platinum are found.

Luster. The shine of a mineral surface, or the manner in which it reflects light. (See p. 14.)

Macroscopic. Visible to the unaided eye; megascopic; in contrast with microscopic.

Magnetic. Capable of attracting the magnetic needle or of being attracted by a magnet.

Malleable. Capable of being hammered or rolled into a sheet.

Mammillary. Having a smooth hummocky surface, with curved protuberances larger than botryoidal.

Massive. Without crystal form or faces.

Meager feel. Rough or harsh to the touch; the opposite of smooth and greasy feel.

Megascopic. Visible to the unaided eye; macroscopic; in contrast with microscopic.

Metallic luster. Having the surface sheen of a metal; with a metal-like reflection.

Metalloidal luster. Reflecting light somewhat like a metal.

Metamorphic rock. A rock (originally either igenous or sedimentary) that has been profoundly changed under the influence of high temperature or great pressure, or both.

Meteorite. A mass of stone or iron that has fallen to the earth from outer space.

Micaceous. Composed of thin plates or scales, or, like mica, capable of being easily split into thin sheets.

Monoclinic. The system of crystallization containing three unequal axes, two at an oblique angle and the third at right angles to these. (Figs. 46–52.)

Mottled. Having spots or irregular patches, as of color or shading.

Nodular. Consisting of rounded lumps or nodules.

Nodule. A somewhat irregularly rounded mass.

Nugget. A rounded, irregular lump of native metal.

Ocherous. Earthy, powdery; usually red, yellow, or brown.

Octahedron. An eight-sided form in the isometric system of crystallization (Fig. 1).

Oolitic. Containing or consisting of small rounded particles, suggesting fish-roe.

Opalescence. A milky or pearly internal reflection.

Opaque. Incapable of transmitting light.

Orthorhombic. The system of crystallization containing three unequal axes at right angles to one another. (Figs. 38–45.)

Parting. A capacity for splitting, much like cleavage, but limited to certain definite planes of weakness (often due to twinning), while true cleavage can be produced in a given direction at any point.

Pearly luster. Like that of mother of pearl.

Peat. The brown to black partially decomposed vegetable matter accumulated in swamps.

Pegmatite. An igneous rock of extremely coarse texture, the most common kind (granitic) consisting chiefly of quartz, feldspar, and mica.

Penetration twin. A pair of crystals developed in reverse position with reference to one another and each penetrating through the other. (Figs. 12, 44, 45.)

Peridotite. A very basic igneous rock, consisting chiefly of olivine and pyroxenes.

Phonolite. A dense volcanic rock composed chiefly of microscopic feldspar, nephelite, and pyroxene.

Phosphorescence. The glow induced in some substances by the action of moderate heat, friction, ultraviolet light, or other forms of energy, the glow continuing in some cases a few seconds, or even minutes, after the removal of the cause. (See p. 15.)

Pinacoidal. Having crystal forms of two parallel planes which are also parallel to two or more crystallographic axes, or developed (as cleavage or parting) parallel to such a form.

Pisolitic. Composed of or containing rounded masses the size of peas.

Pitchy luster. Resembling a fresh surface of pitch.

Placer deposits (or placers.) Accumulations of sand and gravel containing gold or other constituent of value.

Plastic. Capable of being molded or pressed into shape.

Plates. Broad flat tabular masses, thicker than sheets or leaves.

Platy. Consisting of or readily splitting into plates.

Play of colors. Change of colors in rapid succession on turning the mineral.

Pleomorphism. Synonym of polymorphism.

Plumose. Feather-like.

Pocket. An irregularly rounded bunch or mass of minerals, particularly of rich ore, within a rock or in a local enlargement of a fissure.

Polymorphism. The occurrence of two or more minerals having the same composition but differing in physical, and often also in certain chemical, properties. Dimorphism refers to groups of two, trimorphism to three, etc.

Precipitate. The solid produced (generally in powdery or minutely crystalline form) when chemical reaction produces an insoluble compound. (See p. 173.)

Prismatic. Having elongation (of crystals) in one direction, commonly parallel to one of the crystallographic axes; also parallel to the faces of a crystal, as prismatic cleavage.

Pseudohexagonal (pseudotetragonal, etc.). Having a false and misleading resemblance to crystals of the hexagonal (tetragonal, etc.) system.

Pseudomorph. A mineral aggregate having the form of the crystal of another mineral, due to alteration, replacement, etc.

Pulverulent. Powdery; finely divided, incoherent material.

Pungent. Sharp, prickling, stinging.

Pyramidal. Possessing the form of or pertaining to the pyramid, a crystal form the faces of which commonly intersect three crystallographic axes.

Pyritohedron. A form of the isometric system of crystallization possessing twelve five-sided faces (Fig. 15).

Pyroelectricity. The electric charge produced in certain minerals by moderate heat, so that minute particles of paper or other light bodies are attracted.

Radiated. Having fibers, columns, scales, or plates diverging from a point.

Rectangular. Making right angles, or angles of 90°.

Reniform. Kidney-shaped, or having a surface like a kidney, composed of numerous slightly curved surfaces, the curved parts much lower and less prominent than in mammillary.

Resinous luster. Reflecting light like resin, somewhat like greasy luster.

Reticulated. Having slender crystals or fibers crossing like the meshes of a net.

Rhombohedral. Having the form of the rhombohedron; parallel to the faces of such a form, as rhombohedral cleavage.

Rhombohedron. A crystal form in the hexagonal system consisting of six faces intersecting at oblique angles (Figs. 31-33).

Roasting. Heating at a low red heat with a strongly oxidizing blowpipe flame, for the purpose of driving off sulphur, arsenic, etc. (See p. 160.)

Rosette. A cluster of flakes or scales resembling a rose.

Saline taste. Salty; resembling the taste of common salt.

Sandstone. Sedimentary rock consisting of consolidated sand.

Scalenohedron. A twelve-sided crystal form in the hexagonal system, each side being a scalene triangle (Figs. 34, 35).

Scaly. Consisting of scales.

Schiller. A bronze-like, metalloidal luster.

Schist. Metamorphic rock with highly developed parallel or foliated structure, along which it splits easily.

Seam. A thin vein; also a bed in stratified rocks, as a seam of coal.

Sectile. Capable of being cut into slices, or coherent shavings.

Selenious odor. An odor resembling that of horseradish, or decaying horseradish, produced by heating some selenium-bearing minerals in the air.

Shale. A laminated sedimentary rock consisting of solidified mud, clay, or silt.

Silky luster. The luster of satin, due to parallel lustrous fibers.

Skeleton crystals. Those with the edges defined, but with faces not fully filled in.

Slate. Dense metamorphic rock that splits readily into broad thin sheets.

Specific gravity. The weight of a substance compared with that of an equal volume of water. (See p. 12.)

Splendent. Having a brilliant luster.

Splintery fracture. Breaking into elongated, splinter-like fragments.

Stalactitic. Having the form of a stalactite or an icicle.

Stalky. Consisting of slender columns, or long stout fibers.

Stellate. Radiating so as to produce star-like forms.

Streak. The color of the fine powder, or of the mark made by a mineral on a harder substance. (See p. 13.)

Striated. Marked with fine parallel lines or grooves.

Sublimate. A solid formed by the direct solidification of a vapor.

Submetallic luster. Like metallic, but somewhat dulled.

Syenite. A granular igneous rock like granite, but lacking quartz.

Tabular. In broad flat crystals or masses.

Tarnish. A thin surface film formed by exposure and differing in color from the fresh mineral within.

Termination. The faces on the end of a crystal.

Tenacity. The degree or character of cohesion. (See p. 11.)

Tetragonal. The system of crystallization having two equal and interchangeable axes and a third, shorter or longer, at right angles to these. (Figs. 17–25.)

Tetrahedron. A four-sided form in the isometric system of crystallization, each side of which is an equilateral triangle (Fig. 13).

Tough. Difficult to break; the opposite of brittle.

Translucent. Transmitting some light, but objects are not seen clearly through such a substance.

Transparency. The quality of transmitting light; diaphaneity.

Transparent. Transmitting light freely, so that objects may be seen clearly.

Trap rock. A dark, basic, heavy igneous rock, fine grained or dense in texture.

Triclinic. The system of crystallization having three unequal axes intersecting each other at oblique angles. (Figs. 53, 54.)

Trilling. A symmetrical attachment or intergrowth of three crystals.

Trimorphism. See Polymorphism.

Twin. A symmetrical combination or intergrowth of two crystals. (See Figs. 12, 25, 44, 45, 49, 52.)

Unctuous feel. Very smooth and slippery; greasy to the touch.

Variegated. Having different colors.

Vein. A crack, crevice, or fissure filled, or partially filled, with mineral matter.

Vesicular. Having steam or gas bubble cavities, as some igneous rocks.

Vitreous luster. Like that of a surface of broken glass.

Warty. Having small rounded protuberances, like warts.

Zonal. Arranged in zones, belts, or layers.

ABBREVIATIONS

abund.	abundant	mall.	malleable
acic.	acicular	mammil.	mammillary
adamant.	adamantine	mag.	magnetic
alk.	alkaline	mass.	masses, massive
am.	ammonia	micac.	micaceous
am.mol.	ammonium molybdate	mm.	millimeter (1-25 inch)
amorph.	amorphous	mon.	monoclinic
amt.	amount	non-mag.	non-magnetic
anhydr.	anhydrous	non-vol.	non-volatile
at. wt.	atomic weight	oct.	octahedral
b.b.	before the blowpipe	o.f.	oxidizing flame
bd.	bead	opaq.	opaque
blk., blkh.	black, blackish	orth.	orthorhombic
bot., botry.	botryoidal	o.t.	open tube
bp.	blowpipe	P. 1, P. 2, etc.	parting in 1, 2, etc.,
brn., brnh.	brown, brownish		directions
C.1, C.2., etc.	cleavage in 1, 2, etc.,	P., part.	parting
	directions	per.	perfect
capil.	capillary	phys.	physical
ch.	charcoal	pinac.	pinacoidal
cleav.	cleavage	ppt.	precipitate
col.	color, colored	prism.	prismatic
cols.	colorless	pseudm.	pseudomorphic
colum.	columnar	pyram.	pyramidal
comp.	compact	pyrito.	pyritohedral
conc.	concentrated	rad.	radial, radiating
conch.	conchoidal	rdh.	reddish
cp.	compare	reac.	reacts, reaction
c.t.	closed tube	res.	residue, resinous
decrep.	decrepitates, decrepitation	r.f.	reducing flame
dif.	difficulty	rhom.	rhombohedral
dil.	dilute	sil.	silica (SiO$_2$)
direc.	direction	sol.	soluble, solution
dissem.	disseminated	somet.	sometimes
disting.	distinguished	sp.gr., G.	specific gravity
dk.	dark	s.ph.	sodium metaphosphate
dodec.	dodecahedral	splint.	splintery
duct.	ductile	st.	streak
efferv.	effervescence	stalac.	stalactitic
efflores.	efflorescence	subl.	sublimate
F., fract.	fracture	submet.	submetallic
fibr.	fibrous	tab.	tabular
flex.	flexible	tar.	tarnishes, tarnish
fol.	foliated	temp.	temperature
fus.	fuses, fusibility	tetr.	tetragonal
G., sp.gr.	specific gravity	tetrh.	tetrahedral
gel.	gelatinous	transp.	transparent
gran.	granular	transl.	translucent
grn., grnh.	green, greenish	tri.	triclinic
gry., gryh.	gray, grayish	us.	usually
H.	hardness	vesic.	vesicular
hemimor.	hemimorphic	vitr.	vitreous
hex.	hexagonal	vol.	volatilizes, volatile
ign.	ignition	w.	with
incrust.	incrusting	wh., whh.	white, whitish
intumes.	intumescence	xl., xls.	crystal, crystals
iso.	isometric, isomorphic	xln.	crystalline
lamel.	lamellar	yel., yelh.	yellow, yellowish
lt.	light		

CHEMICAL ELEMENTS

Symbol.	Element.	Atomic Weight.	Symbol.	Element.	Atomic Weight.
A	Argon	39.94	Mg	Magnesium	24.32
Ag	Silver (Argentum)	107.88	Mn	Manganese	54.93
Al	Aluminum	26.97	Mo	Molybdenum	96.0
As	Arsenic	74.93	N	Nitrogen	14.008
Au	Gold (Aurum)	197.2	Na	Sodium (Natrium)	22.997
B	Boron	10.82	Nd	Neodymium	144.27
Ba	Barium	137.37	Ne	Neon	20.18
Be	Beryllium	9.02	Ni	Nickel	58.69
Bi	Bismuth	209.0	O	Oxygen	16.000
Br	Bromine	79.916	Os	Osmium	190.8
C	Carbon	12.00	P	Phosphorus	31.027
Ca	Calcium	40.07	Pb	Lead (Plumbum)	207.22
Cb	Columbium	93.1	Pd	Palladium	106.7
Cd	Cadmium	112.41	Pt	Platinum	195.23
Ce	Cerium	140.13	Ra	Radium	225.97
Cl	Chlorine	35.457	Rb	Rubidium	85.44
Co	Cobalt	58.94	Rh	Rhodium	102.91
Cr	Chromium	52.01	Ru	Ruthenium	101.7
Cs	Caesium	132.81	S	Sulphur	32.064
Cu	Copper (Cuprum)	63.57	Sb	Antimony (Stibium)	121.77
Dy	Dysprosium	162.46	Sc	Scandium	45.10
Er	Erbium	167.64	Se	Selenium	79.2
Eu	Europium	152.0	Si	Silicon	28.06
F	Fluorine	19.00	Sn	Tin (Stannum)	118.70
Fe	Iron (Ferrum)	55.84	Sr	Strontium	87.63
Ga	Gallium	69.72	Ta	Tantalum	181.5
Gd	Gadolinium	157.26	Te	Tellurium	127.5
Ge	Germanium	72.60	Th	Thorium	232.12
H	Hydrogen	1.008	Ti	Titanium	47.90
He	Helium	4.00	Tl	Thallium	204.39
Hf	Hafnium	178.6	U	Uranium	238.14
Hg	Mercury(Hydrargyrum)	200.61	V	Vanadium	50.96
Ho	Holmium	163.5	W	Tungsten (Wolframium)	184.0
I	Iodine	126.932			
In	Indium	114.8	Xe	Xenon	130.2
Ir	Iridium	193.1	Y	Yttrium	88.92
K	Potassium (Kalium)	39.10	Yb	Ytterbium	173.6
Kr	Krypton	82.90	Zn	Zinc	65.38
La	Lanthanum	138.90	Zr	Zirconium	91.22
Li	Lithium	6.94			

BIBLIOGRAPHY

CHAMOT, M. E., and MASON, C. W. Handbook Chemical Microscopy. Vol. I, 1930; Vol. II, 1931; John Wiley & Sons.

DANA, E. S. Mineralogy, 6th Ed., 1892. With Appendices I, II, III. John Wiley & Sons.

FARNHAM, C. MASON. Determination of the Opaque Minerals, 1930. McGraw-Hill Book Co.

KRAUS, E. H., and HUNT, W. F. Mineralogy, 2d Ed., 1928. McGraw-Hill Book Co.

LARSEN, E. S. Microscopic Determination Non-Opaque Minerals, U.S.G.S. Bull. 679, 1921.

MOSES, A. J., and PARSONS, A. L. Mineralogy. 1904. D. Van Nostrand Co.

PHILLIPS, A. H. Mineralogy, 1912. John Wiley & Sons.

ROGERS, A. F. Mineralogy. McGraw-Hill, 1921.

WINCHELL, A. N. Elements of Optical Mineralogy, 1928. John Wiley & Sons.

SUPPLEMENT TO

LEWIS AND HAWKINS'

DETERMINATIVE MINERALOGY

The following descriptions include some mineral species which were deleted from this book at the time of the preparation of the Fourth Edition, and which, the opinion of competent teachers in mineralogy indicates, should be restored to their proper places therein. Two species which have lately become important have been also now included.

The authors will appreciate any criticisms which will help to make this a better book.

A. C. HAWKINS

300 LIVINGSTON AVENUE,
NEW BRUNSWICK, NEW JERSEY,
    April 10, 1934.

PHYSICAL TABLES

SECTION 1

On p. 21, after Sylvanite, insert:

H.   G. 6.4–6.5   *Bismuthinite (Bismuthine, Bismuth Glance)*, Bi_2S_3; Bi 81.2%.

2   **Struct.**—Granular, foliated, fibrous; slender orthorhombic crystals rare. **Cleavage** perfect one direction lengthwise (010); slightly sectile.
     Color light lead-gray, often yellowish tarnish.   **Streak** dark lead-gray. **Luster** metallic.   Opaque.   (See p. 10s.)*
     In veins with bismuth, chalcopyrite, cassiterite, gersdorffite, wolframite.

SECTION 2

On p. 23, after Graphite, insert:

1   G. 1.–1.8   ASPHALT (*Asphaltum, Mineral Pitch*), C, H, O, etc.

3   **Struct.**—Amorphous; solid or very viscous liquid.   **Cleavage** none; brittle to flexible; fracture conchoidal.
     Color black to brownish black.   **Streak** brownish black.   **Luster** pitchy, resinous, dull.   Opaque.   Bituminous odor; sticky when plastic. (See p. 12s.)
     Massive deposits (" pitch lakes," etc.) and impregnating sedimentary strata.

On p. 23, under Stibnite, insert:

2   G. 6.4–6.5   *Bismuthinite.*   (See p. 10s.)

On p. 25, under Bournonite, insert:

G. 6.2–6.3   STROMEYERITE, AgCuS; Ag 53.1%;   Cu 31.1%.

$2\frac{1}{2}$ **Struct.**—Compact; rarely twinned pseudohexagonal orthorhombic
3   crystals.   **Cleavage** none; slightly sectile; fracture subconchoidal, uneven.
     Color dark lead-gray.   **Streak** dark lead-gray to black.   **Luster** metallic.   Opaque.   (See p. 10s.)
     In veins with copper and silver ores, argentite, proustite, chalcocite, tetrahedrite.

On p. 25, after Enargite, insert:

G. 6.1–6.2   PEARCEITE, $(Ag, Cu)_9AsS_6$; Ag 55–60%.

3   **Struct.**—Tabular six-sided monoclinic crystals with triangular markings on the base; compact, disseminated.   **Cleavage** none; brittle; fracture conchoidal.
     Color and **streak** black.   **Luster** metallic.   Opaque.   (See p. 10s.)
     In silver ores with galena, chalcopyrite, quartz, calcite, siderite, barite.

---

* References marked " s " refer to this supplement.

H.

On p. 25, at bottom, insert:

3   G. 4.4–5.1   *Tennantite*, Cu_3AsS_3, closely related to Tetrahedrite (which see).

4

At bottom of p. 27, under Columbite, insert:

6   G. 5.3–7.3   *Tantalite*, (Fe, Mn)Ta_2O_6, is a variety of Columbite. (See pp. 10s, 20s.)

Sections 3 and 4 have no additions nor corrections at present.

On p. 34, after Polyhalite: SECTION 5

3   G. 1.95   *Kernite* (*Rasorite*), $Na_2B_4O_7 \cdot 4H_2O$.

Struct.—Masses which are aggregates of long monoclinic crystals. **Cleavage** perfect in one direction; resembles cleavable gypsum.

Color white. **Streak** white. Easily soluble in water; yields borax on evaporation. In ancient lake bed deposits of Kern County, California. (See p. 14s.)

On p. 34, after Glauberite:

2½   G. 2.1–2.2   TRONA (*Urao*), $HNa_3(CO_3)_2 \cdot 2H_2O$.

3   **Struct.**—Incrusting; tabular or acicular monoclinic crystals. **Cleavage** one direction (100); brittle; fracture uneven.

Color white, colorless, yellowish, grayish. **Streak** white. **Luster** vitreous, pearly. Translucent. Alkaline taste. (See p. 14s.)

Efflorescence: crusts about soda lakes; in beds with halite, glauberite, mirabilite, hanksite.

On p. 36:   SECTION 6

Colemanite is frequently radial or sheaf-like in aggregation.

On p. 38, after Andalusite, insert:

7½   G. 3.1   *Lawsonite*, $CaAl_2(OH)_4(SiO_3)_2$.

8   **Struct.**—Prismatic or tabular orthorhombic crystals; lenticular plates. **Cleavage** perfect, two directions at 90° (010) (001); brittle; fracture uneven.

Color pale blue, bluish gray, colorless; white or grayish spots due to alteration. **Streak** white. **Luster** vitreous, greasy. Transparent to opaque. (See p. 16s.)

In schists with glaucophane, actinolite, margarite, epidote, garnet.

(Breunnerite)   SECTION 7

Insert (p. 42) in Sec. 7, as follows:

MAGNESITE, $MgCO_3$; sometimes much Fe (*Bruennerite*), also **Mn**. (See p. 18s.)

Section 8

After Cryolite on p. 48, as follows:

H.

$2\frac{1}{2}$ G. 1.0–1.1   AMBER (*succinite, retinite*), $C_{20}H_{32}O_2$.

3

Section 9

No additions nor corrections.

Section 10

On p. 55 expand description as follows:

6   G. 3.5–3.6   *Aegirite (Aegirine, Acmite, a pyroxene)*, $NaFe(SiO_3)_2$.

$6\frac{1}{2}$ **Struct.**—Long prismatic monoclinic crystals with terminations blunt (*aegirite*) or sharp (*acmite*); acicular, fibrous. **Cleavage** distinct, two directions at 87° and 93° (110); brittle; fracture uneven.

Color greenish black to reddish and brownish black; **acmite** often green interior, brown exterior. **Streak** pale yellowish gray. **Luster** vitreous, resinous. Translucent to opaque. (See pp. 14s, 16s.)

In igneous rocks rich in soda and iron—aegirite granite, nepheline syenite, phonolite, pegmatite.

On p. 55 after Aegirite:

6   G. 3.0–3.1   *Glaucophane* (an amphibole).

$6\frac{1}{2}$

Section 11

No additions nor corrections.

Section 12

On p. 57, after Glauconite:

1   G. 0.9–1.0   OzOCERITE (*Mineral Wax, Native Paraffin*), C_nH_{2n+2}.

2   **Struct.**—Amorphous, compact, fibrous, lamellar; plastic; may be sticky.

Color black, brownish black, brownish yellow, leek-green. **Streak** yellowish brown, pale yellow. **Luster** waxy, greasy, submetallic. Translucent, sometimes greenish opalescence. Like wax; greasy feel. **Burns** with bright smoky flame and odor of paraffin. (See p. 12s.)

In veins in sedimentary rocks.

Section 13

On p. 60, after Copiapite:

2   G. 2.9–3.0   ROSCOELITE (*Vanadium Mica*), approx. $H_2K(Al, V)_3(SiO_4)_3$;
V_2O_3 20–29%; some Mg, Fe.

H.

Struct.—Minute micaceous scales.
Color dark green to brown. Luster pearly. Translucent. (See p. 16s.)
In veins with quartz, gold, and tellurides; disseminated in sandstone with carnotite.

On p. 60, after Thenardite:

$2\frac{1}{2}$ G. 2.1–2.2 TRONA (*Urao*). (See p. 44s.)
3

SECTION 14

No additions nor corrections.

SECTION 15

On p. 65, under Magnesite, add:

var. *Breunnerite.* (See p. 44s.)

On p. 66, expand as follows:

$5\frac{1}{2}$ G. 4.0 *Perovskite* (*Perofskite*), CaTiO$_3$; some Fe.
6   Struct.—Isometric (or pseudoisometric) crystals, commonly cubes
(Fig. 5), often highly modified and striated; reniform aggregates, rounded
grains. Cleavage distinct, three directions at 90° (100); brittle; fracture
uneven.
Color pale yellow to orange-yellow, reddish brown, grayish black.
Streak white, grayish. Luster adamantine, submetallic. Transparent to
opaque. (See pp. 10s, 18s.)
In schists, crystalline limestone, serpentine, basic igneous rocks;
with chlorite, magnetite, garnet, vesuvianite, rutile, ilmenite, corundum.

SECTION 16

On p. 67, after Carnallite:

1   G. 0.9–1.0 OBOCERITE. (See p. 5s.)
2

On p. 67 insert after Cryolite:

2   G. 5.8–6.0 *Bromyrite* (*Bromargyrite*), AgBr; Ag 57.4%.
3   Struct.—Compact, incrusting, concretionary; isometric crystals rare.
Cleavage none; sectile; fracture uneven.
Color bright yellow to amber-yellow, greenish; often grass-green or
olive-green externally; little altered on exposure. Streak pale yellow,
greenish yellow. Luster resinous, adamantine. Transparent to translucent. (See p. 12s.)
With cerargyrite, embolite, cerussite, calcite, in oxidized portions of
silver ores.

H.

On p. 67, immediately following the above:

2½   G. 1.0–1.1   AMBER (*Succinite, Retinite*), $C_{20}H_{32}O_2$.

3   **Struct.**—Amorphous, irregular lumps, grains; fracture conchoidal; brittle; sometimes inclusions of insects, vegetable remains, liquids, minerals.

Color yellow, brownish yellow, brownish red, whitish. **Streak** white. **Luster** greasy, resinous. Transparent to translucent. Electrified by friction. (See p. 12s.)

Fossil resin in clays, sands, coal beds, sedimentary rocks.

Section 17

On p. 72, after Copiapite:

2   G. 2.9–3.0   Roscoelite.   (See p. 5s.)

On p. 73, just before Cordierite:

G. 3.2   *Dumortierite*, $Al_2(AlO)_6(SiO_4)_3$.

7   **Struct.**—Fibrous, columnar, massive; rarely orthorhombic crystals, commonly indistinct. **Cleavage** distinct, one direction (100), also imperfect in two other directions (110); brittle; fracture uneven.

Color bright blue to greenish blue. **Streak** white. **Luster** vitreous. Transparent to translucent. (See p. 20s.)

In pegmatite, gneiss, quartzite, etc., with other silicate minerals.

Section 19

No additions nor corrections.

Section 20

On p. 78, after Glauconite:

1   G. 0.9–1.0   Ozocerite.   (See p. 5s.)
2

On p. 79, at top, after Chrysocolla:

2   G. 5.8–6.0   *Bromyrite*.   (See p. 6s.)
3

Section 21

On p. 82, at beginning, before Sulphur, insert:

1   G. 0.9–1.0   Ozocerite.   (See p. 5s.)
2

Immediately following this, insert:

1   G. 1.0–1.8   Asphalt.   (See p. 3s.)
3

H.

Under Tetrahedrite insert:

var. *Tennantite.*   (See p. 25 in text.)

On p. 83, after Psilomelane at bottom, insert:

5   G. 5.6–5.8   *Samarskite*, $(Fe, Ca, UO_2)_3(Ce, Y, Er)_2(Cb, Ta)_6O_{21}$.

6   **Struct.**—Compact, apparently amorphous, disseminated; orthorhombic crystals rare.   **Cleavage** none; brittle; fracture conchoidal.
     Color velvet-black, black.   **Streak** reddish-brown, grayish-brown.
Luster vitreous, greasy, submetallic.   Opaque.   (See pp. 10s, 16s.)
     Brilliant luster and conchoidal fracture often conspicuous.   In pegmatite with columbite, quartz, mica, feldspars.

Section 22

On p. 85, expand as follows:

1   G. 5.6–5.7   *Iodyrite (Iodargyrite)*, AgI; Ag 46%.

1½   **Struct.**—Thin scales, lamellar, compact; hexagonal prisms.   **Cleavage** conspicuous, one direction crosswise (0001); sectile; thin flakes flexible.
     Color yellow, yellowish green, brownish.   **Streak** yellow.   **Luster** resinous, wax-like.   Translucent.   (See p. 12s.)
     In veins with other silver minerals, vanadinite, descloizite.

Immediately following the above, insert (p. 85):

1   G. 0.9–1.0   Ozocerite.   (See p. 5s.)
2

Then (p. 85) after Molybdite, insert:

1   G. 1.0–1.8   Asphalt.   (See p. 3s.)
3

On p. 87, at top before Calaverite, insert (after Autunite):

2   G. 5.8–6–0   *Bromyrite.*   (See p. 6s.)
3

Section 23

On p. 90, after Vivianite, insert:

2   G. 2.9–3.0   Roscoelite.   (See p. 5s.)

Also on p. 90, expand as follows:

3   G. 2.6–2.7   *Zaratite (Emerald Nickel, Texasite)*, $Ni_3(OH)_4CO_3 \cdot 4H_2O$;
             Ni 46.8%.

     Struct.—Incrusting, mammillary, minutely crystalline, compact.
Cleavage none; brittle; fracture smooth.
     Color emerald-green.   **Streak** green.   **Luster** vitreous.   Transparent to translucent.   (See p. 18s.)
     In peridotite and serpentine with chromite; in nickeliferous magnetite.

Section 1, p. 140

		Name.	Composition.
Cu flame on ch. after roasting and moistening with HCl. SO₂ fumes in o.t. Pearceite has triangular markings on basal planes	Disting. by phys. properties.	*Tennantite* (See p. 4s)	Cu₃AsS₃ (Ag,Zn,Fe,Sb, iso.)
	Ag w. soda on ch. (Cp. Polybasite)	Pearceite (See p. 3s)	(Ag,Cu)₉AsS₆
Cu flame on ch. as above; no SO₂ fumes in o.t.	Disting. by phys. properties. Tar. to bnh. color.	*Domeykite*	Cu₃As

Section 3, p. 144

Cu flame on ch. after roasting and moistening w. HCl.	Not mag. in o.f. (unless impure from admixture of bornite, etc.). Ag reac. in HNO₃ sol.	Stromeyerite (See p. 3s)	AgCuS
Bi reac. w. von Kobell's flux	Te reac. w. H₂SO₄.	*Tetradymite*	Bi₂(Te,S)₃
	Contains only Bi and S. Fuses with spirting.	*Bismuthinite* (Bismuth Glance) (See p. 3s)	Bi₂S₃

Section 4, p. 148

W. reac. after fus. w. soda Mag. w. little soda	Little or no Mn reac.	Ferberite (See p. 26 in text)	FeWO₄ (Some Mn)
Cb. reac. after fus. w. borax	Mn in soda bd.; U in s.ph.bd.	*Samarskite* (See p. 8s)	(Fe,Ca,UO₂)₃ (Co,Y,Er)₁ (Cb,Ta)₆O₂₁
Bi reac. w. von Kobell's flux	Te reac. w. H₂SO₄.	*Tetradymite*	Bi₂(Te,S)₃

Section 7, p. 152

H₂O₂ test for Ti after fus. w. borax	Ca reac. in HCl sol. after fus. w. soda and precipitating Ti w. am.	*Perovskite* (Perofskite) (See p. 6s)	CaTiO₃ (Fe iso. w. Ca)
Cb. reac. after fus. w. soda or borax, dissolving in HCl, and boiling w. Sn.	W. little soda becomes mag.; us. Mn reac. also	*Tantalite* (See p. 4s)	(FeMn)Ta₂O₆ (Cb. iso. w. Ta; slight Sn and W)

TABLES

Color.	Streak.	Hardness.	Specific Gravity.	Fusibility.	Crystallization and Structure.	Cleavage and Fracture.
Dk. Pb-gry. to Fe-blk.	Blk. to dk. cherry-red	3–4	4.4–5.1	$1\frac{1}{2}$	Iso. tetrh.; xls. Figs. 13,14; comp.	F. uneven
Blk.	Blk.	3	6.1–6.2	1	Mon.; tabular, comp.	F. conch.
Sn-wh. to steel-gray	Gry.	$3 -3\frac{1}{2}$	7.2–7.7	2	Massive	F. uneven
Dk. steel-gry.	Dk. steel-gry.	$2\frac{1}{2}$–3	6.2–6.3	$1\frac{1}{2}$	Orth.; us. comp.	F. uneven slightly sectile
Pale steel-gry.	Gry.	$1\frac{1}{2}$–2	7.2–7.6	$1\frac{1}{2}$	Hex. rhom.; us. bladed	C. basal per., slightly sectile
Lt. Pb-gry.	Lt. Pb-gry.	2	6.4–6.5	1	Orth.; gran., fol., fibr.	C. 1, pinac., per., slightly sectile
Blk.	Brnh-blk.	5	7.5	$3\frac{1}{2}$	Mon.	C. 1, pinac., per., F. uneven
Velvet-blk.	Dk. rdh.-brn.	5 –6	5.6–5.8	$4\frac{1}{2}$–5	Orth.; us. comp., dissem.	F. conch.
Pale steel-gry.	Gry.	$1\frac{1}{2}$–2	7.2–7.6	$1\frac{1}{2}$	Hex. rhom.; us. bladed	C. basal per., slightly sectile
Yel. and brn. to blk.	Wh. to gryh.	$5\frac{1}{2}$–6	4.0		Iso., cubes, Fig. 5; striated; dissem.	C. 3, cubic, 90°; F. uneven
Blk.	Blk.	6	6.5–7.3		Orth.; short prism. xls.	F. conch., uneven; C. 1, pinac., poor

SECTION 8, p. 154

		Name.	Composition.
As_2O_3 subl. on ch.; wh.xln., vol.; far from assay	Vol. on ch.; As_2O_3, subl. in c.t.	*Arsenolite*	As_2O_3
Sb_2O_3 subl. on ch.; dense wh. and near assay	Easily fus. in c.t.w. slight wh. subl.	*Senarmontite* (See p. 47 in text)	Sb_2O_3
Str. bnh-blk. Sticky when plastic	Bright flame and pitchy odor	ASPHALT (Mineral Pitch) (See p. 3s)	C,H,O, etc.
Str. wh. Electrified by friction	Dense wh. aromatic fumes on ign.	AMBER (Succinite) (See p. 7s)	$C_{20}H_{32}O_2$
Str. bnh-yel., pale yel. Plastic	Smoky yel. flame, paraffin odor, Somet. sticky	OZOCERITE (Native Paraffin) (See p. 5s)	C_nH_{2n+2}

SECTION 10, p. 156

Deflagrates on ch.; As fumes on ch.; As mirror w. ch. in c.t.	Globule xln. after fus.; little H_2O at red heat	*Olivenite* (See p. 90 in text)	$Cu_2(OH)AsO_4$

SECTION 11, p. 156

Mall. Ag globule; Cl,Br, or I reac. w. powdered galena in c.t.	Subl. yel. hot, wh. cold. Not disting. by bp. methods. Sectile	*Bromyrite* (See p. 6s)	AgBr
	Subl. orange-red hot, lemon-yel. cold. Sectile; flakes flex.	*Iodyrite* (See p. 8s)	AgI
Brittle Bi globule; red subl. w. von Kobell's flux	CO_2 efferv. in HCl; H_2O in c.t.	*Bismutite*	$BiO \cdot Bi(OH)_2CO_3$

TABLES—*Continued*

Color.	Streak.	Hard-ness.	Specific Gravity.	Fusi-bility.	Crystallization and Structure.	Cleavage and Fracture.
Cols. to wh.	Vitreous or silky	$1\frac{1}{2}$	3.7	1	Iso.; us. capil.	F. uneven
Cols. to wh. and gryh.	Resinous	$2 -2\frac{1}{2}$	5.2–5.3	$1\frac{1}{2}$	Iso., oct.; Fig. 1; gran.	F. uneven
Blk. to bnh-blk.	Pitchy, dull	1 –3	1.0–1.8	1	Amorph.	F. conch.
Yel., bnh., whitish	Greasy, resinous	$2\frac{1}{2}$–3	1.0–1.1	1	Amorph.	F. conch.
Bnh-blk., yel., grn.	Waxy, greasy, submet.	1 –2	0.9–1.0	1	Amorph.	F. uneven
Blkh-grn. to olive-grn. and brn.	Vitreous to adaman-tine	3	4.1–4.6	2–$2\frac{1}{2}$	Hex. rhom.; us. tab.	C. basal, per.
Grn. or yel.	Resinous to adaman-tine	2 –3	5.8–6.0	1	Iso.; us. comp.	F. uneven, sectile
Yel. to grnh. and brhn.	Resinous to adaman-tine	1 –$1\frac{1}{2}$	5.6–5.7	1	Hex. hemimor.; prisms, scales	C. 1, basal, per. Sectile. Thin flakes flex.
Wh., grn., yel., gry.	Dull	4 –$4\frac{1}{2}$	6.8–7.7	$1\frac{1}{2}$	Amorph., earthy	F. earthy

Section 12, p. 158

		Name.	Composition.
Sol. in cold H_2O; wh. ppt. $BaSO_4$ w. $BaCl_2$ in HCl sol. Acid H_2O in c.t. The ferric salts give $Fe(OH)_3$ ppt. in boiling water	Ferric Fe only; K flame; little H_2O in c.t.	*Jarosite*	$KFe_3(OH)_6(SO_4)_3$ (Ni iso. w. K)
P reac. w. am. mol. Much ferrous Fe	Mn in borax bd. Little or no H_2O in c.t. Li flame.	*Triphylite*	$LiFePO_4$ (Mn iso. w. Fe)
P reac. w. am. mol.	Ferric Fe. H_2O in c.t.	*Dufrenite*	$Fe_2(OH)_3PO_4$

Section 14, p. 160

Na flame; fus. quietly	Prism and cl. angles near 90°	*Aegirite* (Acmite) (See p. 5s)	$NaFe'''(SiO_3)_2$

Section 15, pp. 162–164

Wh. AgCl ppt. w. HNO_3 sol. and $AgNO_3$	Wh. $BaSO_4$ ppt. in H_2O sol. w. HCl and $BaCl_2$. Na flame; salty taste	*Hanksite*	$9Na_2SO_4 \cdot 2Na_2CO_3 \cdot$ KCl
CO_2 efferv. w. HCl. H_2O sol. gives alkaline reac. w. turmeric paper	H_2O and CO_2 when gently heated in c.t.; alkaline taste	Trona (See p. 4s)	$HNa_3(CO_3)_2 2H_2O$
	H_2O in c.t.; partly sol. in H_2O	*Gay-Lussite*	$Na_2Ca(CO_3)_2 \cdot 5H_2O$
Sulphates.—H_2O sol. w. HCl and $BaCl_2$ gives wh. ppt. $BaSO_4$	B.b. swells and gives K flame; H_2O sol. w. HCl and am. gives ppt. of $Al(OH)_3$	*Kalinite* (Potash Alum)	$KAl(SO_4)_2 \cdot 12H_2O$
B reac. w. turmeric paper	Swells and fus. to clear glass; taste sweetish alk.	*Kernite* (See p. 4s)	$Na_2B_4O_7 \cdot 4H_2O$

Section 16, p. 164

(Same as above)		*Gay-Lussite*	

TABLES—*Continued*

Color.	Streak.	Hardness.	Specific Gravity.	Fusibility.	Crystallization and Structure.	Cleavage and Fracture.
Ocher-yel. to clove-brn.	Vitreous	$2\frac{1}{2}$–$3\frac{1}{2}$	3.1–3.3	$4\frac{1}{2}$	Hex. rhom.; us. xls.	C. 1, basal F. uneven
Lt. blue, grn. or gry.	Vitreous to resinous	$4\frac{1}{2}$–5	3.5–3.6	$1\frac{1}{2}$	Orth.; us. comp.	C. 2, basal, per. and pinac.
Dull olive to blk-grn.	Silky, weak	$3\frac{1}{2}$–4	3.2–3.4	$2\frac{1}{2}$	Orth. us. fibr.	F. splint
Grnh. to brnh-blk.	Vitreous	6 –6.5	3.5–3.6	3.5	Mon.; prism.	C. 2, prism. F. uneven
Cols., wh. to redh.	Vitreous	3 –$3\frac{1}{2}$	2.5–2.6	$1\frac{1}{2}$	Hex.; us. xls.	C. 1, basal F. uneven
Cols., gry., wh., yelh.	Vitreous	$2\frac{1}{2}$–3	2.1–2.2	$1\frac{1}{2}$	Mon.; incrusting	C. 1, pinac., per. F. uneven
Cols., wh., yelh., gryh.	Vitreous	2 –3	1.9–2.1	$1\frac{1}{2}$	Mon., us. xls.	C. 2, prism., per., 111°; F. conch.
Wh., gryh.	Vitreous to pearly	3	1.95	$1\frac{1}{2}$	Mon., us. comp.	C. 1, pinac., per.

Section 17, p. 166

		Name.	Composition.
P reac. w. am. mol.	Mn in soda bd. Li flame.	*Lithiophilite*	$LiMnPO_4$ (Fe iso. w. Mn)
B reac. w. turmeric paper	B flame. Slowly vol.; sol. in H_2O small scales; greasy feel	*Sassolite* (Boric Acid) (See p. 32 in text)	H_3BO_3

Section 22, p. 172

Not decomposed by boiling conc. H_2SO_4. (Flakes retain luster and transp., acid remains clear.)	Na flame; Thin flakes elastic	PARAGONITE (Soda Mica) (See p. 33 in text)	$H_2NaAl_3(SiO_4)_3$
	Fus. easily to blk. glass; V in s.ph. bead	ROSCOELITE (Vanadium Mica) (See p. 5s)	$H_2K(Al,V)_3(SiO_4)_3$ (Some Mg,Fe)

Section 23, pp. 174–176

Amphibole group. Fus. quietly or w. little intumes.	Strong Na flame; fus. easily	*Glaucophane* (See p. 5s)	$Na(Mg,Ca,Fe)$ $Al(SiO_3)_3$
Pyroxene group. Fus. quietly or w. little intumes.	Fus. to blk. globule, somewhat mag.; strong Na flame	*Aegirite* (Acmite) (See p. 5s)	$NaFe'''(SiO_3)_2$

Section 24, p. 178

Cb reac. after fus. w. borax; U reac. in s.ph.bd.		*Samarskite* (See p. 8s)	$(Fe,Ca,UO_2)_3$ $(Ce,Y,Er)_2$ $(Cb,Ta)_6O_{21}$

Section 25, pp. 178–180

Li flame; may be yelh-red or obscured by Na	Blue phosphorescence with gentle heat. Fus. to wh. enamel	*Petalite*	$LiAl(SiO_3)_2$ (Na iso. w. Li)
Fus. easily to cols. blebby glass	Sol. w. gel. after ign.; H_2O in c.t.; very hard	*Lawsonite* (See p. 4s)	$CaAl_2(OH)_4(SiO_3)_2$

TABLES—*Continued*

Color.	Streak.	Hardness.	Specific Gravity.	Fusibility.	Crystallization and Structure.	Cleavage and Fracture.
Salmon-color, yel. to brn.	Vitreous to resinous	$4\frac{1}{2}$–5	3.4–3.5	$1\frac{1}{2}$	Orth., us. mass.	C. 2, basal, per. and pinac.
Cols., wh., yel., gry.	Pearly	1	1.4–1.5	$\frac{1}{2}$	Tri., small scales	C. 1, basal, per. greasy feel
Yelh., grnh., gryh-wh.	Pearly to vitreous	2 –3	2.8–2.9	5	Mon., us. scaly, comp.	C. 1, basal, per. Flakes tough, elastic.
Dk. grn. to brn.	Pearly	2	2.9–3.0	$2\frac{1}{2}$	Mon.? Minute scales.	C. 1, basal, per.
Lavender-blue to azure-blue; gryh., and bluish-blk.	Vitreous to pearly	6 –$6\frac{1}{2}$	3.0–3.1	3–$3\frac{1}{2}$	Mon., us. columnar or fibr.	C. 2, prism. per. 58° F. uneven, conch. Fibers flex.
Grnh. to brnh.-blk.	Vitreous	6 –$6\frac{1}{2}$	3.5–3.6	$3\frac{1}{2}$	Mon.; prism.	C. 2, prism., 87°, poor. F. uneven
Velvet-blk.	Vitreous to res.	5 –6	5.6–5.8	$4\frac{1}{2}$–5	Orth.; us. mass.	F. conch.
Wh., gry., pink, grnh.	Vitreous; C. pearly	6 –$6\frac{1}{2}$	2.4–2.5	4	Mon.; us. mass.	C. 1, basal, per. F. uneven
Pale blue to gryh-blue	Vitreous to greasy	$7\frac{1}{2}$–8	3.1	3	Orth.; us. xls.	C. 2, basal and pinac., per., 90°

Section 26, pp. 182–184

			Name.	Composition.
CARBON-ATES.— CO₂ efferv. in dil. HCl	Contains Mg— little or no ppt. w. am. oxalate in HCl sol., but much w. Na Phosphate. Al-kaline reac. w. turmeric paper may be weak	Scarcely affected by cold dil. HCl. Wh. fragments become pale pink on ign. w. Co(NO₃)₂. Much Fe(OH)₃ ppt. w. am. after boiling HCl sol. w. a drop of HNO₃.	*Breunnerite* (Fe Magnesite; Brown Spar) (See p. 4s)	(Mg,Fe)CO₃ (also iso. with Mg)
SULPHATES. —Wh. ppt. BaSO₄ w. BaCl₂ in HCl sol.	Al. reac. w. Co(NO₃)₂ on ch.	Readily sol. in H₂O: K flame	*Kalinite* (Potash Alum)	KAl(SO₄)₂·12H₂O

Section 27, p. 184

(Same as above)			*Kalinite*	
CARBON-ATES.— CO₂ efferv. in dil HCl.	Ni in borax bead.	H₂O in c.t.	*Zaratite* (See p. 8s)	Ni₃(OH)₄CO₃·4H₂O

Section 29, p. 188

Al reac. w. Co(NO₃)₂ on ch.	Clay - like; sometimes transl. or transp. in H₂O	*Halloysite* (See p. 46 in text)	H₄Al₂Si₂O₉·nH₂O

Section 30, pp. 190–192

P reac. w. am. mol. after fus. w. soda; us. pale blue-grn. flame	Blue col., bb. swells, loses col. and crumbles	*Lazulite* (See p. 80 in text)	(Mg,Fe)(AlOH)₂ (PO₄)₂
S.ph.bd. in o.f.grnh. hot, cols. cold; inr.f.grnh.hot, violet-blue cold	Ti reac. w. H₂O₂	*Perovskite* (Perofskite) (See p. 6s)	CaTiO₃ (Fe iso. w. Ca)

TABLES—*Continued*

Color.	Streak.	Hard-ness.	Specific Gravity.	Fusi-bility.	Crystallization and Structure.	Cleavage and Fracture.
Yelh., brnh., gry. Seldom wh.	Vitreous	$3\frac{1}{2}$–$4\frac{1}{2}$	3.0–3.2		Hex. rhom.; us. comp., gran.	C. 3, rhom. per., $72\frac{1}{2}$°; F. conch.
Cols., white	Vitreous	2 –$2\frac{1}{2}$	1.7–1.8		Iso. pyr.; us. fibr.	F. conch.
Emerald-grn.	Vitreous	3	2.6–2.7		Compact, incrust.	F. smooth
Wh., gry., grnh., yelh., bluish, redh.	Pearly, waxy, dull	1 –2	2.0–2.2		Mass.; earthy	F. uneven
Azure-blue	Vitreous	5 –6	3.0–3.1		Mon.; xls., gran.	C. 2, prism., poor F. uneven
Yel. and brn. to blk.	Adamant. to submet.	$4\frac{1}{2}$–5	5.9–6.1		Tetr.; xls. like oct.; gran.	C. 4, pyram., $49\frac{1}{2}$°, 80°, F. uneven

SECTION 31, pp. 194–196

		Name.	Composition.
Little or no Cb; Mn in soda bd.	Fe in s.ph.bd.; very heavy (G above 6)	*Tantalite* (See p. 4s)	$(Fe, Mn)Ta_2O_6$ (Cb iso. w. Ta; slight Sn and W)
Al reac. w. $Co(NO_3)_2$ on ch.	Bladed or fibrous also massive	*Dumortierite* (See p. 7s)	$Al_2(AlO)_6(SiO_4)_3$

TABLES—*Continued*

Color.	Streak.	Hard-ness.	Specific Gravity.	Fusi-bility.	Crystallization and Structure.	Cleavage and Fracture.
Blk.	Resinous to submet.	6	6.5–7.3		Orth., short prism. xls.	F. uneven, conch. C. 1, pinac., poor
Bright blue to grnh-blue	Vitreous	7	3.2		Orth., fibr. comp., mass.	C. 3 (1 distinct) F. uneven

INDEX TO SUPPLEMENT

Aegirite, 5, 14, 16
Amber, 5, 7, 12
Arsenolite, 12
Asphalt, 3, 7, 8, 12

Bismuthinite, 3, 10
Bismutite, 12
Breunnerite, 4, 6, 18
Bromyrite, 6, 7, 8, 12

Domeykite, 10
Dufrenite, 14
Dumortierite, 7, 20

Ferberite, 10, and p. 26 in text

Gay-lussite, 14
Glaucophane, 5, 16

Halloysite, 18
Hanksite, 14

Iodyrite, 8, 12

Jarosite, 14

Kalinite, 14, 18
Kernite, 4, 14

Lawsonite, 4, 16
Lazulite, 18
Lithiophyllite, 16

Olivenite, p. 90 in text
Ozocerite, 5, 6, 7, 8, 12

Paragonite, 16
Pearceite, 3, 10
Perovskite, 6, 10, 18
Petalite, 16

Roscoelite, 5, 7, 8, 16

Samarskite, 8, 10, 16
Sassolite, 16
Senarmontite, p. 47 in text
Stromeyerite, 3, 10

Tantalite, 4, 10, 20
Tennantite, 4, and p. 25 in text
Tetradymite, 10
Triphylite, 14
Trona, 4, 6, 14

Zaratite, 8, 18

INDEX

NOTE.—A dash (—) separates references to the physical tables from those to the blowpipe tables. Mineral names are printed in **heavy-faced** type.

Abbreviations, 217
Acids, 97, 112
Acmite, 55
Actinolite, 74—174
Adularia, 38
Aegirite, 55
Agate, 51
 mortar, 96
Aggregates, crystal, 10
Alabandite, 91—144
Alabaster, 32
Albite, 38, 174
Alexandrite, 76
Algodonite, 140
Allanite, 58, 148, 160, 168
Allophane, 48, 68, 79—188
Allotropy, 17
Almandite, 70—180
Altaite, 28, 31—148
Alum stone, 49
Aluminum, tests for, 117
Alunite, 49, 68—184, 190
Alunogen, 184
Amalgam, 28—202, 31—146
Amazonite, 38
Amazonstone, 38
Amber mica, 72
Amblygonite, 38, 63, 75—178
Amethyst, 50
Ammonia, 98, 116
Ammonium carbonate, 116
 hydroxide, 98, 116
 molybdate, 98
 oxalate, 116
Amorphous minerals, 1, 205
Amosite, 91
Amphibole asbestos, 45

Amphibole group:
 Actinolite, 74—174
 Anthophyllite, 38, 54, 62, 74—160, 174, 192
 Asbestos, 45
 Hornblende, 54, 62, 74, 83, 89, 91—160, 174
 Nephrite, 50
 Tremolite, 37, 54, 62, 174
Analcite, 49, 69, 80, 170
Anatase, 56
Andalusite, 39, 55, 63, 76—194
Andesine, 38—174
Andradite, 70—180
Anglesite, 40, 56, 64, 76—154
Anhydrite, 41, 56, 64—164
Anhydrous gypsum, 41
Ankerite, 41—182
Annabergite, 78, 90, 158
Anorthite, 38, 168, 174
Anorthoclase, 38
Anthophyllite, 38, 54, 62, 74—160, 174, 192
Antimonial silver, **31**
Antimonite, 23
Antimony, 31—140
 glance, 23
 tests for, 117
Anvil, 95
Apatite, 34, 60, 68, 80—166, 186
Apophyllite, 34, 60, 73—170
Apparatus, 93
Aqua fortis, 98,
Aquamarine, 81
Aqua regia, 98
Aragonite, 41, 56, 64, 76—182
Argentite, 22, 24, 142

245

Arsenic, 31—140
tests for, 118
Arsenical pyrites, 22
Arsenopyrite, 22—140
Asbestos, 45, 54, 90—160, 174, 192
Asterism, 13
Atacamite, 90—156
Augite, 74, 160, 176
Aurichalcite, 184
Autunite, 86—166
Aventurine, 50
feldspar, 38
Axinite, 35, 54, 61, 73—178
Azurite, 91—156

Balas ruby, 82
Barite, 40, 64, 76—164
Barium chloride, 116
Barium, tests for, 118
Barytes, 40
Basanite, 51
Bases in silicates, 129
Bauxite, 44, 46, 66—192
Bead tests, 113—115
Bentonite, 46
Beryl, 52, 71, 81—180, 194
Biotite, 53, 60, 72, 148, 160, 172
Bismuth, 30—146
tests for, 119
Black band ore, 41
Black diamond, 44
Black jack, 64
Black lead, 23
Black mica, 53
Black oxide of copper, 26
Blast, 98
Blende, 64
Bloodstone, 51
Blowpipe, 93
determination by, 93, 135
operations, 98
tables, 135, 138
Blue asbestos, 90
Blue carbonate of copper, 91
Blue glass, 96
Blue iron earth, 72
Bog iron ore, 83
Bog manganese, 24

Boracite, 52, 71, 81—166, 178
Borax, 33, 52, 72—164, 166
Borax (glass), 97
bead, 113
Boric acid, 32
Bornite, 28—142
Boron, tests for, 119
Bort, 44
Bournonite, 25—142
Braunite, 22, 28, 30, 84—150
Brittle silver, 24
Brochantite, 91—156
Bronze mica, 72
Bronzite, 37
Brookite, 58, 69—152, 196
Brown clay ironstone, 83
Brown hematite, 83
Brown ocher, 83
Brucite, 32, 72—184, 186
Burners, 94
Bytownite, 38—174

Cadmium, tests for, 120
Caesium, test, 120
Cairngorm, 50
Calamine, 36, 43—186
Calaverite, 28, 30, 87—148
Calc sinter, 40
Calc spar, 40
Calc tufa, 40
Calcareous marl, 40
Calcite, 40, 56, 64, 76—182
Calcium, tests for, 120
Calomel, 45, 57, 67—154
Cancrinite, 43, 56, 65, 77—168
Carbonado, 44
Carnallite, 45, 67—162
Carnelian, 51
Carnotite, 85—166
Cassiterite, 50, 58, 70, 84, 89—196
Cat's eye, 50, 76
Caustic potash, 98
Celestite, 41, 64, 76—164
Cerargyrite, 45, 57, 66, 77—156
Cerussite, 48, 57, 68—154
Chabazite, 42, 65—170
Chalcanthite, 79—156
Chalcedony, 51, 58, 71, 81, 196

Chalcocite, 22, **25—144**
Chalcopyrite, **28—142**
Chalcotrichite, 88
Chalk, 45
Chalybite, 41
Change of color, 13
Charcoal, 95
Chemical determination, 93, **135**
  elements, 218
    properties, 16
  reagents, 97
  tests, 98
Chert, 51
Chiastolite, 39
Chile saltpeter, 47
China clay, 46
Chloanthite, 22
Chlorine, tests for, 121
Chlorite, 72, 90—172, 190
Chloritoid, 54, 73, 92
Chondrodite, 50, 69—188
Chromic iron, 84
Chromite, 84, 89—**150, 152, 192, 194**
Chromium, tests for, 121
Chrysoberyl, 39, 63, **76—194**
Chrysocolla, 78, 90—**188**
Chrysolite, 63
Chrysoprase, 51
Chrysotile, 45
Cinnabar, 85, 86—144, 154
Citrine, 50
Classification, crystallographic, 198
  physical, 20
Clay ironstone, 41
Cleavage, 10
Cleiophane, 64
Clinochlore, 72
Closed tube, 95, 108
  sublimates in, 109
Cobalt, bloom, 158
  glance, 21
  nitrate, 98, 116
  pyrites, 22
  tests for, 122
Cobaltite, 21, 29—**140**
Cockscomb pyrites, 29
Cogwheel ore, 25
Colemanite, 36—166

Color, 13
Color screens, **102**
Columbite, 27, 84—**148, 152, 178**
Columbium, tests for, 122
Common mica, 33
Common salt, 39
Composition, 16
Contact twins, 2
Copiapite, 60, 72, 86—**158**
Copper, 87—146
  glance, 25
  pyrites, 28
  tests for, 122
Copperas, 78
Cordierite, 54, 61, **73—180, 194**
Corundum, 44, 52, 57, 59, 66, 71, **77,**
  82—**194**
Covellite, 23, 144
Cristobalite, 51
Crocidolite, 45, 90, **91, 162**
Crocoite, 87—154
Cryolite, 48, 67, **166**
Crystal, definition of, **1**
  aggregates, 10
  tables, 198
Crystallization, **1**
Cuprite, 82, 88, 146, 156
Cyanite, 36, 39, 42, 43, 54, 55, 56, **74,**
  75, 77—**190, 194**

Danburite, 52, 71—178
Dark ruby silver, 82
Datolite, 49, 69, **80—168**
Decrepitation, 100
Definition of mineral, 1
Descloizite, 82, 88—154
Descriptions of minerals, 21
Determination, by blowpipe, **93,**
  135
  by crystallization, 198
  optical properties, 8
  by physical properties, 18
Determinative tables, 18, 138, **198**
Diamond, 44, 57, 66, **77—196**
  mortar, 96
Diaphaneity, 14
Diaspore, 35, 53, 61, **73—194**
Diatomaceous earth, 45, 50

Dimorphism, 17
Diopside, 35, **37**, 43, 55, 56, 75—**176**
Dioptase, **91**—**188**
Dogtooth spar, 40
Dolomite, **41**, 56, 64, 76—**182**
Dyscrasite, **31**—142

Electric calamine, 36
Electrum, 87
Elements, table of, 218
  tests for, 98
Embolite, 66, 78—**156**
Emerald, 81
Emery, 44
Enargite, **25**, **140**
Enstatite, **37**, 43, 62, 65, 75—**176**, **192**
Epidote, **61**, 73—**162**, **180**
Epsom salt, 45
Epsomite, **45**, **47**, **164**
Erythrite, **158**
Essonite, 70

False topaz, 50
Fayalite, 63
Feather ore, 21
Feel, 15
Feldspar group:
  Albite, **38**—174
  Andesine, **38**—174
  Anorthite, **38**—174
  Bytownite, **38**—174
  Labradorite, **38**—174
  Microcline, **38**—174
  Oligoclase, 38—174
  Orthoclase, **38**—174
Ferberite, **26**, **162**
Fergusonite, 58
Ferruginous quartz, 50
Fibrolite, 35
Filter paper, 96
Fire opal, 50
Flame, blowpipe, 98
Flame colors, 103
Flame-color screens, 102
Flint, 51
Flos ferri, 41
Fluorescence, 14
Fluorine, tests for, 123

Fluorite, **42**, 65, 77—**166**
Fluorspar, 77
Fontainebleau limestone, **40**
Fool's gold, 29
Forceps, or tweezers, **95**
Forsterite, **63**
Fowlerite, 62
Fracture, 10
Franklinite, **27**, 84—**150**
Freibergite, **25**—142
French chalk, 32
Fuller's earth, 46
Funnel, glass, 96
Fusibility, scale of, 101
Fusion, 99

Gadolinite, 58
Gahnite, **82**—**196**
Galena, **24**, 142
Galenite, 24
Garnet group:
  Almandite, **70**—**180**
  Andradite, **70**—**180**
  Grossularite, **43**, **50**, **70**—**180**
  Pyrope, **70**—**180**
  Spessartite, **70**—**180**
Garnierite, **78**, 79, 90—**188**, **192**
Gersdorffite, **21**—**140**
Geyserite, 50
Gibbsite, **48**, **60**, 73—**192**
Glass funnel, 96
Glauberite, **33**, **164**
Glauber salt, 46
Glauconite, **57**, **78**, 90—**160**
Glossary, 207
Gmelinite, 170
Goethite, **83**, 85, 89—**146**, **150**, **158**.
  186
Gold, **87**—**146**
  tests for, 123
Graphite, **23**—**152**
Gray copper, 25
Green carbonate of copper, 90
Green vitriol, 78
Greenockite, **85**, **87**—**184**
Greensand, 78
Grossularite, **43**, **50**, **70**—**180**
Gypsite, 32

Gypsum, 32, 39, 46, 52, 55, 60, 63—
162, **164**

Halite, 39, 55, 63, 76—**162**
Halloysite, 46
Hammer, mineralogical, 95
Hardness, 11
Harmotome, 36—170
Hausmannite, 83, 89—**150**
Heavy spar, 40
Hedenbergite, 74
Heliotrope, 51
Hematite, 84, 85, 89—146, 150, 158,
186
Hessite, 21, 25, **31—148**
Heulandite, 34, 60—170
Hexagonal system, 2, 4, 8, 9, 203, 204,
205, 210
Hiddenite, 39
Hornblende, 54, 62, 74, 83, 89, 91—
160, 174
Horn silver, 45
Hornstone, 51
Horseflesh ore, 28
Huebnerite, 26—172
Hyacinth, 52
Hyalite, 50
Hyalophane, 38
Hydrochloric acid, 97—116
Hydrocuprite, 88
Hydromagnesite, 182
Hydrozincite, 47, 67—184
Hypersthene, 53, 56, 61, 65, 73, 75,
83, 89, 160, 192

Iceland spar, 40
Ignition, 99—101
on charcoal, 104
Ilmenite, 26, 83—150, 152
Ilvaite, 27
Indicolite, 59
Infusorial earth, 45, 50
Instructions and precautions, 18
Iodide sublimates, 107
Iodine, tests for, 123
Iodyrite, 85
Iolite, 73
Iridescence, 13

Iridium, 31
tests for, 124, 128
Iridosmine, 31
Iridosmium, 31
tests for, 128
Iron pyrites, 29
Iron, tests for, 124
Isinglass, 33
Isomerism, 17
Isometric system, 1, **2, 3, 8, 198, 199,
211**
Isomorphism, 16

Jade, 37, **50,** 81—**176**
Jadeite, **50, 176**
Jamesonite, 21, 24—**142**
Jargon, 52
Jasper, 51
Jefferisite, 59
Jeffersonite, 176

Kainite, 40, 63—**162**
Kaolin, 44
Kaolinite, 44, 46, 66, 67—**192**
Kidney ore, 84
Krennerite, 21, 28, **30—148**
Kunzite, 39

Laboratory records, 136
Labradorite, 38, 172, 174
Lamps, 94
Lapis lazuli, 91
Laumontite, 42, 64—168
Lazulite, 80
Lazurite, 91—168
Lead, glance, 24
tests for, 125
Lepidolite, 33, 60, 73, 172
Leucite, 50, 57, 69—**188**
Light ruby silver, 86
Light filters, 102
Lime feldspar, 174
Lime-soda feldspar, 38
Limestone, 182
Limonite, 83, 85, 88—146, 150, 158,
186
Linnaeite, 22—144
Lithia mica, 33

Lithium, tests for, 125
Lodestone, 27
Luster, 14

Magnesite, 42, 65, 182, 184
Magnesium, tests for, 125
Magnet, 96
Magnetic iron ore, 27
Magnetic pyrites, 29
Magnetism, 15
Magnetite, 27—146, 148
Malachite, 90—156
Malacolite, 37
Manganese,
    tests for, 126
Manganite, 26, 83—150
Marble, 182
Marcasite, 22, 29—144
Margarite, 34, 53, 60, 172, 190
Marl, calcareous, 40
    greensand, 78
Martite, 84
Meerschaum, 47
Melaconite, 22, 26—146
Melanite, 70
Melanterite, 47, 67, 78—158
Mercury, 30—146
    tests for, 182
Merwin's flame-color screen, 102
Mica group:
    Biotite, 53, 60, 72—148, 160, 172
    Lepidolite, 33, 60, 73—172
    Muscovite, 33, 53, 60, 72—172
    Paragonite, 33, 53, 60, 73
    Phlogopite, 33, 53, 60, 72—148, 172
Microcline, 38—174
Microcosmic salt, 97
Microperthite, 38
Milky quartz, 50
Millerite, 28—144
Mimetite, 48, 68—154
Mineral, definition of, 1
Mirabilite, 46—164
Mixed crystals, 16
Molybdenite, 22—152
Molybdenum, tests for, 126
Molybdite, 66, 85
Monazite, 69, 80, 190

Monoclinic system, 2, 5, 6, 9, 201,
    202, 203, 212
Moonstone, 38
Morganite, 81
Mortars, 96
Moss agate, 51
Mountain cork, 45
    leather, 45
    paper, 45
    wood, 45
Muriatic acid, 97, 116
Muscovite, 33, 53, 60, 72—172

Nail head spar, 40
Native antimony, 31
    arsenic, 31
    bismuth, 30
    boric acid, 32
    copper, 87
    gold, 87
    iridium, 124
    mercury, 126
    platinum, 128
    silver, 130
    sulphur, 131
    tellurium, 132
Natrolite, 37, 62, 166
Nemalite, 32
Nephelite, 43, 56, 65, 77—168
Nephrite, 50
Niccolite, 29, 89—140
Nickel,
    pyrites, 28
    tests for, 127
Niobium, see Columbium
Niter, 47—164
Nitric acid, 97
Nitrogen, tests for, 127
Nitrohydrochloric acid, 97

Ocher, brown, 83
    red, 84
    yellow, 83
Octahedrite, 56, 66
Odor, 15
Oil of vitriol, 97
Oligoclase, 38—174
Olivenite, 87, 90

Olivine, **63**, 69, 76, 81—188
Onyx, 51
Opal, **50**, 58, 69, 81—190, 194, 196
Opal agate, 50
Opalescence, 13
Open tube, 95, 110, 112
  sublimates in, 110
Ophicalcite, 79
Optical properties, 6
Optical tables, 8
Orpiment, **86—152**
Orthoclase, **38**, 55, 63, 75—174
Orthorhombic system, 2, 5, 9, 200, 201, 213
Osmiridium, 31
Osmium, tests for, 127
Ottrelite, **54**
Oxidizing flame, 99
Oxygen, tests for, 127

Palladium, tests for, 127
Paragonite, **33**, 53, 60, 73
Parting, 10
Peacock copper, 28
Pearl spar, 40
Pectolite, **49**, 69—**170**
Penetration twins, 2
Pentlandite, 29—144
Peridot, 63
Perofskite, 66
Perovskite, **56**, **66**
Perthite, 38
Petzite, **25**, 31, **148**
Phenacite, **44**, 66—**196**
Phillipsite, **36**, 61
Phlogopite, 33, 53, 60, **72**—148, 172
Phosphate nodules, 68
  rock, 68
Phosphorescence, 15
Phosphorus, bead, 115
  salt, 97
  tests for, 128
Physical classification, 20
  properties, 10
  tables, 18
Pitchblende, 27
Plagioclase feldspars, **38**—174

Plaster tablets, 96
  sublimates on, 107
Platiniridium, 31
Platinum, **31**—152
  tests for, 128
  wire, 95, 111
Play of colors, 13
Pleomorphism, 17
Plumbago, 23
Polybasite, **24**, 28—142
Polyhalite, **34**, **60**, 87, 164
Polymorphism, 17
Porcelain clay, 44
Potash, test for, 128
  feldspar, 38
  mica, 33
Potasssium bisulphate, 97
  hydroxide, 98
Precautions, 18, 135
Precious opal, 50
Precipitates, 116
Prehnite, 50, 58, **81**—170, 180
Prochlorite, 72
Properties of minerals, 1
Proustite, **86**—140, **156**
Psilomelane, **26**, 83—150
Pyrargyrite, **82**, 87—**142**, **156**
Pyrite, 29—144
Pyrites, 29—144
Pyroelectricity, 16
Pyrolusite, 22, **24**, 150
Pyromorphite, 48, 57, 68, **79**, 88—**154**
Pyrope, **70**—180
Pyrophyllite, **32**, 52, 59, 71—**190**
Pyroxene, 55, 56, 62, 65, **74**, 83, 89, 92—**160**, 176
Pyroxene group:
  Aegirite, **55**
  Augite, **74**, **160**, **176**
  Bronzite, 37
  Diopside, 35, **37**, 43, 55, 56, 75—**176**
  Enstatite, **37**, 43, 62, 65, 75—**176**, 192
  Fowlerite, 62
  Hypersthene, **53**, 56, 61, 65, **73**, 75, 83, 89—**160**, 192
  Jadeite, 50

Pyroxene group:
    Jeffersonite, 176
    Pyroxene, 55, 56, 62, 65, 74, 83, 89,
        92—160, 176
    Rhodonite, 62, 74—176
    Spodumene, 39, 55, 63, 75—176,
        178
    Wollastonite, 37, 62—172
Pyrrhotite, 29—144

Quartz, 50, 58, 71, 81—196
Quicksilver, 30

Reactions of the elements, 117
Reagents, 97
Realgar, 85—152
Records, laboratory, 137
Red iron ore, 84
Red ocher, 84
Red oxide of copper, 88
Red zinc ore, 88
Reducing flame, 99
Reduction of metals, 106
Rhodochrosite, 42, 64—184
Rhodonite, 62, 74—176
Roasting on charcoal, 106
Rock, definition of, 1
Rock crystal, 50
Rock salt, 39
Rose beryl, 81
Rose quartz, 50
Rosin jack, 64
Rubellite, 59
Ruby, 44
Ruby silver, 82, 86
Ruby spinel, 82
Rutile, 55, 58, 69, 84, 89—152, 196

Salt, 39
Salt of phosphorus, 97
    bead of, 115
Saltpeter, 47
Sanidine, 38
Sapphire, 44
Sard, 51
Sardonyx, 51
Sassolite, 32—59
Satin spar, 32

Scale, of fusibility, 101
    of hardness, 11
Scapolite (Wernerite), 43, 65, 77-172,
    180
Scheelite, 42, 65, 77, 88—172, 188, 192
Scolecite, 37
Scorodite, 57, 68, 80, 91—158
Selenite, 32
Selenium, tests for, 129
Senarmontite, 47, 57
Sepiolite, 47, 67—170, 188
Sericite, 33
Serpentine, 48, 57, 68, 79—170, 188
Siderite, 41, 56, 64, 82, 88—158, 184
Silicates, bases in, 129
Siliceous sinter, 50
Silicon, tests for, 129
Sillimanite, 35, 61, 73—194
Silver, 30—146
    amalgam, 31
    glance, 24
    nitrate, 116
    tests for, 130
Smaltite, 22—140
Smithsonite, 43, 49, 65, 69, 77, 80—
    184, 186
Smoky quartz, 50
Soapstone, 32
Soda, 97
    bead, 111
    feldspar, 38
    mica, 33
Soda niter, 46, 67—164
Soda-lime feldspar, 38
Sodalite, 49, 57, 69, 80—168
Sodium, ammonium phosphate, 97
    carbonate, 97
    carbonate bead, 111
    metaphosphate bead, 115
    phosphate, 117
    tests for, 130
    tetraborate, 97
Spathic iron, 41
Spearhead pyrites, 29
Specific gravity, 12
Specular hematite, 84
    iron, 84
Spessartite, 70—180

Sphalerite, 42, 56, **64**, 76, 82, 88—144, 166, 184, 190
Sphene, 62
Spinel, 59, 71, 82—196
Spinel ruby, 82
Spodumene, 39, 55, 6ё, 75—**176, 178**
Stalactite, stalagmite, 40
Stannite, 21, 26, **29**—**142**
Staurolite, 59, 71—**194**
Steatite, 32
Stephanite, 24—**142**
Stibnite, 23, 140
Stilbite, 34, 60—**170**
Streak, 13
  plate, 96
Stream tin, 70
Strontianite, 36, 54, 61, **74**—182
Strontium, tests for, 131
Sublimates, in closed tube, 109
  in open tube, 110
  on charcoal, 105
  on plaster, 107
Sulphates, tests for, 132
Sulphides, tests for, 131
Sulphur, 47, **67,** 78, 82, 86, 152
  tests for, 131
Sulphuric acid, 97
Sunstone, 38
Sylvanite, 21, 30—**148**
Sylvite, 40, 55, 63, 76—**162**
Systems of crystallization, 1

Tables, crystallographic, 198
  determinative, 18, 135, 198
  of bead tests, 111 to 115
  of flame colors, 102, 103
  of sublimates, 105 to **110**
  optical, 8
Talc, 32, 34, 52, 53, 72, **73**—172, 182, 190
Tantalite, 84
Tarnish, 13
Taste, 15
Tellurium, 30—**148**
  tests for, 132
Tennantite, 25—**140**
Tenacity, 11
Tenorite, 26

Tephroite, 55, 62, 168˙
Test tubes, 96
  holder, 96
  support, 96
Tetragonal system, 1, 3, 8, 9, 199, 216
Tetrahedrite, 25, 82—**140**
Thaumasite, 182
Thenardite, 33, 60—**162**
Thinolite, 40
Thomsonite, 49, 69, 80—**168**
Tiger eye, 50
Tin and zinc, 97
Tin, pyrites, 21
  tests for, 132
Tinstone, 70
Titanic iron, 26
Titanite, 54, 62, 74—**172, 182**
Titanium, tests for, 133
Topaz, 35, 61, 73—194
Touchstone, 51
Tourmaline, 52, 59, 71, 81—**162, 178**˲ **192**
Transparency, 14
Travertine, 40
Tremolite, 37, 54, **62**—**174**
Triclinic system, 6, 9, 203, **216**
Tridymite, 51
Trimorphism, 17
Tripolite, 45, 46, 50, 67
Troostite, 65, 168
Tungsten, tests for, 133
Turgite, 84, **85,** 89—146, 150, **158**
Turner's flux, 97
Turquois, 81, 92—**186, 190, 194**
Tweezers, or forceps, 95
Twinning, 2

Ulexite, 45—**166**
Uraninite, 27, 84, **92**—**152**
Uranium, tests for, 133

Vanadinite, 67, 87—**154**
Vanadium, tests for, 133
Verdantique, 79
Vermiculite, 59, 71—**170**
Vesuvianite, 70, 81, 180
Vivianite, 32, 52, 72, 90, **158**
Von Kobell's flux, 97
  scale of fusibility, 101

Wad, 23, 26, 27—150, **186**
Watch glasses, 96
Water, 97
Wavellite, 48, 68, **80**—186, 190
Wernerite, **43**, 65, 77—**172, 180**
White lead ore, 48
White mica, 33
Willemite, 43, **65**, 77—**168, 186**
Witherite, **48**, 57, 68—164
Wolframite, **26**, 29, 83, 89—148, 162,
　　178
Wollastonite, **37**, 62—**172**
　opal, 50
Wulfenite, 48, 68, 79—**154**

Yellow ocher, 83

Zaratite, 90
Zeolites:
　Analcite, **49**, 69, 80—170

Zeolites:
　Apophyllite, **34**, 60, 73, **170**
　Chabazite, **42**, 65, **170**
　Gmelinite, 170
　Harmotome, **36**—170
　Heúlandite, **34**, 60—**170**
　Laumontite, **42**, 64—168
　Natrolite, **37**, 62, 166
　Phillipsite, **36**, 61
　Scolecite, 37
　Stilbite, 34, 60—170
　Thomsonite, **49**, 69, 80—168
Zinc and tin, 97
Zinc, blende, 64
　rhodonite, 62
　spinel, 82
　tests for, 134
Zincite, 88—**186**
Zircon, **52**, 59, 71, 81—**196**
Zirconium, tests for, 134
Zoisite, **35**, 53, 61, 73—**180**